DISPERSION THEORY IN HIGH-ENERGY PHYSICS

DISPERSION THEORY IN HIGH-ENERGY PHYSICS

N. M. QUEEN

Department of Mathematical Physics, University of Birmingham

G. VIOLINI

Istituto di Fisica dell'Università di Roma

M

First published 1974 by
THE MACMILLAN PRESS LIMITED
London and Basingstoke
Associated companies in New York
Dublin Melbourne Johannesburg and Madras

SBN 333 16792 9

Filmset at The Universities Press, Belfast, Northern Ireland
Printed by Thomson Litho Ltd, East Kilbride, Scotland

To the memory of
Comrade Salvador Allende

Preface

In the absence of a complete dynamical theory of strong interactions, high-energy physics in its present form rests heavily on those few general principles which can be regarded as firmly established. One of the ideas which has had the greatest impact on the development of high-energy physics is that scattering amplitudes have certain simple analyticity properties as functions of their kinematic variables. The hypothesis of analyticity imposes stringent constraints on the possible behaviour of amplitudes and leads to deep and intimate relationships among various physical quantities. In phenomenological applications, the constraints due to analyticity are usually expressed in the form of dispersion relations or dispersion sum rules.

Many new books on high-energy physics continue to appear, and some of them offer an excellent coverage of the subject as a whole. Although aspects of dispersion theory are treated in individual chapters of many books and in a number of more specialised review articles, we are not aware of any broad and systematic exposition of this important branch of high-energy physics. The purpose of this book is to fill this gap.

This book is aimed at the student or research worker in either theoretical or experimental high-energy physics who wishes to acquire a working knowledge of the basic concepts and methods of dispersion theory. Part of the material is an expanded version of lecture notes for a course given by one of us (N.M.Q.) at the University of Birmingham. Additional material has been drawn from reviews which we have written jointly on phenomenological applications of dispersion relations and sum rules and from our other work in this field.

It should be stressed that this book is limited in scope and is not intended to serve as an overall survey of high-energy physics. Interpreting the term 'dispersion theory' of the title in its broad sense, our central theme is the application of analyticity. This includes not only the formulation and utilisation of dispersion relations and dispersion sum rules, but also the derivation of certain theoretical consequences of analyticity, such as the Froissart bound and the Pomeranchuk theorem, as well as problems of analytic continuation. We have concentrated on those aspects of the subject which appear to be well established, with emphasis on the basic ideas and methods. Particular phenomenological applications are cited to illustrate the general methods and to give an indication of what dispersion theory has achieved, but we have made no attempt to review the rapidly changing status of phenomenology. We have also not developed the formalism for the most general case when the complications of full generality would tend to obscure the basic ideas; thus, our considerations are often restricted to the case of spinless particles and equal-mass kinematics.

To avoid cluttering the text with many references, we have not attributed all results to their original sources. However, original works are cited whenever we feel that they are 'classics' with which anyone working in the field ought to be familiar or that the reader would benefit in some way by consulting them. In the Further Reading sections at the ends of the chapters we provide lists of books and review articles which we recommend for further reading. These should enable the reader not only to study the subject in greater depth, but also to trace further references.

We have endeavoured to make the book self-contained and to use a consistent notation throughout the text. Although our goal has been to achieve a systematic and coherent development of the subject, it seems to us in retrospect that the various chapters can, on the whole, be read independently of one another by anyone with a modest background in high-energy physics.

As the prior knowledge which is required of the reader is kept to a minimum, the material in this book should be comprehensible to most of those who are fairly new to the field of high-energy physics. The main prerequisite is some familiarity with the language, terminology and basic empirical facts of high-energy physics—the types of particles, interactions and quantum numbers which are known, and the types of scattering experiments which have been performed. We also presuppose some familiarity with the elementary properties of analytic functions of a single complex variable. A few ideas are assumed from non-relativistic scattering theory (the relation between scattering amplitudes and cross sections, and the partial-wave expansion of the scattering amplitude, at least for spinless particles) and from relativistic mechanics (the relation between the energy and momentum of a relativistic particle, and the concept of Lorentz invariance). In order to keep the book reasonably self-contained, we have incorporated some fairly traditional material which is essential for an understanding of some of the applications of dispersion theory, such as topics in scattering theory, relativistic kinematics and Regge theory.

There is one significant omission which deserves special comment, namely the important subject of partial-wave dispersion relations. Our reasons for neglecting this subject are twofold: first, an adequate treatment of partial-wave dispersion relations would require a level of technical complexity beyond that of the rest of the book and unrelated to the remaining subject matter; and second, we felt that in any case we would have nothing significant to add to the excellent reviews of this subject which already exist in the literature.

We are indebted to our colleagues J. E. Bowcock, F. Buccella, O. V. Dumbrais, E. Ferrari, R. Gatto, J. Gunson and M. Lusignoli for many constructive criticisms of the manuscript.

N. M. Queen
G. Violini

Contents

CHAPTER 1

General formalisms and theorems in scattering theory

1.1. Introduction

In discussions of the present status of high-energy physics, it is often emphasized that there is as yet no complete dynamical theory of the strong interactions. By this, we mean that no simple set of physical principles has been shown to be both mathematically consistent and, at the same time, comprehensive enough to enable one to predict in principle all the observed characteristics of the strong interactions of hadrons in the same way that the known form of the electro-magnetic interaction and the laws of quantum mechanics are believed to be sufficient in principle to explain all of atomic physics.

For this reason, great prominence has been given to the approach generally known as S-matrix theory, in which one deals primarily with observable quantities such as scattering amplitudes and attempts to extract as much information as possible from a small number of reasonably well-established general physical principles.

Although there is no universal agreement as to precisely what combination of postulates should be adopted or what detailed form they should take, all variants of S-matrix theory are based on principles which can be classified broadly into four categories

(i) Lorentz invariance of the theory and other symmetry principles
(ii) unitarity of the S-matrix
(iii) analyticity
(iv) crossing.

These principles appear to be necessary ingredients or consequences of a complete theory of hadron physics.

It is most difficult to give a precise formulation of the postulate concerning analyticity. In broad terms, it states that scattering amplitudes, when expressed as functions of certain kinematic variables, can be analytically continued into the complex domain and that the resulting analytic functions, at least near the physical regions, have the simplest singularity structure which is consistent with the other general principles of the theory. This postulate is essentially different in character from any of the basic postulates of other physical theories and has had the most profound influence on the development of S-matrix theory. Without it, the subject as we know it today could certainly not exist.

The material of this book concentrates upon those aspects of S-matrix theory and its phenomenological applications in which analyticity plays a central role. For this reason, our main mathematical tools will include some results from the theory of functions of a complex variable. For completeness, we list below the main theorems from this branch of mathematics with which we assume the reader is already familiar. A full account can be found in the books cited in the Further Reading section at the end of this chapter. A small number of less widely known mathematical theorems are stated later in the text when they are required.

The knowledge of complex variable theory which we presuppose is contained mainly in the following four standard theorems.

(i) *Cauchy's theorem.* If the function $f(z)$ is analytic throughout the region enclosed by the closed contour C in the complex z-plane, then

$$\oint_C f(z)\,dz = 0$$

More generally, the value of an integral

$$I = \oint f(z)\,dz$$

of an analytic function $f(z)$ around a closed contour remains invariant if the contour is deformed in a continuous manner entirely within the domain of analyticity of $f(z)$ (without passing through any singularities of the function).

(ii) *The residue theorem.* If $f(z)$ has no singularities other than poles in the interior of the closed contour C, then

$$\oint_C f(z)\,dz = 2\pi i R$$

where R is the sum of the residues of these poles and the integration is taken in the anticlockwise sense. This theorem can be regarded as a generalisation of Cauchy's theorem.

(iii) *Cauchy's integral formula.* If $f(z)$ is analytic throughout the interior of the closed contour C, then at any interior point z of this region

$$f(z) = \frac{1}{2\pi i} \oint_C \frac{f(z')\,dz'}{z' - z}$$

where the integration is taken in the anticlockwise sense.

(iv) *The Schwarz reflection principle.* If $f(z)$ is analytic in a connected region which includes part of the real axis and $f(z)$ is real-valued on this part of the real axis, then

$$f(z^*) = f^*(z)$$

for all points z in this region.

The remainder of this chapter is devoted to a selection of topics in scattering theory. This is by no means a complete exposition of the subject, but it covers much of the basic formalism and notation which is used elsewhere in the book.

1.2. Unitarity

We begin by recalling several elementary formulae describing the purely elastic scattering of two spinless particles, at the same time fixing some notation. The differential cross section in the centre-of-mass system (c.m.s.) is given by

$$d\sigma(\theta)/d\Omega = |f(\theta)|^2 \tag{1.1}$$

where θ is the c.m. scattering angle and $f(\theta)$ is the c.m. scattering amplitude. The partial-wave expansion for $f(\theta)$ reads

$$f(\theta) = \sum_{l=0}^{\infty} (2l + 1)T_l P_l(\cos \theta) \tag{1.2}$$

where T_l is the partial-wave amplitude for orbital angular momentum l and P_l is a Legendre polynomial. Each partial-wave amplitude T_l, like the full amplitude f, is in general energy-dependent. However, we do not indicate this energy dependence explicitly at this stage, since it suffices for our purposes in this section to restrict our attention to scattering at a fixed energy.

It is conventional to write the partial-wave amplitude in the form

$$T_l = [\exp(i\delta_l)\sin \delta_l]/q = [\exp(2i\delta_l) - 1]/2iq \tag{1.3}$$

where δ_l is the phase shift for this partial wave and q is the c.m. momentum of each of the particles (we shall reserve the symbol k for momenta in the laboratory system). The S-matrix is defined by

$$S_l = \exp(2i\delta_l) = 2iqT_l + 1 \tag{1.4}$$

It is a familiar fact that, in the absence of inelastic processes, the conservation of probability in the scattering process requires that each phase shift δ_l be real or, equivalently, that

$$|S_l|^2 = 1 \tag{1.5}$$

We shall now generalise the preceding results to allow for the presence of inelastic processes. For simplicity, we shall continue to consider here only scattering processes involving two spinless particles in both the initial and final states. Let us consider reactions connecting various states having the same complete set of conserved quantum numbers (including l), at a fixed value of the total c.m. energy (also conserved). We shall label the possible 2-particle states, called channels, by Greek letters α, β, ... Different channels having the same set of quantum numbers are said to be coupled; transitions between two coupled channels may occur if the total c.m. energy exceeds the sum of the rest masses of the particles in each channel.

The generalisations of equations (1.1) and (1.2) for a general (possibly inelastic) reaction $\alpha \rightarrow \beta$ are

$$\frac{\mathrm{d}\sigma_{\beta\alpha}(\theta)}{\mathrm{d}\Omega} = \frac{q_\beta}{q_\alpha} |f_{\beta\alpha}(\theta)|^2 \tag{1.6}$$

$$f_{\beta\alpha}(\theta) = \sum_{l=0}^{\infty} (2l + 1)T_{\beta\alpha}^{(l)}P_l(\cos\theta) \tag{1.7}$$

while (1.4) becomes

$$S^{(l)} = 2iq^{1/2}T^{(l)}q^{1/2} + 1 \tag{1.8}$$

Here $S^{(l)}$ and $T^{(l)}$ are matrices in channel space (including all the channels which are open, that is energetically accessible, at the energy in question) and q is now a diagonal matrix whose elements are the c.m. momenta in the various channels, that is $q_{\beta\alpha} = q_\alpha \delta_{\beta\alpha}$; the term 1 in (1.8) denotes the unit matrix. The symmetric ordering of the two factors $q^{1/2}$ in (1.8) allows both of the matrices $S^{(l)}$ and $T^{(l)}$ to be symmetric (this symmetry property is required by time-reversal invariance). In terms of matrix elements, (1.8) takes the form

$$S_{\beta\alpha}^{(l)} = 2iq_\beta^{1/2}T_{\beta\alpha}^{(l)}q_\alpha^{1/2} + \delta_{\beta\alpha} \tag{1.9}$$

Note that (1.9) reduces to (1.4) when $\alpha = \beta$.

As an example of the formalism, the $\bar{K}N$ system at low energies couples to the (open) $\pi\Lambda$ and $\pi\Sigma$ channels; since the $\pi\Lambda$ system can have only isospin $I = 1$, while the others can have both $I = 0$ and $I = 1$, the matrices S and T are 2×2 for the $I = 0$ partial waves and 3×3 for the $I = 1$ partial waves.

The generalization of (1.5) for the multi-channel situation is the matrix equation

$$S^\dagger S = 1 \tag{1.10}$$

which is known as the unitarity condition for the S-matrix. (Here $S^\dagger$ denotes the hermitian conjugate of S, that is the complex conjugate of the transposed matrix; the index l is suppressed for brevity.) Substituting (1.8) into (1.10), one immediately obtains

$$4q^{1/2}T^\dagger qTq^{1/2} + 2iq^{1/2}(T - T^\dagger)q^{1/2} = 0$$

and hence

$$T - T^\dagger = 2iT^\dagger qT \tag{1.11}$$

Since T is a symmetric matrix, $T^\dagger$ is simply its complex conjugate matrix T^*, so that (1.11) can be written

$$2i\text{Im}\,T = 2iT^\dagger qT$$

It follows from this that the diagonal elements of the T-matrix satisfy

$$\text{Im}\,T_{\alpha\alpha} = \sum_\beta (T^\dagger)_{\alpha\beta} q_\beta T_{\beta\alpha} = \sum_\beta q_\beta\,|T_{\beta\alpha}|^2 \qquad (1.12)$$

Now let us integrate the expression for $d\sigma_{\beta\alpha}(\theta)/d\Omega$ obtained from (1.6) and (1.7) over the complete solid angle, using the orthogonality property of the Legendre polynomials

$$\int_{-1}^{1} P_l(x)P_{l'}(x)\,dx = 2\delta_{ll'}/(2l + 1) \qquad (1.13)$$

and the relation

$$d\Omega = 2\pi \sin\theta\,d\theta \qquad (1.14)$$

This gives the total cross section for the reaction $\alpha \to \beta$

$$\sigma_{\beta\alpha} = 4\pi\,\frac{q_\beta}{q_\alpha} \sum_{l=0}^{\infty} (2l + 1)\,|T_{\beta\alpha}^{(l)}|^2 \qquad (1.15)$$

According to (1.15) and (1.12), the total cross section for scattering into *all* final states from a given initial state α is given by

$$\sigma_\alpha = \sum_\beta \sigma_{\beta\alpha} = \frac{4\pi}{q_\alpha} \sum_{l=0}^{\infty} (2l + 1)\text{Im}\,T_{\alpha\alpha}^{(l)}$$

Now, using the partial-wave expansion (1.7) and the fact that $P_l(1) = 1$ for any l, we can express σ_α in terms of the elastic scattering amplitude in the forward direction ($\theta = 0$) in the form

$$\sigma_\alpha = \frac{4\pi}{q_\alpha}\,\text{Im}\,f_{\alpha\alpha}(0) \qquad (1.16)$$

The relation (1.16) is the celebrated optical theorem.

We shall now derive an important alternative form of the unitarity relation. Multiplying (1.11) on the left by $(T^\dagger)^{-1}$ and on the right by T^{-1}, we find

$$2iq = (T^\dagger)^{-1} - T^{-1} = (T^{-1})^* - T^{-1} = -2i\,\text{Im}\,T^{-1}$$

Hence

$$\text{Im}\,T^{-1} = -q \qquad (1.17)$$

This is a convenient expression for the restriction which unitarity imposes on the T-matrix for each partial wave.

Let us now consider the Argand diagram of a partial-wave amplitude for an elastic scattering process corresponding to a particular channel, which we label by the index 1 for definiteness. In particular, we shall plot the quantity $q_1 T_{11}$. If all the other coupled channels are closed at a particular energy, then equation (1.5) shows that $|S_{11}| = 1$, that is S_{11} lies on the unit circle in the complex plane. From the general relation between S and T, equation (1.4), it follows that $q_1 T_{11}$ then lies on a circle of radius $\frac{1}{2}$ centred at $\frac{1}{2}i$ (figure 1.1). This circle is called the unitarity circle.

We turn now to the more general case when additional coupled channels are open. To derive a unitarity constraint on the partial-wave amplitude T_{11} for

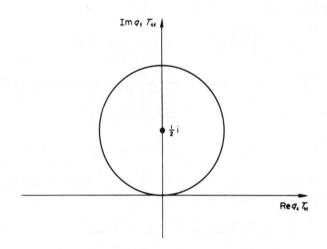

Figure 1.1. The unitarity circle for a partial-wave amplitude.

elastic scattering in channel 1, we partition the S-matrix as follows

$$S = \left(\begin{array}{c|c} S_{11} & A \\ \hline \tilde{A} & B \end{array}\right) \qquad S^\dagger = \left(\begin{array}{c|c} S_{11}^* & A^* \\ \hline \tilde{A}^* & B^\dagger \end{array}\right)$$

where $\tilde{A}$ denotes the transpose of the row matrix A. Then the unitarity condition (1.10) implies in particular that $S_{11}^* S_{11} + A^* \tilde{A} = 1$, that is

$$|S_{11}|^2 = 1 - \sum_{\alpha \neq 1} S_{1\alpha}^* S_{1\alpha} \leq 1 \tag{1.18}$$

Thus, S_{11} lies within the unit circle. Since $S_{11} = 2iq_1 T_{11} + 1$, this means that $q_1 T_{11}$ lies within the unitarity circle. Note that the equality in (1.18) holds only when $S_{1\alpha} = 0$ for all $\alpha \neq 1$, which, by virtue of (1.9), is equivalent to the vanishing of $T_{1\alpha}$. This is the case when the remaining channels are effectively decoupled from channel 1.

When inelastic scattering is possible, the effect of absorption in an elastic scattering process can be described phenomenologically within the 1-channel formalism by allowing the phase shifts to be complex. If

$$T_l = [\exp(2i\delta_l) - 1]/2iq$$

with

$$\delta_l = \alpha_l + i\beta_l \quad (\beta_l \geqslant 0)$$

then the S-matrix $S_l = \exp(2i\delta_l)$ automatically satisfies $|S_l| \leqslant 1$. Sometimes the parametrisation $S_l = \eta_l \exp(2i\alpha_l)$ $(0 \leqslant \eta \leqslant 1)$ is used instead. The relation between these parametrisations is given by $\eta_l = \exp(-2\beta_l)$.

1.3. Threshold branch points

In this section we shall consider the dependence of the partial-wave amplitudes $T_{\beta\gamma}$ on the total c.m. energy W near the threshold for some particular channel α. Let this threshold energy be $W = W_\alpha \equiv m_{1\alpha} + m_{2\alpha}$, where $m_{1\alpha}$ and $m_{2\alpha}$ are the masses of the particles in channel α.

Let us first examine the relation between W and the channel c.m. momentum q_α

$$W = \sqrt{(q_\alpha^2 + m_{1\alpha}^2)} + \sqrt{(q_\alpha^2 + m_{2\alpha}^2)} \tag{1.19}$$

Clearly, q_α is real (positive) for $W > W_\alpha$, but becomes purely imaginary when $W < W_\alpha$, so that $q_\alpha = \pm i \,|q_\alpha|$. To decide which of these two values to consider, we recall that bound states in potential scattering correspond to poles in the partial-wave amplitude on the *upper* half of the imaginary axis of the q_α-plane, where $q_\alpha = +i \,|q_\alpha|$.[1] This is a consequence of the fact that the outgoing spherical wave $\exp(iq_\alpha r)$ in the description of scattering in channel α must be replaced by an exponentially damped wave $\exp(-|q_\alpha| r)$ in the case of a bound state.

The inverse of the function $W(q_\alpha)$ defined by (1.19), namely $q_\alpha(W)$, is double-valued and has a square-root branch point at $W = W_\alpha$. The existence of this branch point can be seen from the fact that, if q_α is taken through an angle of π along a small circular path about the origin in the complex q_α-plane, the corresponding point in the W-plane traverses a closed trajectory about the point $W = W_\alpha$, returning to its original value.

Now the function $q_\alpha(W)$ appears on the right-hand side of the unitarity condition (1.17)

$$\text{Im}(T^{-1})_{\alpha\alpha} = -q_\alpha(W)$$

Thus, if the function $(T^{-1})_{\alpha\alpha}(W)$ is analytically continued into some region of the complex W-plane containing the point $W = W_\alpha$, it must have at least the singularity possessed by the function $q_\alpha(W)$. However, we shall assume that in general the functions $(T^{-1})_{\beta\alpha}(W)$ have no singularities in the physical region apart from those implied by the term $-q$ in the unitarity relation (1.17). This is a particular application of the postulate of *maximal analyticity*, which states that, with certain reservations, the amplitudes have only those singularities which are direct consequences of general principles such as unitarity and crossing.

It is convenient to formulate this idea mathematically by putting

$$T^{-1} = K^{-1} - iq \tag{1.20}$$

where the elements of the matrix K^{-1} have no singularities in the physical region and are real in this region. (Strictly speaking, we allow the elements of K^{-1} (and also those of K) to have certain poles (see sections 1.5 and 1.7).) Note that, although the unitarity condition (1.17) can be deduced from the conservation of probability only when all the channels considered in the matrix T are open, it follows from analyticity that K^{-1} is real in some range of lower energies. In fact, each element of K^{-1} must remain real with decreasing energy until its first singularity is reached. This can be seen, for example, from the fact that its Taylor series expansion about any real energy must have real coefficients. Moreover, since T and q are symmetric matrices, K is also symmetric

$$K_{\alpha\beta} = K_{\beta\alpha}$$

We have seen that $(T^{-1})_{\alpha\alpha}(W)$ has a square-root branch point at $W = W_\alpha$. To make such a function single-valued, we introduce a cut in the W-plane (known in this context as the unitarity cut) along the segment $W > W_\alpha$ of the real axis. As is easily verified, the analytic continuation of a function in the upper half of the q_α-plane from the sub-threshold momenta $+i|q_\alpha|$ to the physical momenta $q_\alpha > 0$ then corresponds to a continuation in the cut W-plane from the region $W < W_\alpha$ to the values of W just *above* the unitarity cut. The entire domain of the function reached from such points in the W-plane along paths which do not cross the cut defines the *physical sheet*.

Now the matrix T can be expressed in terms of its inverse T^{-1} by the standard formula involving the adjoint and determinant

$$T = \mathrm{adj}\,T^{-1}/\det T^{-1} \tag{1.21}$$

Thus, owing to the square-root branch point in $(T^{-1})_{\alpha\alpha}(W)$ at $W = W_\alpha$, *each* T-matrix element $T_{\beta\gamma}$ has a similar branch point at $W = W_\alpha$, even for $\beta \neq \alpha$, $\gamma \neq \alpha$. In other words, there is a branch point in $T_{\beta\gamma}$ at the threshold for each coupled channel. The amplitude has the general cut structure shown in figure 1.2, taking its physical values just above the cut.

As an example, among the branch points possessed by the partial-wave amplitudes for K^-p elastic scattering are those at the $\pi\Lambda$ and $\pi\Sigma$ thresholds (below the elastic region), the elastic threshold, and the threshold for the charge-exchange reaction $K^- + p \rightarrow \overline{K}^0 + n$ (slightly higher).

For some region of real energies below *all* the thresholds, the matrix T^{-1} and hence also T is *real*. By virtue of the Schwarz reflection principle, this implies that each amplitude $T_{\beta\gamma}$, when analytically continued from this region onto the rest of the physical sheet, satisfies the condition

$$T_{\beta\gamma}(W^*) = T^*_{\beta\gamma}(W) \tag{1.22}$$

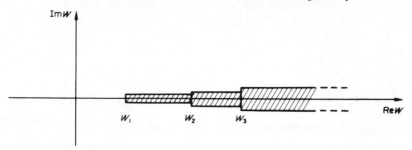

Figure 1.2. The general cut structure of a partial-wave amplitude in the physical region. The thresholds for the various channels are denoted by $W_1, W_2, \ldots$.

In particular, the values of $T_{\beta\gamma}$ at energies just above and just below the unitarity cut are complex conjugates of each other, the former giving the physical amplitude.

Unless specified otherwise, all complex energies in our further considerations will be understood to refer to the physical sheet. It should be noted that an amplitude may have a many-sheeted structure, owing to the presence of branch points at the thresholds for all the coupled channels.

1.4. Threshold cusps

We shall now consider briefly the threshold behaviour of cross sections. We begin with the case of purely elastic scattering in channel α, assuming that all other coupled channels are closed. In this case, we see from (1.20) that $T_{\alpha\alpha}$ is equal to some real constant at threshold, when $q_\alpha = 0$. Equation (1.15) then shows that the cross section tends to some finite limit at threshold.

Let us next suppose that certain other channels remain open below the threshold energy W_α for channel α. As before, $T_{\alpha\alpha}$ and $\sigma_{\alpha\alpha}$ both approach constant values as $W \to W_\alpha$, although the threshold value of $T_{\alpha\alpha}$ is now complex in general. On the other hand, owing to the factor q_β/q_α in (1.15), the cross section for an inelastic process $\alpha \to \beta$ with $W_\beta < W_\alpha$ has the behaviour

$$\sigma_{\beta\alpha} \sim \text{const}/\sqrt{(W - W_\alpha)}$$

as $W \to W_\alpha$, since in this case $q_\beta \to \text{const} \neq 0$, while $q_\alpha \sim \text{const} \sqrt{(W - W_\alpha)}$. The optical theorem (1.16) gives, of course, a similar threshold behaviour for the total cross section σ_α.

Finally, we may consider the threshold behaviour of a production process $\alpha \to \gamma$ with $W_\gamma > W_\alpha$. In this case

$$\sigma_{\gamma\alpha} \sim \text{const} \sqrt{(W - W_\gamma)}$$

as $W \to W_\gamma$.

These results can be applied to K^-p interactions, for example, by associating the channel labels α, β, γ in the foregoing formulae with the K^-p, $\pi Y (Y = \Lambda, \Sigma)$

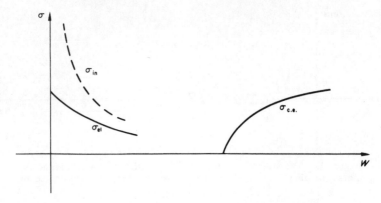

Figure 1.3. The qualitative threshold behaviour of the K^-p elastic, inelastic and charge-exchange cross sections.

and $\bar{K}^0n$ states respectively. The threshold behaviour of the K^-p elastic, inelastic and charge-exchange cross sections are shown in figure 1.3. In this example, the cross sections for elastic scattering and for hyperon production are also expected to have cusps at the charge-exchange threshold; this is a specific example of a general phenomenon which we shall now study in some detail.

From (1.19) and (1.20) we see that, at the threshold for channel α,

$$\mathrm{d}(T^{-1})_{\alpha\alpha}/\mathrm{d}W \rightarrow \begin{cases} -\mathrm{i}\infty & \text{as} \quad W \rightarrow W_\alpha^+ \\ -\infty & \text{as} \quad W \rightarrow W_\alpha^- \end{cases}$$

As the energy W increases through its threshold value W_α, $(T^{-1})_{\alpha\alpha}$ traces out a trajectory in the complex plane of the type shown in figure 1.4. In particular, there is a bend through an angle of $\frac{1}{2}\pi$ at $W = W_\alpha$. For energies W sufficiently near W_α, all elements of T^{-1} other than $(T^{-1})_{\alpha\alpha}$ have finite derivatives and may be regarded as constants. This means that, in expressing each element of T, say $T_{\beta\gamma}$, in terms of the elements of T^{-1} according to (1.21), we can regard $T_{\beta\gamma}$

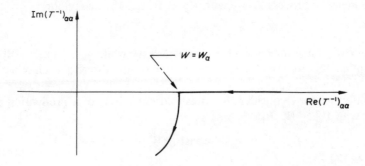

Figure 1.4. A typical trajectory of $(T^{-1})_{\alpha\alpha}$ in the complex plane as a function of energy near the threshold for channel α.

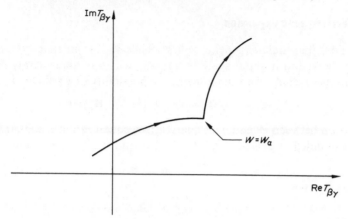

Figure 1.5. A typical form of the cusp in the trajectory of $T_{\beta\gamma}$ as a function of energy near the threshold for channel α.

as a certain function of $(T^{-1})_{\alpha\alpha}$ alone in some sufficiently small range of energies near W_α. Since this function is analytic, the conformal mapping theorem implies that the angle of $\frac{1}{2}\pi$ in the trajectory of $(T^{-1})_{\alpha\alpha}$ corresponds to an angle of $\frac{1}{2}\pi$ in the trajectory of $T_{\beta\gamma}$ (figure 1.5). Note that such a cusp appears in *each* amplitude $T_{\beta\gamma}$, even when $\beta \neq \alpha, \gamma \neq \alpha$. An alternative derivation of this result can be given in terms of the K-matrix formalism.[2]

Since the amplitude has an infinite derivative at the cusp, cusps show up in all observable quantities such as cross sections and polarisations. These cusps may be of the four types shown in figure 1.6. Examples of processes in which the effects of cusps have been clearly seen experimentally are K^-p interactions at the charge-exchange threshold, πN scattering at the ηN production threshold, and the reaction $\pi^- + p \to K + \Lambda$ near the $K\Sigma$ threshold.

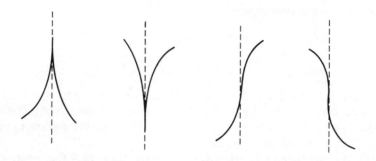

Figure 1.6. The four basic types of threshold cusps.

1.5. Effective-range expansion

We consider the single-channel case first. Since K^{-1} is an analytic function of W, we may expand it about some energy W_0, which is conveniently chosen at threshold (we exclude, for the moment, the possibility of a pole at $W = W_0$)

$$K^{-1} = a + b(W - W_0) + c(W - W_0)^2 + \cdots \tag{1.23}$$

The relation between W and q^2 is analytic (see equation 1.19), so that K^{-1} can also be expanded in powers of q^2. From (1.3) and (1.20), we find that

$$K^{-1} = q \cot \delta$$

Hence we can put

$$q \cot \delta = 1/A + \tfrac{1}{2}Rq^2 + \cdots \tag{1.24}$$

This is the conventional form of the effective-range expansion, where A and R are the scattering length and effective range respectively.

Actually, this form is appropriate only for S-wave scattering, since K_l^{-1} has poles at threshold in the higher partial waves with $l \geqslant 1$. The existence of these poles can be seen from a well-known theorem for potential scattering[3] which states that, for scattering by a potential $V(r)$ of finite range (more precisely, one which falls off faster than any power of r as $r \to \infty$, such as a Yukawa potential), the phase shifts have the threshold behaviour

$$\delta_l \sim \text{const } q^{2l+1} \tag{1.25}$$

(In Chapter 3 we shall derive this threshold behaviour within the framework of S-matrix theory.) Since $\cot \delta_l \sim 1/\delta_l$ for small δ_l, we have

$$q \cot \delta_l \sim \text{const } q^{-2l} \tag{1.26}$$

This means that the function $K_l^{-1}(q^2)$ has a pole of order l at $q^2 = 0$. By removing this pole, we obtain a modified effective-range expansion

$$q^{2l+1} \cot \delta_l = 1/A + \tfrac{1}{2}Rq^2 + \cdots \tag{1.27}$$

In the multi-channel case, the correct generalisation of the effective-range expansion is the matrix expansion

$$q^l K_l^{-1} q^l = a + b(W - W_0) + \cdots \tag{1.28}$$

or

$$q^l K_l^{-1} q^l = A^{-1} + \tfrac{1}{2}(q^2 - q_0^2)^{1/2} R (q^2 - q_0^2)^{1/2} + \cdots \tag{1.29}$$

where $a, b, \ldots$ and $A, R, \ldots$ are real symmetric matrices and q_0 is the value of the matrix q at $W = W_0$. The order of the q-dependent factors in (1.29) ensures that K_l is symmetric whenever the matrices $A, R, \ldots$ are symmetric. In practice, W_0 is taken at one of the thresholds.

Both the multi-channel effective-range expansion and the single-channel expansion (with complex coefficients, to allow for absorption processes) have been used extensively to parametrise low-energy $K^- p$ interactions. The former involves many more parameters, but it has the advantage of automatically taking into account the behaviour of the amplitudes at the thresholds for all the coupled channels which are considered. Such an expansion remains valid within a circle of convergence up to the nearest singularity which is not explicitly taken into account (which may be a pole or cut in an unphysical region or a threshold branch point due to some additional channel).

1.6. Resonances

We shall first consider the single-channel case. In this case, a resonance may be defined as a local maximum of the cross section as a function of energy for a particular partial wave; this obviously corresponds to a phase shift $\delta_l = \frac{1}{2}\pi m$, where m is an odd integer, at some energy $W = W_0$. To investigate the energy dependence of a resonant amplitude, we define the function

$$H(W) = q^{2l+1} \cot \delta_l = q^{2l}K_l^{-1} \tag{1.30}$$

We use this function instead of K_l^{-1} itself because any approximation giving a finite limit for $H(W)$ at threshold will then automatically give the correct threshold behaviour for K_l^{-1} and hence for the amplitude; this is important for resonances near threshold.

At the resonance energy, $H(W_0) = 0$. Since the function $H(W)$ is analytic, we may expand it in a Taylor series about the point $W = W_0$, giving

$$H(W) \approx (W - W_0)[\mathrm{d}H/\mathrm{d}W]_{W=W_0} \tag{1.31}$$

near the resonance. Equations (1.30) and (1.31), together with the relation (1.20), then lead to the *Breit–Wigner resonance formula*

$$T_l \approx \frac{\frac{1}{2}\Gamma/q}{W_0 - W - \frac{1}{2}i\Gamma} \tag{1.32}$$

where the quantity Γ, given by

$$\Gamma(W) = -2q^{2l+1}/[\mathrm{d}H/\mathrm{d}W]_{W=W_0} \tag{1.33}$$

has the dimensions of energy and is called the (energy-dependent) width of the resonance. To see its significance, suppose that the resonance peak is narrow in comparison with its distance from threshold, so that we can neglect the q-dependence in equations (1.32) and (1.33) and set $\Gamma(W) \approx \Gamma(W_0) \equiv \Gamma_0$ within this peak. The position of the resonance is taken to be $W = W_0$, corresponding to the maximum value of $|T_l|^2$. At the energies $W = W_0 \pm \frac{1}{2}\Gamma_0$ the value of $|T_l|^2$ is halved, so that $|\Gamma_0|$ gives the width of the peak in the cross section at half-height.

So far, the sign of Γ_0 is unspecified. We shall now argue that $\Gamma_0 > 0$. We know that, when the scattering is restricted to be purely elastic, qT_l lies on the unitarity circle in the Argand diagram (figure 1.7). If $\Gamma_0 > 0$ ($\Gamma_0 < 0$), the

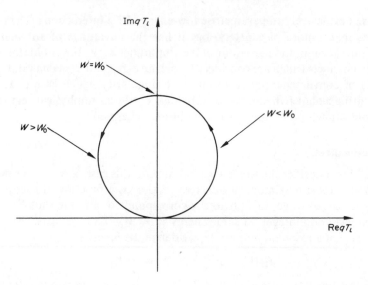

Figure 1.7. Trajectory of a partial-wave amplitude near a resonance energy
$W = W_0$.

Breit–Wigner formula shows that with increasing energy this circle is traced out in the anticlockwise (clockwise) sense, although the two cases would give identical cross sections. It is easily seen that these two cases correspond respectively to a phase shift δ_l which increases (decreases) with W. The maximum rate of change occurs at the top of the circle, where $W = W_0$. The narrower the resonance, that is the smaller $|\Gamma_0|$, the greater the rate of change. A simple argument originally due to Wigner,[4] based on the wave-function interpretation of the phase shift δ_l, shows that, for any finite-range interaction which satisfies a general causality principle (the hypothesis that no scattering occurs before the incoming wave reaches the interaction region), one can impose a certain bound on the rate at which the phase shift can decrease with energy (the *Wigner condition*). If we assume that arbitrarily narrow resonances can exist, we are led to exclude the case $\Gamma_0 < 0$.

In the S-matrix framework, the same conclusion follows from different considerations. The Breit–Wigner resonance formula (1.32) shows that T_l has a pole at a complex energy $W \approx W_0 - \frac{1}{2}i\Gamma_0$. This pole is reached by analytically continuing the amplitude from the physical region just above the unitarity cut, where the resonance peak is observed. Thus, if $\Gamma_0 > 0$, the pole lies below the real axis on an *unphysical* sheet reached by passing through the cut; on the other hand, if $\Gamma_0 < 0$, the pole lies above the real axis on the *physical* sheet. In S-matrix theory, the postulate of maximal analyticity which we have already stated actually applies only to the physical sheet. Thus, the possibility $\Gamma_0 < 0$ is excluded.

1.7. Multi-channel formalism

We now turn to the description of resonances in a multi-channel situation, restricting the discussion at first to the set of open channels in a particular energy region. For the present purpose it is convenient to construct the matrices $t = q^{1/2}Tq^{1/2}$ and $k = q^{1/2}Kq^{1/2}$ in the space of these channels, which, by virtue of (1.8) and (1.20), satisfy the equations

$$S = 2it + 1 \qquad t^{-1} = k^{-1} - i \qquad (1.34)$$

Now K and hence also k is real and symmetric; consequently, k can be diagonalised by an orthogonal transformation, corresponding to a rotation of the coordinate axes in channel space and specified by some matrix U. Equations (1.34) show that t and S are also diagonalised by the same transformation. (This transformation does not also diagonalise T and K, since these matrices are related to k by equations with q-dependent factors, which are diagonal only in the original representation.)

Since S is unitary, its eigenvalues are unimodular, so that we can write its diagonal form as

$$\bar{S} = U^{-1}SU = \begin{pmatrix} \exp(2i\delta_1) & & & \\ & \exp(2i\delta_2) & & \\ & & \cdot & \\ & & & \cdot \end{pmatrix} \qquad (1.35)$$

where the δ_α are real eigenphases. For example, in the 2-channel case the most general form of the S-matrix can be written

$$S = \begin{pmatrix} \cos\theta & \sin\theta \\ -\sin\theta & \cos\theta \end{pmatrix} \begin{pmatrix} \exp(2i\delta_1) & 0 \\ 0 & \exp(2i\delta_2) \end{pmatrix} \begin{pmatrix} \cos\theta & -\sin\theta \\ \sin\theta & \cos\theta \end{pmatrix}$$

where θ is a real parameter. From the relations (1.34), it follows that the diagonal forms of t and k^{-1} are

$$\bar{t} = U^{-1}tU = \begin{pmatrix} \exp(i\delta_1)\sin\delta_1 & & & \\ & \exp(i\delta_2)\sin\delta_2 & & \\ & & \cdot & \\ & & & \cdot \end{pmatrix} \qquad (1.36)$$

$$\bar{k}^{-1} = U^{-1}k^{-1}U = \begin{pmatrix} \cot\delta_1 & & & \\ & \cot\delta_2 & & \\ & & \cdot & \\ & & & \cdot \end{pmatrix} \qquad (1.37)$$

Physically a resonance is expected to correspond to a compound state of a system which can decay into any of the coupled channels. Thus, a resonance must appear in all coupled channels at the same energy. Our general definition of a resonance must also reduce to the previous one for the single-channel case. These conditions are met if a multi-channel resonance is associated with a resonance value of one of the eigenphases, $\delta_\alpha = \frac{1}{2}\pi m$ (m odd). In this case $(\bar{k}^{-1})_{\alpha\alpha} = 0$ and hence $|\bar{k}_{\alpha\alpha}| = \infty$, so that in the physical representation *each* K-matrix element $K_{\beta\gamma}$ has a pole at the same energy. We can also see from the diagonal form (1.37) that det $k^{-1} = 0$ at the resonance energy; alternatively

$$\det K^{-1} = 0 \qquad (1.38)$$

This is a concise form of the condition for a resonance. In terms of the T-matrix, which is more closely related to experiment, it reads

$$\det(\mathrm{Re}\,T^{-1}) = 0 \qquad (1.39)$$

The preceding results are valid when only the open channels are considered. Now suppose that we consider both open and closed channels in the region of the resonance energy and deal accordingly with larger matrices. To see what form the condition for a resonance takes, we partition the matrices with respect to the open and closed channels

$$K = \begin{pmatrix} K_{oo} & K_{oc} \\ \hline K_{co} & K_{cc} \end{pmatrix} \qquad T = \begin{pmatrix} T_{oo} & T_{oc} \\ \hline T_{co} & T_{cc} \end{pmatrix} \qquad q = \begin{pmatrix} q_o & 0 \\ \hline 0 & q_c \end{pmatrix} \qquad (1.40)$$

The full matrices are related by $T^{-1} = K^{-1} - iq$. On the other hand, the K-matrix referring to the set of open channels, known in this context as the *reduced K-matrix K_R*, satisfies the analogous equation

$$T_{oo}^{-1} = K_R^{-1} - iq_o \qquad (1.41)$$

Because of the matrix inversions in (1.41), K_R cannot be identified with K_{oo}. However, by matrix algebra one can show that

$$K_R = K_{oo} + iK_{oc}(1 - iq_cK_{cc})^{-1}q_cK_{co} \qquad (1.42)$$

We have seen that a resonance corresponds to a pole in K_R (in each element), but it turns out that the larger matrix K may or may not have a pole. Resonance poles in K_R can arise in two distinct ways

(i) det $K^{-1} = 0$
(ii) $\det(1 - iq_cK_{cc}) = 0$

In case (i), every element of K has a pole (excluding the exceptional case when some of the cofactors of K^{-1} vanish) and (1.42) shows that this gives a pole in K_R. Case (ii) refers only to the closed channels, and in this case the resonance can be regarded as a virtual bound state of these channels; in the absence of coupling to the open channels into which it can decay, the resonance would be a stable bound state due to the attractive forces in the closed channels. In the sense defined here, the Y_0^* (1405) resonance just below the $\bar{K}N$ threshold is generally believed to be a virtual bound state of the $\bar{K}N$ system, so that the elements of the full K-matrix for the coupled $I = 0$, $\pi\Sigma$ and $\bar{K}N$ channels do not have resonance poles.

Let us finally consider the behaviour of any particular elastic or inelastic scattering amplitude near a resonance in a multi-channel situation. Suppose that one of the eigenphases δ_α passes through a resonance value at $W = W_0$. Then, exactly as in the single-channel case, we can represent the corresponding element of the diagonal matrix (1.36) by the Breit–Wigner formula

$$\bar{t}_{\alpha\alpha} \approx \tfrac{1}{2}\Gamma/(W_0 - W - \tfrac{1}{2}\Gamma) \tag{1.43}$$

From the relation $t = U\bar{t}U^{-1}$, we have, for a typical amplitude

$$t_{\beta\gamma} = \sum_\sigma U_{\beta\sigma}\bar{t}_{\sigma\sigma}(U^{-1})_{\sigma\gamma} = \sum_\sigma U_{\beta\sigma}U_{\gamma\sigma}\bar{t}_{\sigma\sigma} \tag{1.44}$$

where we have used the fact that U is an orthogonal matrix. Separating the contribution from the term with $\sigma = \alpha$ in (1.44), we can write

$$t_{\beta\gamma} \approx \frac{\tfrac{1}{2}(\Gamma_\beta\Gamma_\gamma)^{1/2}}{W_0 - W - \tfrac{1}{2}i\Gamma} + B(W) \tag{1.45}$$

where

$$\Gamma_\delta = \Gamma U_{\delta\alpha}^2$$

and

$$B(W) = \sum_{\sigma \neq \alpha} U_{\beta\sigma}U_{\gamma\sigma}\bar{t}_{\sigma\sigma}$$

The quantity Γ_δ is known as the partial width of the resonance for channel δ, while Γ is now called the total width. It follows directly from the fact that U is an orthogonal matrix that

$$\sum_\delta \Gamma_\delta = \Gamma \tag{1.46}$$

As the energy W increases through the resonance value W_0, the first term of (1.45) describes an anticlockwise circle on the Argand diagram, exactly as in the single-channel case. However, since each partial width is in general smaller than the total width Γ, the resonance loop is now smaller than the unitarity circle which is traversed in the case of purely elastic scattering.

Owing to the additional term $B(W)$ in (1.45), known as the background term, the resonance circle on the Argand diagram may be translated, distorted and rotated. However, if it is assumed that the background term is slowly varying with energy in the region where the eigenphase δ_α rises rapidly through its resonance value, the resonance loop may be expected to retain its circular shape. The characteristic resonance loops on the Argand diagram (figure 1.8) are the usual means of identifying resonances in energy-dependent partial-wave analyses of scattering data.

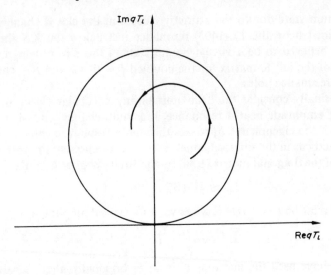

Figure 1.8. A typical resonance loop in a partial-wave amplitude in the
presence of inelasticity.

References

1. See, for example, N. F. Mott and H. S. W. Massey, *The Theory of Atomic Collisions*, 3rd edition,
   Clarendon Press, Oxford, 1965, Chapter 7.
2. R. H. Dalitz, *Strange Particles and Strong Interactions*, Oxford University Press, 1962, Chapter
   11.
3. See, for example, Mott and Massey (reference 1), chapter 2.
4. E. P. Wigner, *Phys. Rev.*, **98** (1955), 145.

Further reading

An excellent coverage of those aspects of the theory of analytic functions which are most relevant
for our purposes can be found in the following references.

1. P. Dennery and A. Krzywicki, *Mathematics for Physicists*, Harper & Row, New York, 1967,
   Chapter 1.
2. H. Burkhardt, *Dispersion Relation Dynamics*, North-Holland, Amsterdam, 1969, Part A.
3. F. W. Byron, Jr. and R. W. Fuller, *Mathematics of Classical and Quantum Physics*, vol. II,
   Addison-Wesley, Reading, Massachusetts, 1970, Chapter 6.

For further reading on topics in scattering theory related to the material of this chapter, the
following books are recommended.

4. H. Pilkuhn, *The Interactions of Hadrons*, North-Holland, Amsterdam, 1967.
5. A. D. Martin and T. D. Spearman, *Elementary Particle Theory*, North-Holland, Amsterdam,
   1970.

CHAPTER 2

Causality, analyticity and dispersion relations

2.1. Some mathematical preliminaries

In this section we shall introduce some important identities which will be required for what follows. Our primary consideration here will be the evaluation of definite integrals having the general form

$$I = \int_a^b \frac{F(z)\,dz}{z - x_0} \tag{2.1}$$

where a, b and x_0 are real constants such that $a < x_0 < b$ and $F(z)$ is an analytic function of the complex variable z in some region containing the real interval from a to b.

The integrand of (2.1) has a pole at $z = x_0$, and it is necessary to specify the contour of integration in such a way that it does not pass through this singularity. There are two distinct ways of doing this, namely to take the contour above or below the pole. In either case, the contour of integration may be deformed arbitrarily within the domain of analyticity of $F(z)$, provided that it is not allowed to pass through the singular point $z = x_0$. Let us denote by I_+ and I_- the values of the integral (2.1) for the upper and lower contours respectively.

We can represent $I_\pm$ as integrals along line segments which approach the real axis from above or from below. For this purpose, we put $z = x \pm i\varepsilon$, where x is a real variable and ε is a small positive imaginary part; we adopt the convention that the limit $\varepsilon \to 0^+$ is implied in any expression containing the quantity ε. Thus

$$I_\pm = \int_a^b \frac{F(x)\,dx}{x \pm i\varepsilon - x_0} \tag{2.2}$$

These integrals can be evaluated by deforming the contour of integration so that it runs along the real axis in the intervals

$$a < x < x_0 - \varepsilon \quad \text{and} \quad x_0 + \varepsilon < x < b$$

and along a semicircle $C_\pm$ of radius ε about the point x_0 in either the upper or the lower half-plane (figure 2.1); the limit $\varepsilon \to 0^+$ is understood. Thus

$$I_\pm = \left[\int_a^{x_0-\varepsilon} \frac{F(x)\,dx}{x-x_0} + \int_{x_0+\varepsilon}^b \frac{F(x)\,dx}{x-x_0} \right] + \int_{C_\pm} \frac{F(z)\,dz}{z-x_0} \qquad (2.3)$$

The quantity in the square brackets in (2.3), after taking the limit as $\varepsilon \to 0^+$, is by definition the principal value of the integral, denoted by

$$P\int_a^b \frac{F(x)\,dx}{x-x_0}$$

To evaluate the last integral in (2.3), we represent z on the semicircular contour

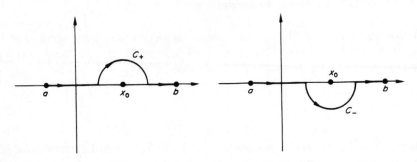

Figure 2.1. Contours of integration for evaluating the integrals $I_\pm$.

$C_\pm$ in the form $z = x_0 + \varepsilon \exp(i\phi)$. Using the fact that $F(x_0 + \varepsilon \exp(i\phi))$ can be replaced by $F(x_0)$ for sufficiently small ε, we find

$$\int_{C_\pm} \frac{F(z)\,dz}{z-x_0} = \int_{\pm\pi}^0 \frac{F(x_0)i\varepsilon \exp(i\phi)\,d\phi}{\varepsilon \exp(i\phi)} = \mp i\pi F(x_0) \qquad (2.4)$$

Thus, comparing (2.2) and (2.3), we have

$$\int_a^b \frac{F(x)\,dx}{x \pm i\varepsilon - x_0} = P\int_a^b \frac{F(x)\,dx}{x-x_0} \mp i\pi F(x_0) \qquad (2.5)$$

This general relation is sometimes represented symbolically by the more compact identity

$$1/(x \pm i\varepsilon - x_0) = P/(x - x_0) \mp i\pi \, \delta(x - x_0) \qquad (2.6)$$

where $\delta(x - x_0)$ is the Dirac delta function, having the formal property

$$\int_c^d F(x)\,\delta(x - x_0)\,dx = \begin{cases} F(x_0) & \text{if } c < x_0 < d \\ 0 & \text{if } x_0 < c \text{ or } x_0 > d \end{cases} \qquad (2.7)$$

for any continuous function $F(x)$. Equation (2.6) leads back to (2.5) if one multiplies by $F(x)$ and then integrates over the range $a < x < b$.

An additional property of the delta function which we shall require is its integral representation

$$\delta(x) = \frac{1}{2\pi} \int_{-\infty}^{\infty} \exp(ixt) \, dt \tag{2.8}$$

Equation (2.8) is a direct consequence of the well-known theorem which states that the inverse of a Fourier transform

$$G(t) = \int_{-\infty}^{\infty} \tilde{G}(x)\exp(-ixt) \, dx \tag{2.9}$$

is given by

$$\tilde{G}(x) = \frac{1}{2\pi} \int_{-\infty}^{\infty} G(t)\exp(ixt) \, dt \tag{2.10}$$

Equation (2.9) shows that $G(t) = 1$ when $\tilde{G}(x) = \delta(x)$. Substituting these values into (2.10), we obtain the required result (2.8).

2.2. The connection between causality and analyticity

To show the physical grounds for expecting scattering amplitudes to have analyticity properties, let us consider the wave-function description of a simple forward scattering process. In particular, we shall suppose that massless particles of energy (and hence also momentum) ω are scattered by a fixed target at the origin. For an incident plane wave in the z-direction, the asymptotic form of the wave function is

$$\psi \sim \exp[i\omega(z - t)] + f(\omega)\exp[i\omega(r - t)]/r \tag{2.11}$$

where $f(\omega)$ is the forward scattering amplitude. More generally, for an incident wave packet given by a superposition of plane waves

$$\psi_{\text{inc}}(z, t) = \int_{-\infty}^{\infty} A(\omega)\exp[i\omega(z - t)] \, d\omega \tag{2.12}$$

the corresponding scattered wave will be

$$\psi_{\text{sc}}(r, t) = \int_{-\infty}^{\infty} A(\omega)f(\omega)\exp[i\omega(r - t)]/r \, d\omega \tag{2.13}$$

To abstract the relevant general features of the problem, let us consider the system as a 'black box' (figure 2.2). We define the *input* $G(t)$ as the incident wave seen by the target at $z = 0$ and the *output* $H(t)$ as the scattered wave seen by a detector near the forward direction at some finite distance R from the origin. Thus

$$G(t) = \psi_{\text{inc}}(0, t) = \int_{-\infty}^{\infty} A(\omega)\exp(-i\omega t) \, d\omega \tag{2.14}$$

$$H(t) = \psi_{\text{sc}}(R, t) = \int_{-\infty}^{\infty} A(\omega)f(\omega) \frac{\exp(i\omega R)}{R} \exp(-i\omega t) \, d\omega \tag{2.15}$$

B

Figure 2.2. The input and output of a general physical system.

Using the general properties of the delta function given by (2.7) and (2.8), we can write (2.15) in the form

$H(t)$

$$= \int_{-\infty}^{\infty} d\omega' f(\omega') \frac{\exp(i\omega' R)}{R} \exp(-i\omega' t) \int_{-\infty}^{\infty} d\omega A(\omega)\, \delta(\omega' - \omega)$$

$$= \frac{1}{2\pi} \int_{-\infty}^{\infty} dt' \int_{-\infty}^{\infty} d\omega' f(\omega') \frac{\exp(i\omega' R)}{R} \exp(-i\omega' t)\exp(i\omega' t') \int_{-\infty}^{\infty} d\omega A(\omega)\exp(-i\omega t')$$

Thus

$$H(t) = \int_{-\infty}^{\infty} L(t, t')G(t')\, dt' \tag{2.16}$$

where

$$L(t, t') = \frac{1}{2\pi} \int_{-\infty}^{\infty} f(\omega') \frac{\exp(i\omega' R)}{R}\exp[i\omega'(t' - t)]\, d\omega' \tag{2.17}$$

Equation (2.16) shows explicitly that *the response of the system is linear*, that is, its output depends linearly on the input. From (2.17) we see that $L(t, t')$ is actually a function of the single variable $\tau = t - t'$

$$L(t, t') = L(t - t') \tag{2.18}$$

Equation (2.18) asserts that the properties of the system are *time-independent*. So far, $f(\omega)$ and hence $L(t - t')$ are arbitrary. However, we now impose the *causality condition*, namely the physical requirement that the output at any time t can depend only on the input at earlier times $t' < t$. This gives the constraint

$$L(\tau) = 0 \qquad \text{for} \qquad \tau < 0 \tag{2.19}$$

Let us now define the Fourier transform

$$\tilde{L}(\omega) = \int_{-\infty}^{\infty} L(\tau)\exp(i\omega\tau)\, d\tau = \int_{0}^{\infty} L(\tau)\exp(i\omega\tau)\, d\tau \tag{2.20}$$

For reasonable asymptotic behaviour of $L(\tau)$ (for example, polynomial boundedness), the integral (2.20) converges absolutely for all complex ω such that $\text{Im}\,\omega > 0$. Since the function $\exp(i\omega\tau)$ is analytic everywhere, we can conclude from a standard theorem on analytic functions that

$$\tilde{L}(\omega) \text{ is analytic for } \text{Im}\,\omega > 0$$

Note that the analyticity of $\tilde{L}(\omega)$ in the upper half-plane follows entirely from the three general conditions (2.16), (2.18) and (2.19) and was deduced without reference to the specific nature of the system. This analysis of general linear causal systems was first given by Toll.[1]

Let us return to the particular scattering problem discussed at the beginning of this section. By comparing the general expression (2.17) for $L(\tau)$ with the relation

$$L(\tau) = \frac{1}{2\pi} \int_{-\infty}^{\infty} \tilde{L}(\omega)\exp(-i\omega\tau)\,d\omega \tag{2.21}$$

obtained by inverting equation (2.20) (compare with equations 2.9 and 2.10), we obtain $\tilde{L}(\omega) = f(\omega)\exp(i\omega R)/R$. Hence *the scattering amplitude $f(\omega)$ is analytic in the upper half of the energy plane*. If $f(\omega)$ obeys the Schwarz reflection principle, then it is necessarily also analytic in the lower half-plane.

It is worth pointing out that such a straightforward proof of analyticity cannot be constructed for the scattering of massive particles. The difficulty arises from the more complicated relation between the energy and momentum of a particle with non-zero mass. For example, a plane wave $\exp[i\omega(z - t)]$ such as that in (2.11) becomes instead

$$\exp[i(\omega^2 - m^2)^{1/2}z - i\omega t]$$

2.3. Analyticity of amplitudes in quantum field theory

Rigorous derivations of analyticity properties of scattering amplitudes have been constructed within the framework of both non-relativistic potential scattering and relativistic quantum field theory. Although we do not expect either of these formalisms to give a full description of the strong interactions, they do provide some useful guidance as to what analyticity properties should be postulated in S-matrix theory (or expected to hold in a future theory of elementary particles).

The quantum field theoretic form of the causality hypothesis is that the commutator (or anticommutator, for particles obeying Fermi statistics) of two Heisenberg field operators must vanish for space-time points having a space-like separation

$$[\phi_1(x_1), \phi_2(x_2)] = 0 \qquad \text{for } (x_1 - x_2) \text{ space-like}$$

Physically, this restriction means that there is no mutual interference between two measurements taken at a space-like separation. We have here a condition of *microcausality*, in contrast with the form of causality assumed in the preceding section, where the distance R to the detector may be taken to be large.

Using the causality condition, rigorous proofs of analyticity properties of amplitudes in quantum field theory have been given for certain specific processes. However, the proofs are straightforward only for the forward scattering of massless particles. Proofs of analyticity in the upper half of the energy plane (required for the derivation of dispersion relations, as we shall see in section 2.4) have also been given for scattering at fixed momentum transfer, but only for a limited range of values of the momentum transfer. For example, a proof has been found for elastic πN scattering at fixed physical t (t is the invariant momentum transfer variable defined in section 3.1) only for $0 \leqslant -t \lesssim 18 \cdot 0 m_\pi^2$. For certain other processes (for example, elastic KN or NN scattering) no proof exists, even in the forward direction. A proof for NN scattering, for example, is known only for the hypothetical case in which the nucleon mass is less than $(1 + \sqrt{2})$ times the pion mass. A similar limitation applies to KN scattering. However, for any fixed $t \leqslant 0$ the scattering amplitude for a given process has been shown to be analytic at least in a cut energy plane minus some finite region.

The breakdown of the proofs of analyticity in quantum field theory for certain processes is generally believed to be due to the inadequacy of the mathematical techniques which are used and not to some intrinsic limitation of the theory. In S-matrix theory we simply postulate all the analyticity properties which are expected to hold.

For further details of the rigorously established analyticity properties of scattering amplitudes, we refer the reader to the reviews cited at the end of this chapter.

2.4. Derivation of the basic dispersion relation

Consider a function $F(z)$ having the following properties

(i) $F(z)$ is analytic in the upper half of the z-plane, but has cuts and poles on the real axis

(ii) $|F(z)| \leqslant O(|z|^{-\alpha})$ as $|z| \to \infty$ in the upper half-plane, for some $\alpha > 0$ (this notation means that $|F(z)| \leqslant C |z|^{-\alpha}$ for sufficiently large $|z|$, where C is some constant; that is, $|F(z)|$ decreases to zero asymptotically at least as fast as some negative power of z)

(iii) $F(z^*) = F^*(z)$

The bound in assumption (ii) is actually too restrictive for scattering amplitudes, and we shall relax it in section 2.5.

Beginning with assumption (i), we shall apply Cauchy's integral formula for $F(z)$ to a certain contour C in the complex z-plane. The contour (figure 2.3), chosen to exclude all the singularities of $F(z)$, consists of a straight line segment just above the real axis between the points $z = -R + i\varepsilon$ and $z = R + i\varepsilon$, closed by a semicircle of radius R in the upper half-plane. Thus, for any point z

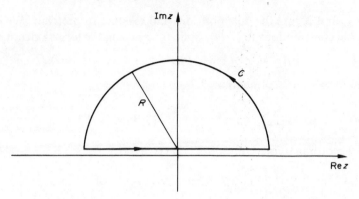

Figure 2.3. The contour of integration C used to derive the dispersion relation.

inside the contour

$$F(z) = \frac{1}{2\pi i} \oint_C \frac{F(z')\,dz'}{z' - z} \tag{2.22}$$

Since we shall usually be interested in physical energies, we shall evaluate $F(z)$ at the point $z = x + i\varepsilon$ for real x. To ensure that this point remains inside the contour C, we must first take the limit as the contour of integration approaches the real axis and then the limit as z approaches the real axis from above. This is equivalent to adding a small negative imaginary part in the denominator of the integrand, giving

$$F(x + i\varepsilon) = \frac{1}{2\pi i} \int_{-R}^{R} \frac{F(x' + i\varepsilon')\,dx'}{x' - x - i\varepsilon} + \frac{1}{2\pi i} \int_{S(R)} \frac{F(z')\,dz'}{z' - x - i\varepsilon} \tag{2.23}$$

where the second integral is over the semicircle $S(R)$ of radius R. Equation (2.23) is valid for any value of the radius R, but the second integral vanishes when $R \to \infty$ by virtue of assumption (ii). Thus

$$F(x) = \frac{1}{2\pi i} \int_{-\infty}^{\infty} \frac{F(x' + i\varepsilon')\,dx'}{x' - x - i\varepsilon} \tag{2.24}$$

As is customary, we have written $F(x)$ for the physical scattering amplitude $F(x + i\varepsilon)$ on the left-hand side of this relation. However, we retain the $i\varepsilon$ and $i\varepsilon'$ terms in the integral to indicate whether the path of integration runs above or below the poles of the integrand. Note that the limit $\varepsilon \to 0^+$ is to be taken after the integration is performed.

The integrand has poles due to (a) the poles of $F(z)$ on the real axis, and (b) the zero of the denominator; the path of integration passes above the former and below the latter. The poles of $F(z)$ give a contribution of the form

$$F^{(\text{pole})}(z) = \sum_n X_n/(z - x_n) \tag{2.25}$$

where x_n and X_n are the pole positions and residues respectively. We evaluate both pole contributions to (2.24) explicitly by using the formal identity

$$1/(x' - x \pm i\varepsilon) = P/(x' - x) \mp i\pi \, \delta(x' - x) \qquad (2.26)$$

derived in section 2.1. Equation (2.24) then becomes

$$F(x) = \frac{1}{2\pi i}\left[-i\pi \sum_n \frac{X_n}{x_n - x - i\varepsilon} + i\pi F(x + i\varepsilon) + P\int_{-\infty}^{\infty} \frac{F(x' + i\varepsilon') \, dx'}{x' - x} \right]$$

which, according to our conventions, we write as

$$F(x) = \frac{1}{2\pi i}\left[-i\pi \sum_n \frac{X_n}{x_n - x} + i\pi F(x) + P\int_{-\infty}^{\infty} \frac{F(x') \, dx'}{x' - x} \right] \qquad (2.27)$$

The first and second terms in the square brackets arise from the poles of types (a) and (b) defined above, and the integral is principal-valued with respect to each of the poles. Simplifying (2.27), we have

$$F(x) = \sum_n \frac{X_n}{x - x_n} + \frac{1}{\pi i} P\int_{-\infty}^{\infty} \frac{F(x') \, dx'}{x' - x} \qquad (2.28)$$

This is the *unsubtracted dispersion relation* for the function $F(z)$. Using assumption (iii), which implies that $F(x')$ is real on the singularity-free part of the real axis and also that the residues X_n are real, we obtain the more usual form of the dispersion relation

$$\text{Re}F(x) = \sum_n \frac{X_n}{x - x_n} + \frac{1}{\pi} P\int_{\text{cuts}} \frac{\text{Im}F(x') \, dx'}{x' - x} \qquad (2.29)$$

Note that the dispersion integral runs only over the cuts.

If, on the other hand, we take the imaginary part instead of the real part of (2.28), we obtain the so-called inverse dispersion relation

$$\text{Im}F(x) = -\frac{1}{\pi} P\int_{-\infty}^{\infty} \frac{\text{Re}F(x') \, dx'}{x' - x} \qquad (2.30)$$

Dispersion relations of this type will be discussed in more detail in section 7.1.

2.5. Subtractions

If the asymptotic condition assumed in section 2.4 is not satisfied, the integral over the semicircle may not tend to zero as $R \to \infty$.

Suppose instead that $F(z)$ satisfies the weaker condition

$$|F(z)| \leqslant O(|z|^{N-\alpha}) \qquad \text{as } |z| \to \infty \qquad (2.31)$$

in the upper half-plane, for some $\alpha > 0$ and positive integer N. A function satisfying such a condition is said to be *polynomially bounded*. We assume that the conditions (i) and (iii) enumerated in section 2.4 remain valid. Then all three conditions required for the derivation of the unsubtracted dispersion relation hold for the function obtained by dividing $F(z)$ by a real polynomial of degree N. Let us define in particular

$$G(z) = F(z) \Big/ \prod_{i=1}^{N} (z - a_i) \qquad (2.32)$$

where the a_i are real constants, which we choose to be all distinct.

The dispersion relation for G reads

$$\text{Re}G(x) = \sum_n \frac{X_n}{(x - x_n) \prod_{i=1}^{N} (x_n - a_i)} + \sum_{i=1}^{N} \frac{Y_i}{x - a_i} + \frac{1}{\pi} P \int_{\text{cuts}} \frac{\text{Im}G(x')\, dx'}{x' - x}$$

$$(2.33)$$

where X_n are the residues of the poles in the original function $F(z)$ and Y_i are the residues of the new poles introduced by the denominator of (2.32). If any of the a_i are equal, then the corresponding poles are no longer simple and the dispersion relation written here needs modification; we shall not consider this case.

In terms of $F(z)$, the dispersion relation becomes

$$\text{Re}F(x) = \left[\prod_{i=1}^{N} (x - a_i) \right] \sum_n \frac{X_n}{(x - x_n) \prod_{i=1}^{N} (x_n - a_i)}$$

$$+ A_0 + A_1 x + \cdots + A_{N-1} x^{N-1}$$

$$+ \frac{1}{\pi} \left[\prod_{i=1}^{N} (x - a_i) \right] P \int_{\text{cuts}} \frac{\text{Im}F(x')\, dx'}{(x' - x) \prod_{i=1}^{N} (x' - a_i)} \qquad (2.34)$$

where the polynomial of degree $N - 1$ arises from the product of $\Pi_i(x - a_i)$ and $\Sigma_i Y_i/(x - a_i)$. The N coefficients $A_0, \ldots, A_{N-1}$ can be related to the N residues $Y_1, \ldots, Y_N$, which in turn can be expressed in terms of $F(a_1), \ldots,$ $F(a_N)$. The points $z = a_1, \ldots, a_N$ are called the *subtraction points* and the coefficients $A_0, \ldots, A_{N-1}$ (or, alternatively, $F(a_1), \ldots, F(a_N)$) are known as the *subtraction constants*. The dispersion relation in this form is said to be one with N subtractions.

The minimum number of subtractions required for the validity of the dispersion relation is determined by the asymptotic behaviour of $F(z)$ for complex z. However, scattering amplitudes are physically accessible only for real energies. Fortunately, it turns out to be possible to replace the asymptotic condition which we have been assuming so far by a corresponding condition along the real axis alone. To do this, we make use of the following powerful theorem due to Sugawara and Kanazawa.[2]

Theorem. Let $F(z)$ have the properties

(i) $F(z)$ is analytic except for poles and cuts on the real axis, the cuts extending in general to $\pm \infty$

(ii) $F(z)$ is polynomially bounded in both the upper and lower half-planes

(iii) The limits $F(\pm\infty \pm i\varepsilon)$ along the cuts exist and are finite. Then

$$\lim_{|z|\to\infty} F(z) = \begin{cases} F(\pm\infty + i\varepsilon) \text{ in the upper half-plane} \\ F(\pm\infty - i\varepsilon) \text{ in the lower half-plane} \end{cases}$$

In particular, the theorem asserts that the corresponding limits along the cuts to the left and to the right are equal. This theorem is closely related to the better known Phragmén–Lindelöff theorem of complex variable theory but is more convenient for our purposes.

Hypotheses (i) and (ii) of the theorem imply that $F(z)$ satisfies a dispersion relation with some finite number of subtractions. If hypothesis (iii) is added, then the conclusion of the theorem implies that only a single subtraction is actually needed.

Suppose now, more generally, that $F(z)$ does not have finite limits at $z = \pm\infty \pm i\varepsilon$, but instead increases polynomially. Then we can apply the theorem to the function $F(z)/H(z)$, where $H(z)$ is a known function which diverges as strongly as $F(z)$, but has no singularities off the real axis; for example, we can choose $H(z)$ to be a polynomial of the appropriate degree.

Let us assume in particular that

$$|F(x)| \leqslant O(|x|^{N-\alpha}) \qquad \text{as } x \to \pm\infty \pm i\varepsilon \tag{2.35}$$

with $\alpha > 0$. Applying the theorem to the function $F(z)/z^{N-\alpha}$, we find that in the upper and lower half-planes this function has the (finite) limits

$$\lim_{|z|\to\infty} F(z)/z^{N-\alpha} = \lim_{x\to\infty\pm i\varepsilon} F(x)/x^{N-\alpha}$$

so that

$$|F(z)| \leqslant O(|z|^{N-\alpha}) \qquad \text{as } |z| \to \infty$$

This is exactly what is required to derive a dispersion relation for $F(z)$ with N subtractions. Thus, it is sufficient to assume such an asymptotic behaviour only along the real axis, as in (2.35).

In a subsequent chapter we shall consider the question as to exactly how many subtractions are required in realistic cases. Note that it is always possible to make more subtractions than the minimum number which is theoretically necessary. The greater the number of subtractions, the more rapid the convergence of the dispersion integrals, owing to the additional factors in the denominators. Extra subtractions were particularly advantageous in some early applications of dispersion relations, since they suppressed the dependence on the (then) poorly known high-energy contributions to the integrals. On the other hand, a disadvantage of extra subtractions is the introduction of additional subtraction constants.

References

1. J. S. Toll, *Phys. Rev.*, **104** (1956), 1760
2. M. Sugawara and A. Kanazawa, *Phys. Rev.*, **123** (1961), 1895

Further reading

For a discussion of the analyticity properties of scattering amplitudes in non-relativistic potential theory, see, for example, the following references.
1. M. L. Goldberger and K. M. Watson, *Collision Theory*, Wiley, New York, 1964.

A detailed survey of the rigorous proofs of analyticity properties of scattering amplitudes in relativistic quantum field theory appears in
2. G. Sommer, *Fortschritte der Physik*, **18** (1970), 577

The following papers are reviews of the derivation of dispersion relations and the early historical development of dispersion theory in high-energy physics
3. J. Hamilton, *Progr. in Nucl. Phys.*, **8** (1960), 143
4. J. D. Jackson, in *Dispersion Relations*, ed. G. R. Screaton, Oliver and Boyd, Edinburgh, 1961, p. 1
5. D. Amati and S. Fubini, *Ann. Rev. Nucl. Science*, **12** (1962), 359
6. S. Mandelstam, *Reports on Progr. in Phys.*, **25** (1962), 99

CHAPTER 3

Relativistic kinematics, crossing and the Mandelstam representation

3.1. Relativistic kinematics

A relativistic theory must be invariant under general Lorentz transformations. These include rotations of the coordinate axes as well as transformations between two coordinate systems having a uniform relative velocity. Thus, a total of 6 parameters are required to specify a general transformation, 3 for the rotation and 3 for the relative velocity.

We introduce the 4-momentum of a particle $p \equiv (\mathbf{q}, E)$, where $\mathbf{q}$ is its 3-momentum and E is its energy. We shall adopt the natural system of units in which $\hbar = c = 1$ and a metric such that $p^2 = E^2 - q^2$. For a particle of mass m, we have the mass-shell condition $p^2 = m^2$. More generally, the scalar product of any two 4-vectors $p_1 = (\mathbf{q}_1, E_1)$ and $p_2 = (\mathbf{q}_2, E_2)$ is given by $p_1 \cdot p_2 = E_1 E_2 - \mathbf{q}_1 \cdot \mathbf{q}_2$ and is a Lorentz invariant.

As a practical example of the application of 4-vectors to the kinematics of a two-body system, let us derive the relation between the energy ω_1 of particle 1 in the rest system of particle 2 (the laboratory energy of particle 1 when particle 2 is the target) and the total c.m. energy W of the system. Consider the invariant $(p_1 + p_2)^2$, where the subscripts label the particles. Evaluated in the c.m.s., in which $\mathbf{q}_1 + \mathbf{q}_2 = 0$, it gives $(p_1 + p_2)^2 = (E_1 + E_2)^2 - (\mathbf{q}_1 + \mathbf{q}_2)^2 = W^2$. Evaluated in the rest system of particle 2, in which particle 1 has 3-momentum $\mathbf{k}_1$, we find $(p_1 + p_2)^2 = (\omega_1 + m_2)^2 - k_1^2 = 2m_2\omega_1 + m_2^2 + m_1^2$. By equating these two expressions, we obtain the required relation

$$W^2 = 2m_2\omega_1 + m_1^2 + m_2^2 \tag{3.1}$$

Another useful result is the relation between the c.m. and laboratory momenta q_1 and k_1 of particle 1. To derive it, we shall first obtain a relation between the energies of particle 1 in the c.m. and laboratory systems, E_1 and ω_1. The equality $q_1^2 = q_2^2$ can be rewritten in the form

$$E_1^2 - m_1^2 = (W - E_1)^2 - m_2^2$$

Solving for E_1 and using (3.1), we have

$$E_1 = (W^2 + m_1^2 - m_2^2)/2W = (2m_2\omega_1 + 2m_1^2)/2W$$

Thus

$$q_1^2 = E_1^2 - m_1^2 = (m_2^2\omega_1^2 + 2m_1^2m_2\omega_1 + m_1^4 - m_1^2W^2)/W^2$$

Substituting the expression (3.1) for W^2 in the numerator, we have

$$q_1^2 = (m_2^2\omega_1^2 - m_1^2m_2^2)/W^2 = m_2^2k_1^2/W^2$$

Hence we finally obtain

$$q_1/k_1 = m_2/W \tag{3.2}$$

We now consider a general scattering process (which we refer to as the s-channel) with two particles in the initial and final states

$$a_1 + a_2 \to \bar{a}_3 + \bar{a}_4 \qquad \text{(s-channel)}$$
$$(p_1) \quad (p_2)(-p_3)(-p_4)$$

Below each particle we indicate its 4-momentum; note that the 4-momenta of the final particles are defined here with minus signs and that we have chosen to describe the final-state particles $\bar{a}_3$ and $\bar{a}_4$ as antiparticles (indicated by the bars).

In order to introduce the principle of crossing, we shall need the notion of a crossed process. The crossed processes corresponding to any given reaction are those in which one or more ingoing (outgoing) particles are replaced by their corresponding outgoing (ingoing) antiparticles. Two crossed processes are kinematically equivalent if each of these particles is replaced by its antiparticle having a 4-momentum equal to the negative of that of the original particle.

The crossing principle relates a given reaction to its kinematically equivalent crossed processes. In particular, associated with the original s-channel process specified above there is a (more symmetric) process in which each of the four particles a_i ($i = 1, 2, 3, 4$) is ingoing with 4-momentum p_i. We represent this process by a diagram such as that shown in figure 3.1. The other related

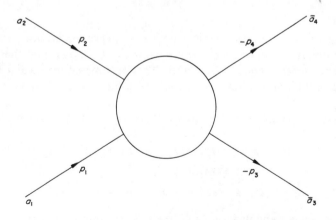

Figure 3.1. Diagram for a general two-body process.

two-body crossed processes, also represented by the same diagram, are

$$a_1 + a_3 \to \bar{a}_2 + \bar{a}_4 \quad \text{(t-channel)}$$
$$(p_1) \quad (p_3)(-p_2)(-p_4)$$
$$a_1 + a_4 \to \bar{a}_2 + \bar{a}_3 \quad \text{(u-channel)}$$
$$(p_1) \quad (p_4)(-p_2)(-p_3)$$

as well as the *CPT*-equivalent reactions

$$a_3 + a_4 \to \bar{a}_1 + \bar{a}_2$$
$$a_2 + a_4 \to \bar{a}_1 + \bar{a}_3$$
$$a_2 + a_3 \to \bar{a}_1 + \bar{a}_4$$

also referred to as the *s*-, *t*- and *u*-channels, respectively. Assuming *T* and *C* invariance separately, the amplitude for the *s*-channel process also describes the related processes

$$\bar{a}_3 + \bar{a}_4 \to a_1 + a_2$$
$$\bar{a}_1 + \bar{a}_2 \to a_3 + a_4$$

Including the remaining four processes similarly related to the *t*- and *u*-channels, we find that the same diagram represents in all 12 related processes.

If, in addition, one of the masses exceeds the sum of the other three, say $m_1 > m_2 + m_3 + m_4$, then there is still another crossed process which may occur physically, namely the decay process $a_1 \to \bar{a}_2 + \bar{a}_3 + \bar{a}_4$.

There are a total of 16 components of the four 4-momenta p_1, p_2, p_3 and p_4. However, energy-momentum conservation leads to 4 relations among them, namely the components of the relation

$$\sum_{i=1}^{4} p_i = 0 \tag{3.3}$$

as well as the 4 mass-shell conditions $p_i^2 = m_i^2$. Using in addition the fact that Lorentz invariance imposes 6 conditions, it can be shown that there are only *two* independent kinematic invariants. This means that any scalar (invariant) function of the four 4-momenta p_i must be a function of these two invariants alone.

A convenient set of kinematic invariants is given by the so-called Mandelstam variables

$$s = (p_1 + p_2)^2 = (p_3 + p_4)^2$$
$$t = (p_1 + p_3)^2 = (p_2 + p_4)^2 \tag{3.4}$$
$$u = (p_1 + p_4)^2 = (p_2 + p_3)^2$$

where the second equality on each line follows from energy-momentum conservation. Since only two of the three Mandelstam variables can be independent, there must be one relation among them. Using the definitions of s, t and u, the mass-shell conditions and energy-momentum conservation, the required relation is found to be

$$s + t + u = 3m_1^2 + m_2^2 + m_3^2 + m_4^2 + 2p_1 \cdot (p_2 + p_3 + p_4)$$

or

$$s + t + u = \sum_{i=1}^{4} m_i^2 \qquad (3.5)$$

The variables s, t and u can be related to the kinematic variables conventionally used to describe the scattering in any one of the crossed channels. Consider, for example, s-channel scattering in the c.m.s., in which the initial and final 3-momenta obey

$$\mathbf{q}_1 + \mathbf{q}_2 = \mathbf{q}_3 + \mathbf{q}_4 = 0 \qquad (3.6)$$

(see figure 3.2). Evaluating s, t and u in this system, we find

$$s = (E_1 + E_2)^2 - (\mathbf{q}_1 + \mathbf{q}_2)^2 = W^2$$
$$t = (E_1 - E_3)^2 - (\mathbf{q}_1 - \mathbf{q}_3)^2$$
$$= m_1^2 + m_3^2 - 2\sqrt{[(q^2 + m_1^2)(q'^2 + m_3^2)]} + 2qq' \cos \theta \qquad (3.7)$$
$$u = (E_1 - E_4)^2 - (\mathbf{q}_1 - \mathbf{q}_4)^2$$
$$= m_1^2 + m_4^2 - 2\sqrt{[(q^2 + m_1^2)(q'^2 + m_4^2)]} - 2qq' \cos \theta$$

The minus signs in the expressions for t and u arise from the fact that we have used $\mathbf{q}_3$, $\mathbf{q}_4$ and E_3, E_4 for the 3-momenta and energies of the final *outgoing* particles in the reaction, while p_3 and p_4 are ingoing; W is the total c.m. energy, $q = |\mathbf{q}_1| = |\mathbf{q}_2|$, $q' = |\mathbf{q}_3| = |\mathbf{q}_4|$, and the scattering angle θ is defined here as the angle between the directions of motion of the ingoing particle 1 and the outgoing particle 3. We could, of course, have defined θ as the angle between the directions of particles 1 and 4; in this case the signs of $\cos \theta$ in the formulae for t and u would be reversed.

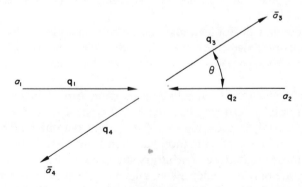

Figure 3.2. The c.m. momenta of the initial and final particles in a two-body scattering process.

In certain considerations we shall restrict ourselves to the equal-mass case $m_1 = m_2 = m_3 = m_4$ for simplicity. In this case $q = q'$, so that

$$t = -2q^2(1 - \cos \theta)$$
$$u = -2q^2(1 + \cos \theta)$$

(3.8)

The quantities $-t$ and $-u$ are then equal to the squares of the momentum transfers from particles 1 to 3 and from 1 to 4. More generally, when the masses are not necessarily equal, t and u give the squares of the corresponding 4-momentum transfers. Note that the equal-mass result for t in (3.8) depends only on the mass equalities $m_1 = m_3$, $m_2 = m_4$ (as, for example, in elastic scattering of two distinct particles), while that for u depends only on the equalities

$$m_1 = m_4, \qquad m_2 = m_3$$

Exactly analogous expressions can be written for s, t and u in terms of t- or u-channel quantities in the c.m.s., since everything is completely symmetric with respect to the variables s, t and u.

Note that the physical region for the s-channel is characterized by values of s greater than both $(m_1 + m_2)^2$ and $(m_3 + m_4)^2$; in the equal-mass case, t and u are always negative in this physical region.

3.2. Crossing

Let f be the s-channel c.m. scattering amplitude which we have employed so far in our considerations. We now define the new amplitude

$$A = \tfrac{1}{2}Wf$$

(3.9)

which can be shown to be Lorentz invariant and is called the (s-channel) *invariant amplitude*. Being invariant, A must be a function of any two of the three related kinematic invariants s, t and u, so that we may write $A = A(s, t)$, $A = A(t, u)$ or $A = A(u, s)$. However, to preserve the overall symmetry one may also write $A = A(s, t, u)$, with the understanding that s, t and u are related by the condition (3.5).

We are now in a position to give the precise statement of the principle of *crossing*, sometimes also called the *substitution law:* The invariant amplitudes for the s, t and u-channel processes are given by a single analytic function $A(s, t, u)$.

In general, the s, t and u-channel physical regions can be shown to be disjoint. Hence the concept of crossing has non-trivial content only if we assume that there exists an analytic continuation of $A(s, t, u)$ from one region to another. The existence of such a continuation has been rigorously proved in quantum field theory for the scattering of arbitrary stable particles.

Since there are only two independent kinematic invariants, all possible values of s, t and u can be represented on a two-dimensional plot. The symmetry among these three variables suggests the use of equilateral triangular coordinates

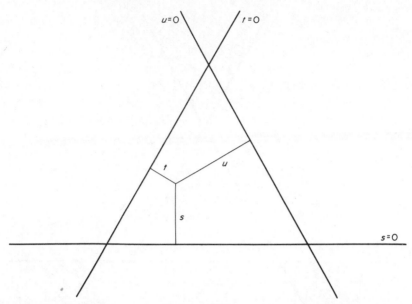

Figure 3.3. Representation of the variables s, t and u on the Mandelstam diagram.

(figure 3.3). From geometry it is known that the sum of the perpendicular distances to the three sides of an equilateral triangle from any point inside the triangle is a constant; the result remains true for points in the plane outside the triangle, provided that the perpendicular distances on the opposite sides of the lines are regarded as negative. Choosing the sides of the triangle as the coordinate axes and the perpendicular distances to them from a given point in the plane to represent (s, t, u) for that point, we can satisfy the constraint (3.5) for the sum $s + t + u$ by choosing the size of the triangle appropriately. In particular, its altitude must be equal to $\sum_i m_i^2$. Such a plot is called a Mandelstam diagram.

Let us consider some illustrative examples, beginning with the equal-mass case. Figure 3.4 shows the Mandelstam diagram for elastic $\pi\pi$ scattering. The altitude of the triangle is equal to $4m_\pi^2$. The s, t and u-channel physical regions, which all represent the same process in this case, are indicated by the shaded areas. The boundaries of the physical region in each channel correspond to forward and backward scattering in that channel. As is easily verified, for example by putting $t = \text{const } u$ in (3.8), the set of points on any straight line passing through one of the vertices corresponds to scattering at some fixed angle.

The symmetry of the diagram is broken when the masses are unequal. As an example of a case with four distinct masses, we show in figure 3.5 the Mandelstam diagram for the three related processes $\pi + \bar{K} \to \bar{N} + \Lambda$, $\pi + N \to K + \Lambda$ and $\bar{K} + N \to \pi + \Lambda$, taken to be the s, t and u-channels, respectively. Although the boundaries of the physical regions in the unequal-mass case (representing forward and backward scattering) are in general more

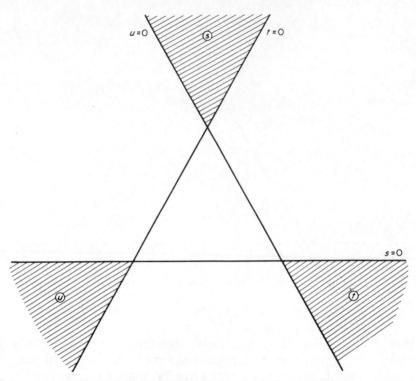

Figure 3.4. The Mandelstam diagram for elastic $\pi\pi$ scattering.

complicated than in the preceding example, they always approach the coordinate axes as the energy variable increases asymptotically. This can be seen by setting $\cos\theta = \pm 1$ in our general s-channel formulae (3.7) for t and u and letting $s \to \infty$.

Finally, we give in figure 3.6 the Mandelstam diagram for the process $\pi + \omega \to \pi + \pi$ and its associated crossed scattering channels (all representing the same process); in this case there is also a fourth physical region at the centre of the diagram, representing the decay channel $\omega \to \pi + \pi + \pi$.

To conclude this section, we return to the invariant amplitude A which we have introduced by equation (3.9). Since it is often convenient to work with this amplitude, we shall now write out the formulae for the total and differential cross sections in terms of $A(s, t)$ in the case of an elastic scattering process

$$\sigma(s) = \frac{4\pi}{q} \operatorname{Im} f(s, 0) = \frac{8\pi}{q\sqrt{s}} \operatorname{Im} A(s, 0) \qquad (3.10)$$

$$d\sigma/d\Omega = |f|^2 = 4|A|^2/s \qquad (3.11)$$

For many purposes it is advantageous to specify the differential cross section in terms of $d\sigma/d|t|$ instead of $d\sigma/d\Omega$. To obtain the relation between these two

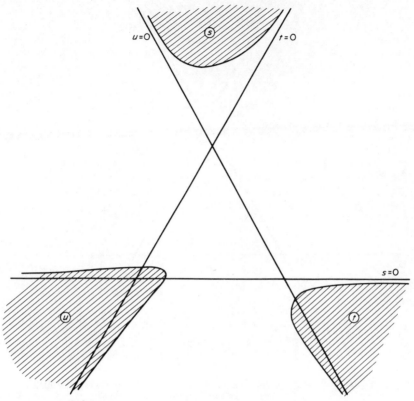

Figure 3.5. A Mandelstam diagram for three processes with unequal masses.

quantities, we first note that

$$d\Omega = 2\pi \sin \theta \, d\theta$$
$$dt = -2q^2 \sin \theta \, d\theta$$

for a given scattering angle θ, so that $d\Omega/d|t| = \pi/q^2$. Hence

$$\frac{d\sigma}{d|t|} = \frac{\pi}{q^2} \frac{d\sigma}{d\Omega} = \frac{4\pi}{q^2 s} |A|^2 \qquad (3.12)$$

Later we shall often use the asymptotic forms of these relations. As $s \to \infty$, we have $s \sim 4q^2$ and hence

$$\sigma(s) \sim \frac{16\pi}{s} \, \mathrm{Im} A(s, 0) \qquad (3.13)$$

$$\frac{d\sigma}{d|t|} \sim \frac{16\pi}{s^2} |A|^2 \qquad (3.14)$$

We adopt the symbol $\sim$ to denote an asymptotic equality as $s \to \infty$, in the sense that the ratio of the two quantities in question approaches unity.

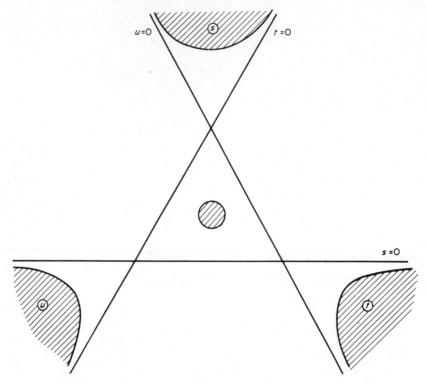

Figure 3.6. A Mandelstam diagram with a fourth physical region representing
a decay channel.

3.3. One-particle exchange model

As an illustration of the principle of crossing, it is instructive to consider its
application to a simple version of the ρ-exchange model for the process
$\pi^- + p \rightarrow \pi^0 + n$ (figure 3.7).

In figure 3.8 we show the Mandelstam diagram for this process and its
associated crossed channels. The three channels are as follows

$$\pi^- + p \rightarrow \pi^0 + n \qquad \text{(s-channel)}$$

$$\pi^- + \pi^0 \rightarrow \bar{p} + n \qquad \text{(t-channel)}$$

$$\pi^- + \bar{n} \rightarrow \pi^0 + \bar{p} \qquad \text{(u-channel)}$$

To simplify the algebra, we shall ignore the presence of spin and suppose that
there is only a single invariant amplitude A. The one-particle exchange model
for small-angle scattering in the s-channel ($t \approx 0$) consists in keeping only the
important low-lying single-particle states in the t-channel (corresponding to a
sum of poles in t at positive values of $\mathrm{Re}\,t$), neglecting all u-channel states;
crossing is then invoked to obtain the corresponding amplitude in the s-channel.

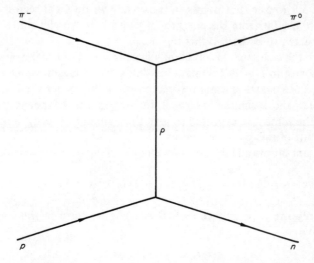

Figure 3.7. Diagram representing the ρ-exchange model for the process
$\pi^- + p \rightarrow \pi^0 + n$.

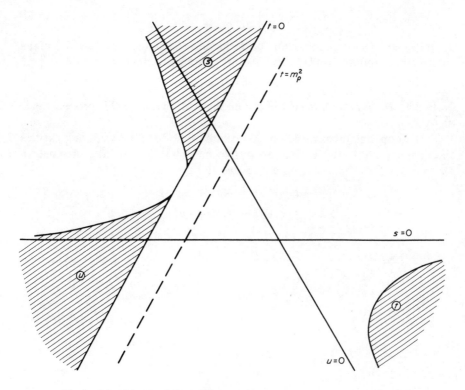

Figure 3.8. The Mandelstam diagram for the process $\pi^- + p \rightarrow \pi^0 + n$
and its associated crossed channels.

From figure 3.8 we see that points in the s-channel physical region with large s and small $|t|$ are far from the energies of possible u-channel states. Thus, the model is expected to be best in this region.

In our case the t-channel involves only isospin $I = 1$, since the $\bar{p}n$ system is a state of pure isospin $I = 1$. The main low-lying $I = 1$ meson which can couple to the $\pi\pi$ and $\bar{N}N$ states is the ρ resonance at $t = m_\rho^2$. Since the line $t = m_\rho^2$ is relatively near the s-channel physical region on the Mandelstam diagram (figure 3.8), the ρ may be expected to give the dominant energy dependence in the nearby part of this physical region.

The invariant amplitude in the t-channel has the partial-wave expansion

$$A(s, t) = \tfrac{1}{2}\sqrt{t} \sum_{l=0}^{\infty} (2l + 1)T_l(t)P_l(\cos \theta_t) \tag{3.15}$$

Retaining only the ρ resonance as a Breit–Wigner term in the $l = 1$ partial wave, we have

$$A(s, t) \approx K(t)P_1(\cos \theta_t) \tag{3.16}$$

where (see section 1.7)

$$K(t) = \frac{3\sqrt{t}}{2\sqrt{(q_\pi q_N)}} \frac{\tfrac{1}{2}x\Gamma}{m_\rho - \sqrt{t} - \tfrac{1}{2}i\Gamma} \tag{3.17}$$

q_π and q_N being the c.m. momenta for the $\pi\pi$ and $\bar{N}N$ states; Γ is the width of the ρ resonance, and the factor x describes its coupling to the process

$$\pi + \pi \to \bar{N} + N$$

Note that the ρ meson appears in the unphysical region for this process, since $m_\rho < 2m_N$.

Before applying crossing to our approximation (3.16), we shall first express the quantity $\cos \theta_t$ (which has no simple interpretation in the s-channel) in terms of s and t. The momenta are related to t by

$$t = 4E_\pi^2 = 4(q_\pi^2 + m_\pi^2)$$
$$t = 4E_N^2 = 4(q_N^2 + m_N^2)$$

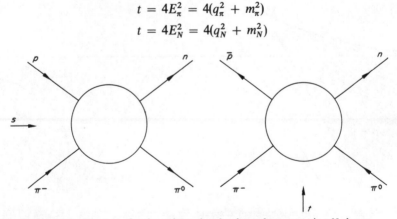

Figure 3.9. Diagrams for the s-channel and t-channel processes in πN charge exchange.

To find $\cos \theta_t$ in terms of s and t, we note that

$$s = (p_\pi + p_p)^2 = m_\pi^2 + m_N^2 + 2p_\pi p_p \tag{3.18}$$

where p_π and p_p are the 4-momenta of the initial particles in the s-channel. Consider the diagrams in figure 3.9 showing the related s-channel and t-channel reactions. We see that p_p is related to the variables describing the antiproton in the t-channel by

$$p_p = -p_{\bar{p}} = (-\mathbf{q}_{\bar{p}}, -E_{\bar{p}})$$

In terms of quantities referring to the t-channel c.m.s., we have

$$\begin{aligned} p_\pi p_p &= -E_\pi E_{\bar{p}} + q_\pi q_{\bar{p}} \cos \theta_t \\ &= -\tfrac{1}{4}t + \tfrac{1}{4}\sqrt{[(t - 4m_\pi^2)(t - 4m_N^2)]}\cos \theta_t \end{aligned} \tag{3.19}$$

Using (3.18) and (3.19) (and implicitly applying crossing), we finally obtain the amplitude in the s-channel

$$A(s, t) \approx K(t)\cos \theta_t = K(t)\left[\frac{2(s - m_\pi^2 - m_N^2 + \tfrac{1}{2}t)}{-\sqrt{[(4m_\pi^2 - t)(4m_N^2 - t)]}}\right] \tag{3.20}$$

We have rewritten the factors in the square root so that they are positive in the physical region of the s-channel (where $t < 0$). The minus sign in front of the square root in (3.20) (which is not present in the description of t-channel scattering) comes from choosing the branch of the square root function reached by analytically continuing from the t-channel region considered above ($t > 0$) to the s-channel physical region with $t < 0$.

It is of interest to examine the s-dependence of (3.20): $A(s, t) \sim$ const s as $s \to \infty$ with t fixed. This s-dependence is governed entirely by the spin of the exchanged particle, that is the value of l for the t-channel partial-wave amplitude which is assumed to dominate. To obtain the result in the general case, $P_1(\cos \theta_t)$ in the preceding argument must be replaced by $P_l(\cos \theta_t)$. Since $P_l(x) \sim$ const x^l as $x \to \infty$, we find in general that $A(s, t) \sim$ const s^l as $s \to \infty$ at fixed t. Such a behaviour in the case of an elastic scattering process would lead to an asymptotic total cross section

$$\sigma(s) \sim \text{const } s^{l-1} \tag{3.21}$$

in violent disagreement with both experiment and theory (see chapter 4) when $l > 1$. As we shall see later, this inconsistency can be removed by 'reggeising' the exchange.

3.4. Crossing relations

For definiteness, let us consider an elastic scattering process $a_1 + a_2 \to a_1 + a_2$, which we call the s-channel. Its amplitude $A(s, t_0)$ at fixed $t = t_0$ is assumed to be analytic in a cut s-plane with the unitarity cut for $s > s_0$, where s_0 is the threshold for the two-particle state of lowest mass which couples to the state $a_1 + a_2$.

An analogous statement holds for the amplitude for the u-channel process $\bar{a}_1 + a_2 \rightarrow \bar{a}_1 + a_2$ in the u-plane at fixed t. Suppose that its unitarity cut begins at $u = u_0$. Then from the relation $s + t + u = 2m_1^2 + 2m_2^2$ we see that $A(s, t_0)$ also has a cut in the s-plane for $s < 2m_1^2 + 2m_2^2 - t_0 - u_0 \equiv s_L$; this cut is called the *left-hand* (or *crossed*) *cut*.

Now the physical region for the s-channel process corresponds to values $s + i\varepsilon$, above the unitarity cut in the s-plane. Since the u-channel physical region is similarly given by values $u + i\varepsilon$, it follows from the relation for $s + t + u$ that in the s-plane at fixed (real) t the u-channel physical region corresponds to points just *below* the left-hand cut.

Between the left- and right-hand cuts there may be poles on the real axis associated with stable particles in either the s or u-channel. In particular, s-channel poles must lie in the interval $0 < s < s_0$ (the possible range of squares of the masses of s-channel particles), while u-channel poles must lie in the interval $0 < u < u_0$, that is

$$s_L < s < 2m_1^2 + 2m_2^2 - t_0$$

The general analytic structure of the amplitude $A(s, t_0)$ in the s-plane is shown in figure 3.10. The crosses on the real axis between the two cuts indicate possible poles.

Let us now define the amplitudes $A_s \equiv A_s(s, t)$ and $A_u \equiv A_u(u, t)$ appropriate for describing scattering in the s and u-channels, respectively. These two amplitudes are connected by crossing, but are written as functions of different sets of arguments, the first argument in each case being the energy variable appropriate to the channel in question. Applying crossing, we obtain the *crossing relation*

$$A_s(s, t) = A_u(2m_1^2 + 2m_2^2 - t - s, t) \tag{3.22}$$

This relation can be written in a more symmetric manner by introducing new energy-type variables for the s and u-channels

$$v_s = (s - u)/4m_2 \qquad v_u = (u - s)/4m_2 \tag{3.23}$$

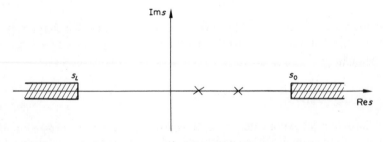

Figure 3.10. The general analytic structure of the scattering amplitude in the s-plane at fixed t.

We note that

$$v_s = (2s + t - 2m_1^2 - 2m_2^2)/4m_2 = \omega_s + t/4m_2 \qquad (3.24)$$

where ω_s is the energy of particle 1 in the rest system of particle 2 (its laboratory energy) for s-channel scattering. Similarly

$$v_u = \omega_u + t/4m_2 \qquad (3.25)$$

In the special case of forward scattering ($t = 0$), each variable v reduces to the corresponding ω.

The analyticity properties of amplitudes in the cut s-plane at fixed t imply similar analyticity properties in a cut v-plane. However, the v variable is more convenient for certain purposes because of the relation $v_s = -v_u$, which holds for any set of values of s, t and u. To exploit this property, we regard the amplitudes instead as functions of v and t and write

$$A_s = A_s(v_s, t) \qquad A_u = A_u(v_u, t)$$

The crossing relation then takes the simple form

$$A_s(-v, t) = A_u(v, t) \qquad (3.26)$$

Note that the significance of the first argument is different on the left and right-hand sides of the crossing relation (3.26) (v_s and v_u, respectively). This relation holds in general in the (cut) complex v-plane. In the formulation of dispersion relations we shall be particularly concerned with the value of the amplitude just above the cuts in the s-plane (and hence also in the v-plane). Evaluating the crossing relation (3.26) at $v + i\varepsilon$ and applying the Schwarz reflection principle, we obtain

$$A_s^*(-v + i\varepsilon, t) = A_u(v + i\varepsilon, t) \qquad (3.27)$$

3.5. The left-hand cut in fixed-t dispersion relations

Consider the related scattering processes

$$a_1 + a_2 \rightarrow a_1 + a_2 \qquad \text{and} \qquad \bar{a}_1 + a_2 \rightarrow \bar{a}_1 + a_2$$

whose amplitudes we shall now write as $A(v, t)$ and $\bar{A}(v, t)$ respectively. Let us suppose that the left and right-hand cuts cover the ranges

$$-\infty < v < -v_L \qquad \text{and} \qquad v_R < v < \infty$$

respectively. For example, in the special case in which no inelastic channels are open at threshold

$$v_L = v_R = m_1 + t/4m_2 \qquad (3.28)$$

Assuming the absence of additional singularities apart from poles on the real axis (maximal analyticity), we can write the unsubtracted dispersion relation (cf. equation 2.29)

$$\mathrm{Re}A(v, t) = \sum_n \frac{X_n}{v - v_n} + \frac{1}{\pi} P \int_{\mathrm{cuts}} \frac{\mathrm{Im}A(v', t)\, dv'}{v' - v} \qquad (3.29)$$

(we ignore the possible need for subtractions here; later we shall apply the same technique to more realistic subtracted forms). We recall that the dispersion integrals run *above* the cuts. Using the crossing property

$$\mathrm{Im}A(v + i\varepsilon, t) = -\mathrm{Im}\bar{A}(-v + i\varepsilon, t) \qquad (3.30)$$

the integral over the left-hand cut can be expressed in terms of one involving the crossed amplitude over its right-hand cut

$$\int_{-\infty}^{-v_L} \frac{\mathrm{Im}A(v', t)\, dv'}{v' - v} = \int_{-\infty}^{-v_L} \frac{-\mathrm{Im}\bar{A}(-v', t)\, dv'}{v' - v}$$

$$= -\int_{\infty}^{v_L} \frac{\mathrm{Im}\bar{A}(v'', t)\, dv''}{v'' + v}$$

$$= \int_{v_L}^{\infty} \frac{\mathrm{Im}\bar{A}(v'', t)\, dv''}{v'' + v} \qquad (3.31)$$

Thus, the dispersion relation can be written

$$\mathrm{Re}A(v, t) = \sum_n \frac{X_n}{v - v_n} + \frac{1}{\pi} P \int_{v_R}^{\infty} \frac{\mathrm{Im}A(v', t)\, dv'}{v' - v} + \frac{1}{\pi} \int_{v_L}^{\infty} \frac{\mathrm{Im}\bar{A}(v', t)\, dv'}{v' + v} \qquad (3.32)$$

Similarly, the dispersion relation for the amplitude $\bar{A}$ is

$$\mathrm{Re}\bar{A}(v, t) = -\sum_n \frac{X_n}{v + v_n} + \frac{1}{\pi} P \int_{v_L}^{\infty} \frac{\mathrm{Im}\bar{A}(v', t)\, dv'}{v' - v} + \frac{1}{\pi} \int_{v_R}^{\infty} \frac{\mathrm{Im}A(v', t)\, dv'}{v' + v} \qquad (3.33)$$

where the pole positions v_n and the residues X_n are again defined as those in the amplitude $A(v, t)$ (and not in $\bar{A}(v, t)$). The dispersion relation (3.33) can be derived directly in analogy with the dispersion relation (3.32) for the amplitude $A(v, t)$. Alternatively, it can be obtained from the latter by simply making the substitution $v \to -v$ and applying the crossing property

$$\mathrm{Re}A(-v, t) = \mathrm{Re}\bar{A}(v, t)$$

Finally, we note the important fact that the dispersion relation which we have derived for the invariant amplitude A also holds for the forward amplitude F in the laboratory system, say the rest system of particle 2. This is a consequence of the fact that the invariant amplitude A is simply proportional to F, since in this case

$$A = \tfrac{1}{2}Wf = \tfrac{1}{2}W \frac{q_1}{k_1} F = \tfrac{1}{2}W \frac{m_2}{W} F = \tfrac{1}{2}m_2 F \qquad (3.34)$$

In phenomenological applications, forward dispersion relations are usually written for the laboratory amplitudes.

The c.m. amplitude f does *not* satisfy a simple dispersion relation of the same type, since f contains an additional kinematic singularity in the s-plane at $s = 0$ due to the factor W in the relation between A and f.

3.6. The Mandelstam representation

The singularities of the amplitude $A(s, t, u)$ when one variable is fixed include the unitarity cuts for $s > s_0, t > t_0$ and $u > u_0$ and possible pole terms associated with single-particle states in the variables s, t and u. We have not yet considered the analytic structure of the amplitude as a function of two independent complex variables. Mandelstam conjectured that, apart from subtractions, $A(s, t, u)$ has the structure

$$A(s, t, u) = \frac{1}{\pi^2} \int_{s_0}^{\infty} ds' \int_{t_0}^{\infty} dt' \frac{\rho_{st}(s', t')}{(s' - s)(t' - t)} + \frac{1}{\pi^2} \int_{t_0}^{\infty} dt' \int_{u_0}^{\infty} du' \frac{\rho_{tu}(t', u')}{(t' - t)(u' - u)}$$

$$+ \frac{1}{\pi^2} \int_{s_0}^{\infty} ds' \int_{u_0}^{\infty} du' \frac{\rho_{su}(s', u')}{(s' - s)(u' - u)} + \text{pole terms} \tag{3.35}$$

where the functions ρ_{st}, ρ_{tu} and ρ_{su} (double spectral functions) are all real. This is the unsubtracted form of the Mandelstam representation (also known as the double dispersion relation). It gives the analytic structure of $A(s, t, u)$ for all complex s, t and u and implies maximal analyticity in each channel, with singularities only for real values of s, t and u. It turns out that certain processes have so-called 'anomalous thresholds', where the lower limits of the double integrals are not determined simply by the masses of the possible states which couple to a given channel. In such cases the Mandelstam representation must be appropriately modified, but we shall not consider this problem here.

We shall now show that the ordinary fixed-variable dispersion relations are consequences of the Mandelstam representation. Consider, for example, the fixed-t case. First of all, we split the third double integral in (3.35) into two integrals by means of the identity

$$\frac{1}{(s' - s)(u' - u)} = \left(\frac{1}{s' - s} + \frac{1}{u' - u} \right) \left(\frac{1}{s' - s + u' - u} \right)$$

Using the relation (3.5) for $s + t + u$, we find

$$s' - s + u' - u = s' - \left(\sum_i m_i^2 - t - u' \right) = u' - \left(\sum_i m_i^2 - t - s \right)$$

so that (3.35) becomes

$$A(s, t, u) = \frac{1}{\pi} \int_{s_0}^{\infty} \frac{ds'}{s' - s} \left[\frac{1}{\pi} \int_{t_0}^{\infty} \frac{\rho_{st}(s', t')\, dt'}{t' - t} + \frac{1}{\pi} \int_{u_0}^{\infty} \frac{\rho_{su}(s', u')\, du'}{u' - (\sum_i m_i^2 - t - s')} \right]$$

$$+ \frac{1}{\pi} \int_{u_0}^{\infty} \frac{du'}{u' - u} \left[\frac{1}{\pi} \int_{t_0}^{\infty} \frac{\rho_{tu}(t', u')\, dt'}{t' - t} \right.$$

$$\left. + \frac{1}{\pi} \int_{s_0}^{\infty} \frac{\rho_{su}(s', u')\, ds'}{s' - (\sum_i m_i^2 - t - u')} \right] + \text{pole terms} \tag{3.36}$$

If we replace s by $s + i\varepsilon$ with $s > s_0$ in this result and apply the formal identity

$$1/(s' - s - i\varepsilon) = P/(s' - s) + i\pi\, \delta(s' - s)$$

we find that the imaginary part of the s-channel amplitude $\text{Im}A_s(s + i\varepsilon, t)$ is equal to the first square bracket in (3.36) evaluated at $s' = s$. Similarly, $\text{Im}A_u(u + i\varepsilon, t)$ for $u > u_0$ is equal to the second square bracket with u' replaced by u. Hence, with the usual notation

$$A(s, t, u) = \frac{1}{\pi} \int_{s_0}^{\infty} \frac{\text{Im}A_s(s', t)\, ds'}{s' - s} + \frac{1}{\pi} \int_{u_0}^{\infty} \frac{\text{Im}A_u(u', t)\, du'}{u' - u} + \text{pole terms} \tag{3.37}$$

This is precisely the fixed-t dispersion relation in either of the variables s or u. Note that this dispersion relation follows from the Mandelstam representation for any value of t, which shows that the Mandelstam representation is considerably stronger than what has been rigorously proved in quantum field theory. The fixed-s and fixed-u relations can be derived from the Mandelstam representation in a similar way.

In general, the asymptotic behaviour of the amplitude may require subtractions in the Mandelstam representation. For example, a typical once-subtracted form is

$$A(s, t, u) = A(s_0, t_0, u_0)$$

$$+ \frac{(s - s_0)(t - t_0)}{\pi^2} \int_{s_0}^{\infty} ds' \int_{t_0}^{\infty} dt' \frac{\rho_{st}(s', t')}{(s' - s_0)(s' - s)(t' - t_0)(t' - t)}$$

$$+ \text{two analogous terms} + \text{pole terms} \tag{3.38}$$

This implies the usual once-subtracted fixed-variable dispersion relations.

Although the Mandelstam representation has not been proved within the framework of quantum field theory, it has had a decisive influence on the development of S-matrix theory.

3.7. Threshold behaviour

In this section we shall show that the existence of fixed-variable dispersion relations implies the threshold behaviour of the partial-wave amplitudes which we assumed in section 1.5. We begin by writing the partial-wave expansion for the s-channel amplitude, expressed as a function of s and the variable $x = \cos\theta_s$, in the form

$$A_s(s, x) = \tfrac{1}{2}\sqrt{s} \sum_{l=0}^{\infty} (2l + 1)T_l(s)P_l(x) \tag{3.39}$$

Using the orthogonality property of the Legendre polynomials, equation (1.13), the individual partial-wave amplitudes are given by

$$T_l(s) = \frac{1}{\sqrt{s}} \int_{-1}^{1} A_s(s, x)P_l(x)\,dx \tag{3.40}$$

For simplicity, we restrict the discussion here to the equal-mass case, when

$$s = 4(q^2 + m^2)$$
$$t = -2q^2(1 - x)$$
$$u = -2q^2(1 + x)$$

As a function of q, equation (3.40) becomes

$$T_l(q) = \frac{1}{2\sqrt{(q^2 + m^2)}} \int_{-1}^{1} A_s(q, x)P_l(x)\,dx$$

Substituting the fixed-s dispersion relation for A_s, namely

$$A_s(q, x) = \frac{1}{\pi} \int_{t_0}^{\infty} \frac{\text{Im}A_t(q, t')\,dt'}{t' + 2q^2(1 - x)} + \frac{1}{\pi} \int_{u_0}^{\infty} \frac{\text{Im}A_u(q, u')\,du'}{u' + 2q^2(1 + x)}$$

(dropping the pole terms, if any, for simplicity), we find

$$T_l(q) = \frac{1}{2\pi\sqrt{(q^2 + m^2)}}\left[\int_{t_0}^{\infty} dt'\,\text{Im}A_t(q, t')\int_{-1}^{1} dx\,\frac{P_l(x)}{t' + 2q^2(1 - x)}\right.$$
$$\left. + \int_{u_0}^{\infty} du'\,\text{Im}A_u(q, u')\int_{-1}^{1} dx\,\frac{P_l(x)}{u' + 2q^2(1 + x)}\right]$$

For small q we may expand the integrands in powers of q^2; for example

$$\int_{-1}^{1} \frac{P_l(x)\,dx}{t' + 2q^2(1 - x)} = \int_{-1}^{1} P_l(x)\left[\frac{1}{t'} - \frac{2q^2}{t'^2}(1 - x) + \cdots\right] dx$$

Now the factors $(1 \pm x)^m$ associated with the q^{2m} terms in these expansions ($m = 0, 1, 2, \ldots$) can be expressed as certain linear combinations of the Legendre polynomials $P_n(x)$ for $n = 0, 1, \ldots, m$. Since $P_n(x)$ is orthogonal to $P_l(x)$ if $n \neq 1$, the first non-vanishing contribution to each integral comes from the q^{2l} term in the expansion of the integrand. The q-dependent factor multiplying the integrals tends to a constant as $q \to 0$. Hence we have the threshold behaviour

$$T_l(q) \sim q^{2l} \qquad \text{as} \qquad q \to 0 \tag{3.41}$$

Note that the validity of the power-series expansion required for the foregoing argument would break down if we had either $t_0 = 0$ or $u_0 = 0$, since in this case q^2 could not be made small in comparison with all the values of t' or u' in the range of integration. This means that the result depends on the existence of a lowest non-zero mass which can be exchanged, that is the finite range of the interaction. It is interesting to note that in potential theory the threshold behaviour (3.41) is also a consequence of the finite range of the interaction.

Further reading

More detailed discussions on the topics covered in this chapter can be found in many books on high-energy physics. The following are examples.

1. G. F. Chew, *S-Matrix Theory of Strong Interactions*, Benjamin, New York, 1962
2. H. Pilkuhn, *The Interactions of Hadrons*, North-Holland, Amsterdam, 1967
3. H. Burkhardt, *Dispersion Relation Dynamics*, North-Holland, Amsterdam, 1969
4. A. D. Martin and T. D. Spearman, *Elementary Particle Theory*, North-Holland, Amsterdam, 1970

CHAPTER 4

Constraints on high-energy behaviour

4.1. Heuristic derivation of some bounds

In this section we shall obtain two simple bounds on the high-energy behaviour of amplitudes. More rigorous derivations of the same bounds will be presented in subsequent sections. The preliminary derivations given here are especially instructive in elucidating the physical origin of these bounds.

We shall first derive an upper bound on elastic scattering amplitudes at high energy, using an argument based on unitarity and the finite range of the interaction. As in deriving most of the bounds here, our starting point is the partial-wave expansion for the invariant amplitude at high energy

$$A(s, \theta) \sim \sum_{l=0}^{\infty} (2l + 1)t_l(s)P_l(\cos \theta) \qquad (4.1)$$

(We recall that the symbol $\sim$ denotes an asymptotic relation as $s \to \infty$; t_l is the partial-wave amplitude introduced in section 1.7.) Suppose that the inter-action has some finite range R, so that scattering can occur only for impact parameters less than R. According to a semi-classical picture, there are con-tributions only from angular momenta $l \lesssim qR \equiv L$. The higher partial waves would actually be expected to fall off exponentially with increasing l (see section 4.3), but at this stage we shall simply ignore them completely.

Using the unitarity bound $|t_l(s)| \leqslant 1$, we find for the forward scattering amplitude

$$|A(s, 0)| \lesssim \sum_{l=0}^{L} (2l + 1) |t_l(s)| \leqslant \sum_{l=0}^{L} (2l + 1) \sim q^2R^2 \qquad (4.2)$$

where in the last step we have used the fact that

$$\sum_{l=0}^{L} (2l + 1) = (L + 1)^2 \qquad (4.3)$$

The forward differential cross section is therefore bounded by

$$\frac{d\sigma}{d |t|} (s, 0) \lesssim \pi R^4 \qquad (4.4)$$

Applying the asymptotic form of the optical theorem, equation (3.13), we obtain in the same way a bound for the total cross section

$$\sigma(s) \sim \frac{4\pi}{q^2} \sum_{l=0}^{L} (2l + 1) \operatorname{Im} t_l(s) \lesssim 4\pi R^2 \tag{4.5}$$

Thus, both $d\sigma/d |t|$ and σ are bounded by certain constants.

A sharper estimate is obtained if we adopt the hypothesis of pure absorption in each partial wave as $s \to \infty$. In this case $t_l = [\eta_l \exp(2i\alpha_l) - 1]/2i$ with $\eta_l \to 0$, so that $t_l(s) \to \frac{1}{2}i$. This gives

$$|A(s, 0)| \sim \tfrac{1}{2}q^2 R^2 \qquad \sigma(s) \sim 2\pi R^2 \tag{4.6}$$

(σ tends to twice the geometric cross section). These are precisely the high-energy limits for scattering by a black sphere of radius R.

These results are consistent with the current experimental data at least up to about 60 GeV, which have traditionally been interpreted in terms of constant total interaction cross sections at asymptotic energies. A significant real part is seen experimentally in the forward elastic scattering amplitudes for certain processes at high energy, although these real parts appear to be decreasing in importance with increasing energy, in accordance with the pure absorption model.

Our theoretical estimate of the total cross section turns out to be correct in order of magnitude if we take a reasonable value for R. For example, taking $R \sim 1$ fm (the pion Compton wavelength is 1·4 fm), we find $\sigma \sim 60$ mb, which is somewhat larger than, but of the same order of magnitude as, the NN and $\bar{N}N$ total cross sections at high energy. The πN, KN and $\bar{K}N$ cross sections, for which the lowest mass that can be exchanged is that of two pions, are expected to be smaller by about a factor of 4; this is indeed the case experimentally.

We next establish, as a consequence of unitarity alone, a relation between the width of the forward diffraction peak and the total cross section. Writing σ as the sum of its elastic and inelastic parts and applying the optical theorem in the form (3.13), we have

$$(16\pi/s) \operatorname{Im} A(s, 0) \sim \int (d\sigma/d |t|) \, dt + \sigma_{\text{in}} \gtrsim (16\pi/s^2) \int [\operatorname{Im} A(s, t)]^2 \, dt \tag{4.7}$$

In the last step we have made use of equation (3.12) for $d\sigma/d |t|$, as well as the positivity of $[\operatorname{Re} A(s, t)]^2$ and σ_{in}. If we now define Δt to be the width of the forward peak in $(\operatorname{Im} A)^2$, that is the range of t which gives a significant contribution to the last integral, we can approximate the integral by

$$[\operatorname{Im} A(s, 0)]^2 \, \Delta t$$

Hence we are left with the estimate

$$\operatorname{Im} A(s, 0) \, \Delta t \lesssim s \tag{4.8}$$

Applying the optical theorem again, this gives

$$\Delta t \lesssim 16\pi/\sigma \tag{4.9}$$

If $A(s, t)$ is assumed to be predominantly imaginary near $t = 0$ (as expected from a simple diffraction picture of high-energy scattering), then Δt coincides with the width of the diffraction peak in $d\sigma/d|t|$. Equation (4.9) shows that, if asymptotically $\sigma \sim$ const, then Δt is bounded by a constant; such a bound is consistent with the semi-classical diffraction scattering model. On the other hand, the diffraction peak must shrink with energy if σ grows as $s \to \infty$.

A defect of the preceding discussion is that a precise meaning has not actually been assigned to Δt. A more satisfactory definition, which we shall adopt in deriving rigorous bounds, is

$$\Delta t \equiv \frac{[\mathrm{Im}A(s, 0)]^2}{\{d[\mathrm{Im}A(s, t)]^2/dt\}_{t=0}}$$

$$= \frac{\mathrm{Im}A(s, 0)}{2\{d[\mathrm{Im}A(s, t)]/dt\}_{t=0}}$$

$$= \frac{1}{2\{d \log[\mathrm{Im}A(s, t)]/dt\}_{t=0}} \qquad (4.10)$$

4.2. Rigorous results from field theory

We quote here some rigorously established consequences of axiomatic quantum field theory which we shall require for the derivation of certain bounds in the following sections.

(i) *The Lehmann ellipse.* Lehmann[1] first proved that the scattering amplitude at a fixed energy has definite analyticity properties as a function of the momentum transfer. In particular, he showed that for fixed physical values of s (the s-channel energy variable), the amplitude $A(s, \theta)$ is analytic in the variable $\cos \theta$ within an ellipse with foci at $\cos \theta = \pm 1$ and semi-major axis $1 + c/s^2$, where c is some positive constant.

To see the connection with the variable t, let us consider for simplicity the equal-mass case, when

$$t = -2q^2(1 - \cos \theta) = -2(\tfrac{1}{4}s - m^2)(1 - \cos \theta) \qquad (4.11)$$

Then the extreme point of the Lehmann ellipse, with $\cos \theta = 1 + c/s^2$, corresponds to a point in the t-plane with $|t| \sim$ const/s as $s \to \infty$. In this limit the Lehmann ellipse shrinks to the line segment $-1 \leqslant \cos \theta \leqslant 1$.

(ii) *The Martin extension.*[2] The amplitude $A(s, t)$ is analytic in t for $|t| < R$, for physical values of s, where R is a constant independent of s. One would expect from crossing that $\sqrt{R}$ is given by the lowest mass which can be exchanged in the t-channel. This has been shown to be the case for certain processes. For example, it is found that $R = 4m_\pi^2$ for elastic $\pi\pi$ or πN scattering.

(iii) *Polynomial boundedness.*[3]   The amplitude satisfies a bound of the form

$$|A(s, t)| \leq O(|s|^N) \qquad \text{as} \qquad |s| \to \infty \qquad (4.12)$$

for any fixed t with $|t| < R$ (R being the same constant as above). It can be shown further that one can take $N = 1 + \varepsilon$ for any $\varepsilon > 0$ (this excludes a behaviour like s^α with $\alpha > 1$, but allows a growth of the type $s \log^2 s$).

4.3. The Froissart bound

We begin with the partial-wave expansion for an elastic scattering process, as in section 4.1. Our method will be based on the use of the partial-wave expansion for $A(s, t)$ with $s \to \infty$ at a certain value $t = t_0(s) > 0$ at which the expansion is known to converge. From the theory of expansions in Legendre polynomials, it follows that the partial-wave series converges within the largest ellipse in the $\cos \theta$ plane whose foci are at $\cos \theta = \pm 1$ and which does not enclose any singularities of the amplitude. If we assume analyticity in the Lehmann ellipse, we can therefore take $t_0 = \text{const}/s$. On the other hand, analyticity in the Martin domain allows us to take $t_0 = \text{const}$. Although the second case is stronger than the first, we shall carry out the derivation for both cases in parallel to show how the result depends on the choice of t_0; the first case is now mainly of historical interest.

From the partial-wave expansion (considering the equal-mass case for simplicity)

$$\text{Im}A(s, t_0) \sim \sum_{l=0}^{\infty} (2l + 1)\, \text{Im}t_l(s) P_l(1 + t_0/2q^2) \qquad (4.13)$$

Now the polynomial boundedness property requires that $\text{Im}A(s, t_0) \lesssim \text{const } s^N$ (the symbol $\lesssim$ here denotes an asymptotic inequality as $s \to \infty$). We make no assumption about the specific value of N. From unitarity and the property $P_l(x) > 0$ for $x > 1$, it follows that each term in the partial-wave expansion of $\text{Im}A(s, t_0)$ is non-negative. Therefore each term individually satisfies the same bound as $\text{Im}A(s, t_0)$ itself. We shall use this result to derive an upper bound on $\text{Im}t_l(s)$ for large l and s.

From the mathematical properties of the Legendre polynomials, it can be shown that

$$P_l(1 + t_0/2q^2) > [\text{const}/\sqrt{(2l + 1)}]\exp[l\sqrt{(t_0/q^2)}]$$

when l and q are large. Combining this with the above-mentioned bound on each term in the series (4.13), we have

$$\text{Im}t_l(s) \lesssim [\text{const } s^N/\sqrt{(2l + 1)}]\exp[-2l\sqrt{(t_0/s)}] \qquad (4.14)$$

which in turn implies that

$$\text{Im}t_l(s) \lesssim \text{const } \exp[N \log s - 2l\sqrt{(t_0/s)}] \qquad (4.15)$$

At fixed s, the argument of the exponential function is negative when

$$l > (N\sqrt{s}\,\log s)/2\sqrt{t_0} \equiv L(s) \tag{4.16}$$

and becomes increasingly negative as l increases, leading to negligibly small values of $\mathrm{Im}\,t_l(s)$. This suggests that for large s the partial-wave expansion can be effectively truncated at the value $l = L$. We shall show that this is indeed the case.

Let us write the total cross section in the form

$$\sigma(s) = \sigma_1(s) + \sigma_2(s) \tag{4.17}$$

where $\sigma_1(s)$ and $\sigma_2(s)$ are the total contributions to the partial-wave expansion corresponding to $l \leqslant L(s)$ and $l > L(s)$, respectively. An upper bound on the behaviour of $\sigma_1(s)$ as $s \to \infty$ can be determined by applying the unitarity bound $\mathrm{Im}\,t_1(s) \leqslant 1$

$$\sigma_1(s) \sim (16\pi/s) \sum_{l=0}^{L(s)} (2l + 1)\,\mathrm{Im}\,t_l(s) \leqslant (16\pi/s) \sum_{l=0}^{L(s)} (2l + 1)$$

Using (4.3) and (4.16), we find

$$\sigma_1(s) \lesssim (4\pi N^2/t_0)\log^2 s \tag{4.18}$$

To find an upper bound on the second term in (4.17), we proceed as follows. Making use of (4.14), we have

$$\sigma_2(s) \sim (16\pi/s) \sum_{l=L(s)}^{\infty} (2l + 1)\,\mathrm{Im}\,t_l(s)$$

$$\lesssim \text{const } s^{N-1} \sum_{l=L(s)}^{\infty} (2l + 1)\exp[-2l\sqrt{(t_0/s)}]$$

$$\sim \text{const } s^{N-1} \sum_{l=L(s)}^{\infty} l \exp[-2l\sqrt{(t_0/s)}]$$

This infinite series can be summed explicitly by first summing the simple geometric series

$$\sum_{l=L}^{\infty} \exp(-al) = \exp(-al) \sum_{l=0}^{\infty} [\exp(-a)]^l = \frac{\exp(-aL)}{1 - \exp(-a)} \equiv H(a)$$

and then differentiating the result with respect to a, which gives

$$\sum_{l=L}^{\infty} l \exp(-al) = -H'(a)$$

where the right-hand side is a function which can be evaluated explicitly. An alternative method of summing the series is to replace it by an integral, which can then be evaluated analytically

$$\sum_{l=L}^{\infty} l \exp(-al) \sim \int_{L}^{\infty} l \exp(-al)\,dl$$

C

In either case, straightforward calculations lead to the asymptotic bound

$$\sigma_2(s) \lesssim (\text{const log } s)/t_0 \tag{4.19}$$

Comparing (4.18) and (4.19), we see that the bound on $\sigma_2(s)$ becomes negligible in comparison with the bound on $\sigma_1(s)$ as $s \to \infty$, so that

$$\sigma(s) \lesssim (4\pi N^2/t_0)\log^2 s \tag{4.20}$$

If we assume analyticity in the Lehmann ellipse ($t_0 = \text{const}/s$), then

$$\sigma(s) \lesssim \text{const } s \log^2 s \tag{4.21}$$

This result is known as the Greenberg-Low bound. However, if analyticity in the Martin domain is assumed (so that t_0 can be taken to be any constant less than $4m_\pi^2$), we obtain the stronger bound

$$\sigma(s) \lesssim (\pi N^2/m_\pi^2)\log^2 s \tag{4.22}$$

which is known as the Froissart bound. If the value of N can be specified (see section 4.4), the numerical constant in the Froissart bound can be made precise.

Note that the Froissart bound is stronger than the Greenberg–Low bound by a factor s, although it is still somewhat weaker than the semi-classical estimate derived in section 4.1 (the Froissart bound corresponds to an interaction range which grows logarithmically with s).

4.4. Existence of twice-subtracted dispersion relations

We shall now derive an asymptotic upper bound on $|A(s, t)|$ for $t \leqslant 0$ by using an extension of the method of section 4.3. As a first step, we note that the partial-wave expansion gives

$$|A(s, t)| \lesssim \sum_{l=0}^{\infty} (2l + 1) |t_l(s)| \, |P_l(\cos \theta)| \tag{4.23}$$

We shall show that the series (4.23), like the series considered in the preceding section, can be effectively truncated at the value $l = L(s)$ defined by (4.16). Using the unitarity bound $|t_l(s)| \leqslant 1$, the property

$$|P_l(\cos \theta)| \leqslant 1 \qquad \text{for} \qquad -1 \leqslant \cos \theta \leqslant 1 \tag{4.24}$$

and the specific form of $L(s)$, we find that

$$|A(s, t)| \lesssim \sum_{l=0}^{L(s)} (2l + 1) + M \sim N^2 s \log^2 s/4t_0 + M \tag{4.25}$$

where M is the total contribution to the right-hand side of (4.23) from the terms with $l > L(s)$. It is easy to see that, since we are considering the limit $s \to \infty$, our results will be valid for all $t \leqslant 0$. For example, in the equal-mass case, the range of t corresponding to the physical angular range in which the inequality (4.24) holds at a particular energy is given by $4m^2 - s \leqslant t \leqslant 0$.

Our next step is to show that a suitable bound on M can be derived with the aid of the unitarity condition in the form

$$|t_l(s)|^2 \leqslant \text{Im} t_l(s) \qquad (4.26)$$

This is an inequality which follows from the general representation

$$t_l = [\eta_l \exp(2i\alpha_l) - 1]/2i$$

where $0 \leqslant \eta_l \leqslant 1$ and α_l is real. Direct calculation then gives

$$\text{Re} t_l = \tfrac{1}{2}\eta_l \sin 2\alpha_l$$

$$\text{Im} t_l = \tfrac{1}{2}(1 - \eta_l \cos 2\alpha_l)$$

$$|t_l|^2 = \tfrac{1}{4}(1 + \eta_l^2 - 2\eta_l \cos 2\alpha_l)$$

from which (4.26) follows at once.

Using the inequality (4.26) and the bound on $\text{Im} t_l(s)$ given by (4.15), we find

$$M \lesssim \text{const } s^{(1/2)N} \sum_{l=L(s)}^{\infty} l \exp[-l\sqrt{(t_0/s)}]$$

The resulting series can be summed explicitly by the methods discussed in section 4.3, giving the bound

$$M \lesssim (\text{const } s \log s)/t_0$$

Comparing this with the bound (4.25), we have finally

$$|A(s, t)| \lesssim (N^2 s \log^2 s)/4t_0 \qquad (4.27)$$

If analyticity in the Martin domain is assumed, t_0 can be taken to be any constant less than $4m_\pi^2$. Then

$$|A(s, t)| \lesssim (N^2 s \log^2 s)/16m_\pi^2 \qquad (4.28)$$

as $s \to \infty$ for all $t \leqslant 0$. By crossing, this bound also holds as $s \to -\infty$, since precisely same arguments can be applied to the crossed u-channel process. We note that $|A(s, t)|$ is bounded by const $|s^{2-\alpha}|$ as $s \to \pm\infty$ for some $\alpha > 0$; this implies the important result that two subtractions are certainly sufficient for the fixed-t dispersion relations for $t \leqslant 0$ (see section 2.5).

A comparison of the bound (4.28) with the originally assumed polynomial bound on $|A(s, t)|$ given by (4.12) suggests that $N > 1$. Actually, it is known that N can be taken to be equal to $1 + \alpha$ for any $\alpha > 0$. We are not in a position to prove this on the basis of our results. Although we have made use of the bound (4.12) at some positive value of t, we have derived the bound (4.28) only in the range $t \leqslant 0$. In other words, our proof that $|A(s, t)|$ is bounded by const $|s|^{1+\alpha}$ is valid only for $t \leqslant 0$.

If we make use of the actual value of N, we can specify the precise values of the numerical constants in the Froissart bound (4.22) and in the bound (4.28)

$$\sigma(s) \lesssim (\pi \log^2 s)/m_\pi^2 \tag{4.29}$$

$$|A(s, t)| \lesssim (s \log^2 s)/16m_\pi^2 \tag{4.30}$$

4.5. Width of the forward diffraction peak

In this section we shall derive high-energy bounds on the width of the forward diffraction peak Δt defined by (4.10). As in the preceding sections, we shall consider only equal-mass kinematics for simplicity.

We begin by rearranging the partial-wave series

$$\text{Im}A(s, t) \sim \sum_{l=0}^{\infty} (2l + 1) \, \text{Im}t_l(s) P_l(1 + 2t/s) \tag{4.31}$$

into a power series in t, which we write as

$$\text{Im}A(s, t) \sim 2 \sum_{n=0}^{\infty} \frac{b_n(s)}{(n!)^2} t^n \tag{4.32}$$

The first two coefficients b_n are given by

$$b_0(s) = \tfrac{1}{2} \text{Im}A(s, 0) \sim \tfrac{1}{2} \sum_{l=0}^{\infty} (2l + 1) \, \text{Im}t_l(s) \sim \sum_{l=0}^{\infty} l \, \text{Im}t_l(s)$$

$$b_1(s) = \tfrac{1}{2} \left[\frac{d}{dt} \text{Im}A(s, t) \right]_{t=0} \sim \tfrac{1}{2} \sum_{l=0}^{\infty} (2l + 1) \, \text{Im}t_l(s) \left[\frac{d}{dt} P_l(1 + 2t/s) \right]_{t=0}$$

$$\sim 1/s \sum_{l=0}^{\infty} l^3 \, \text{Im}t_l(s)$$

In the last step we have made use of the identity $P_l'(1) = \tfrac{1}{2}l(l + 1)$. Next we derive an inequality relating b_0 and b_1

$$b_0^2 \sim \left(\sum_{l=0}^{\infty} l \, \text{Im}t_l \right)^2 = \sum_{l=0}^{\infty} l \, \text{Im}t_l \sum_{n=0}^{l-1} n \, \text{Im}t_n + \sum_{n=0}^{\infty} n \, \text{Im}t_n \sum_{l=0}^{n} l \, \text{Im}t_l$$

$$\leqslant 2 \sum_{n=0}^{\infty} n \, \text{Im}t_n \sum_{l=0}^{n} l \sim \sum_{n=0}^{\infty} n^3 \, \text{Im}t_n \sim sb_1$$

where we have used the fact that

$$\sum_{l=0}^{n} l = \tfrac{1}{2}n(n + 1)$$

If in the resulting inequality $b_0^2 \lesssim sb_1$ we substitute the expression obtained for b_1 from the relation

$$g(s) \equiv \{d[\log \text{Im}A(s, t)/dt]\}_{t=0} = \frac{\{d[\text{Im}A(s, t)/dt]\}_{t=0}}{\text{Im}A(s, 0)} \sim \frac{b_1(s)}{b_0(s)}$$

and then eliminate b_0 by using the fact that

$$b_0(s) = \tfrac{1}{2} \operatorname{Im} A(s, 0) \sim (s/32\pi)\, \sigma(s)$$

we find

$$g(s) \gtrsim (1/32\pi)\, \sigma(s) \tag{4.33}$$

The quantity $g(s)$ characterises the width of the forward peak (see equation 4.10). By extending the preceding results, it can be shown that in general

$$b_n(s) \sim (1/s^n) \sum_{l=0}^{\infty} l^{2n+1} \operatorname{Im} t_l(s)$$

Applying the general inequality

$$\sum_{n=0}^{\infty} x_n^2 \sum_{m=0}^{\infty} y_m^2 \geqslant \left[\sum_{n=0}^{\infty} x_n y_n \right]^2 \tag{4.34}$$

we can then derive further relations among the b_n

$$b_{n+1} b_{n-1} \gtrsim \left[(1/s^n) \sum_{l=0}^{\infty} l^{2n+1} \operatorname{Im} t_l \right]^2 \sim b_n^2$$

These relations imply that

$$\frac{b_{n+1}}{b_n} \gtrsim \frac{b_n}{b_{n-1}} \gtrsim \cdots \gtrsim \frac{b_1}{b_0} \sim g$$

or, equivalently

$$b_n \gtrsim g b_{n-1} \gtrsim g^2 b_{n-2} \gtrsim \cdots \gtrsim g^n b_0$$

This set of inequalities can now be used to find an upper bound on $g(s)$. From (4.32) we can deduce that

$$\operatorname{Im} A(s, t) \gtrsim 2 b_0(s) \sum_{n=0}^{\infty} [g(s)t]^n/(n!)^2$$

If the Froissart bound on $\sigma(s)$ were saturated, then the bound (4.33) would correspond to $g(s) \gtrsim \operatorname{const} \log^2 s$. This suggests that we allow for the possibility that $g(s) \to \infty$ as $s \to \infty$ in deriving the upper bound on $g(s)$. In this case, as $s \to \infty$ with some fixed $t > 0$

$$\operatorname{Im} A(s, t) \gtrsim 2 b_0(s) \sum_{n=0}^{\infty} [g(s)t]^{(1/2)n}/n! = 2 b_0(s) \exp\{[g(s)t]^{1/2}\}$$

(We are implicitly assuming analyticity in the Martin domain in order to guarantee the convergence of the partial-wave series at fixed t as $s \to \infty$.) But $|A(s, t)|$ is polynomially bounded in s and cannot increase exponentially. Hence it is necessary that $[g(s)t]^{1/2} \lesssim \operatorname{const} \log s$, that is

$$g(s) \lesssim \operatorname{const} \log^2 s \tag{4.35}$$

It is interesting to note that the upper and lower bounds on $g(s)$ coincide in the case when the Froissart bound is saturated. More generally, a comparison of these upper and lower bounds leads back to the Froissart bound.

Finally, let us rewrite the bounds on $g(s)$ in terms of the width of the diffraction peak Δt defined by (4.10). This gives

$$\text{const}/\log^2 s \lesssim \Delta t \lesssim 16\pi/\sigma(s) \tag{4.36}$$

Note that the upper bound for Δt agrees with that obtained in section 4.1.

4.6. Miscellaneous bounds

In this section we derive several additional asymptotic bounds which follow from the combination of unitarity and analyticity. The results discussed here represent only a small selection of the large number of asymptotic constraints on amplitudes which have been established. We refer the reader to the Further Reading section for further details.

First of all, we obtain a lower bound on the total elastic scattering cross section σ_{el}. According to (1.15)

$$\sigma_{\text{el}} = (4\pi/q^2)\sum_{l=0}^{\infty}(2l+1)|t_l|^2 \geqslant (4\pi/q^2)\sum_{l=0}^{L}(2l+1)(\text{Im} t_l)^2$$

where $L = L(s)$ is defined as in section 4.3. Using now the general inequality (4.34), we have

$$\sigma_{\text{el}} \gtrsim \frac{4\pi}{q^2}\frac{\left[\sum_{l=0}^{L}(2l+1)\,\text{Im} t_l\right]^2}{\sum_{l=0}^{L}(2l+1)} \sim \frac{(q^2/4\pi)\,\sigma^2}{(L+1)^2}$$

Substituting (4.16) for L, we find

$$\sigma_{\text{el}}(s) \gtrsim \text{const}\ \sigma^2(s)/\log^2 s \tag{4.37}$$

If $\sigma(s) \to \text{const}$ as $s \to \infty$, then $\sigma_{\text{el}}(s)$ cannot decrease to zero too rapidly. Thus, the inequality (4.37) has important experimental implications, since it indicates that an appreciable proportion of elastic scattering is expected even at high energies. (Actually, somewhat stronger bounds on σ_{el} can be derived; see the Further Reading section for details.)

Next, we derive an upper bound on non-forward scattering at fixed angle θ. Using the inequality

$$|P_l(\cos\theta)| < \sqrt{[2/(\pi l \sin\theta)]} \qquad \text{for} \qquad |\cos\theta| < 1 \tag{4.38}$$

and the unitarity bound $|t_l| \leqslant 1$, we obtain from the partial-wave expansion for $A(s, \theta)$ the bound

$$|A(s, \theta)| \lesssim \sum_{l=0}^{L} (2l + 1)\sqrt{[2/(\pi l \sin \theta)]} \sim \sqrt{[8/(\pi \sin \theta)]} \int_0^L \sqrt{l} \, dl$$

$$= (\text{const}/\sqrt{\sin \theta})L^{3/2}$$

Using the usual expression (4.16) for $L(s)$, we have

$$|A(s, \theta)| \lesssim \text{const}[s^{3/4}(\log s)^{3/2}]/\sqrt{\sin \theta} \tag{4.39}$$

for fixed angle θ in the range $0 < \theta < \pi$.

This bound is not very strong and can also be improved. In fact, we can easily show that it can be saturated only at discrete angles, since saturation in any finite interval $\theta_1 < \theta < \theta_2$ would lead to a violation of the Froissart bound

$$\sigma_{\text{el}} \geq 2\pi \int_{\theta_1}^{\theta_2} (4/s) |A(s, \theta)|^2 \sin \theta \, d\theta \sim \text{const} \, s^{1/2} \log^3 s$$

It is perhaps not obvious at first sight that we have made use of analyticity in deriving the bounds (4.37) and (4.39). In fact, analyticity in the Martin domain was assumed in obtaining the required expression (4.16) for $L(s)$.

Finally, we derive a general result which is of interest in connection with Regge theory and which follows from unitarity alone. We shall show that if an elastic scattering amplitude has an asymptotic behaviour of the form

$$A(s, t) \sim h(t)(\log s)^\beta \, s^{\alpha(t)} \tag{4.40}$$

for physical s and t (at least for $t \approx 0$), where β is a real constant and the function $\alpha(t)$ is real and continuous, then $\alpha(0) \leq 1$. The proof is based on the fact that, when s is sufficiently large

$$\sigma(s) \geq \sigma_{\text{el}}(s) \gtrsim (16\pi/s^2) \int_{t_0}^0 |A(s, t)|^2 \, dt \tag{4.41}$$

for any fixed $t_0 < 0$. Since $\alpha(t)$ is continuous, for any $\varepsilon > 0$ we may choose a value of t_0 such that $\alpha(0) - \varepsilon < \alpha(t)$ for $t_0 < t < 0$. Applying the optical theorem to the inequality (4.41), assuming the form of $A(s, t)$ given by (4.40), we then get

$$\text{const}(\log s)^\beta s^{\alpha(0)-1} \gtrsim (\text{const}/s^2)(\log s)^{2\beta} s^{2\alpha(0)-2\varepsilon}$$

To ensure that the left-hand side of this inequality grows more rapidly than the right-hand side as $s \to \infty$, it is necessary that

$$\alpha(0) - 1 > 2\alpha(0) - 2 - 2\varepsilon$$

Hence

$$\alpha(0) < 1 + 2\varepsilon$$

Since ε is arbitrary, we have $\alpha(0) \leq 1$.

4.7. The Pomeranchuk theorem

There are many variants of the Pomeranchuk theorem. The following appears to be the simplest and is essentially that originally given by Pomeranchuk.[4]

Let $A(\omega)$ and $\bar{A}(\omega)$ be the scattering amplitudes at $t = 0$ for the elastic scattering processes $a_1 + a_2 \to a_1 + a_2$ and $\bar{a}_1 + a_2 \to \bar{a}_1 + a_2$ respectively and suppose that

(i) $A(\omega)$ satisfies a twice-subtracted dispersion relation
(ii) the total cross sections have finite non-zero limits as $\omega \to \infty$

$$\sigma(\omega) \to \sigma(\infty) \neq 0$$

$$\bar{\sigma}(\omega) \to \bar{\sigma}(\infty) \neq 0$$

(iii) $|\mathrm{Re}A(\omega)|/[\mathrm{Im}A(\omega)\log \omega] \to 0$ as $\omega \to \infty$ (or a similar condition for $\bar{A}$).

The theorem states that, under these conditions the asymptotic limits of the cross sections are equal: $\sigma(\infty) = \bar{\sigma}(\infty)$.

Assumptions (i) and (iii) have not been proved in quantum field theory and no compelling theoretical reasons for their validity are known, although both seem reasonable in view of what is known empirically. These assumptions are also compatible with the high-energy behaviour expected from a simple diffraction picture of the scattering.

The proof of the Pomeranchuk theorem is based on the dispersion relation

$$\mathrm{Re}A(\omega) = \sum_n \frac{X_n(\omega - \omega_1)(\omega - \omega_2)}{(\omega - \omega_n)(\omega_n - \omega_1)(\omega_n - \omega_2)} + A_0 + A_1\omega$$
$$+ \frac{(\omega - \omega_1)(\omega - \omega_2)}{\pi} P \int_{\mathrm{cuts}} \frac{\mathrm{Im}A(\omega')\,d\omega'}{(\omega' - \omega)(\omega' - \omega_1)(\omega' - \omega_2)} \qquad (4.42)$$

with subtractions at the energies ω_1 and ω_2 (compare equation 2.34).

Consider the asymptotic behaviour of the various terms in the dispersion relation (4.42). By inspection, the sum of the pole terms and the subtraction terms $A_0 + A_1\omega$ behaves like const ω as $\omega \to \infty$. We decompose the integral term into the sum $I(\omega) = I_1(\omega) + I_2(\omega)$, where I_1 is the contribution from the region $|\omega'| < W$ and I_2 is the contribution from $|\omega'| > W$ for some fixed energy W. Letting $\omega \to \infty$, we find that the low-energy contribution has the asymptotic behaviour $I_1(\omega) \sim$ const ω.

It remains only to consider the high-energy contribution $I_2(\omega)$. To find its asymptotic behaviour, we first apply crossing to evaluate the high-energy dispersion integral over the left-hand cut in terms of the amplitude $\bar{A}$ for the crossed process (cf. section 3.5, where this was done for the unsubtracted dispersion relation)

$$\int_{-\infty}^{-W} \frac{\mathrm{Im}A(\omega')\,d\omega'}{(\omega' - \omega)(\omega' - \omega_1)(\omega' - \omega_2)} = \int_W^\infty \frac{\mathrm{Im}\bar{A}(\omega')\,d\omega'}{(\omega' + \omega)(\omega' + \omega_1)(\omega' + \omega_2)}$$

The dispersion integrals can then be expressed in terms of the total cross sections by means of the optical theorem

$$\text{Im} A(\omega) \sim C\omega\sigma(\omega) \qquad \text{Im} \bar{A}(\omega) \sim C\omega\bar{\sigma}(\omega)$$

where C is a certain constant which is known but whose specific value is unimportant here.

So far we have not specified the energy W which separates the low-energy and high-energy regions. By assumption (ii), for any $\varepsilon > 0$ we can choose some W such that $\sigma(\omega')$ and $\bar{\sigma}(\omega')$ both differ by less than ε in magnitude from their respective limits $\sigma(\infty)$ and $\bar{\sigma}(\infty)$ whenever $\omega' > W$. Thus, by choosing W sufficiently large, the errors in replacing $\sigma(\omega')$ and $\bar{\sigma}(\omega')$ by their asymptotic limits in the integrands of $I_2(\omega)$ can be made arbitrarily small. Hence we obtain the asymptotic behaviour

$$I_2(\omega) = \frac{(\omega - \omega_1)(\omega - \omega_2)}{\pi} P \left[\int_{-\infty}^{-W} + \int_{W}^{\infty} \right] \left[\frac{\text{Im} A(\omega')\, d\omega'}{(\omega' - \omega)(\omega' - \omega_1)(\omega' - \omega_2)} \right]$$

$$\sim \frac{\omega^2}{\pi} P \left[\int_{W}^{\infty} \frac{C\bar{\sigma}(\infty)\, d\omega'}{(\omega' + \omega)\omega'} + \int_{W}^{\infty} \frac{C\sigma(\infty)\, d\omega'}{(\omega' - \omega)\omega'} \right]$$

The integrals can be evaluated exactly, giving, in the limit as $\omega \to \infty$

$$I_2(\omega) \sim \frac{\omega^2}{\pi} \left[\frac{C\bar{\sigma}(\infty)}{\omega} \log\left(\frac{\omega + W}{W}\right) - \frac{C\sigma(\infty)}{\omega} \log\left(\frac{\omega - W}{W}\right) \right]$$

$$\sim \frac{C\omega}{\pi} [\bar{\sigma}(\infty) - \sigma(\infty)] \log \omega$$

Thus, if $\bar{\sigma}(\infty) \neq \sigma(\infty)$, then $I_2(\omega)$ gives asymptotically the dominant contribution to the dispersion relation and we obtain

$$\text{Re} A(\omega)/\text{Im} A(\omega) \sim \{[\bar{\sigma}(\infty) - \sigma(\infty)]/\pi\sigma(\infty)\} \log \omega \qquad (4.43a)$$

Similarly

$$\text{Re} \bar{A}(\omega)/\text{Im} \bar{A}(\omega) \sim \{[\sigma(\infty) - \bar{\sigma}(\infty)]/\pi\bar{\sigma}(\infty)\} \log \omega \qquad (4.43b)$$

Equation (4.43b) can be derived from (4.43a) by simply interchanging the roles of the two processes. The behaviour (4.43) would contradict assumption (iii) unless $\bar{\sigma}(\infty) = \sigma(\infty)$. This completes the proof of the theorem.

One conventionally speaks of 'violation of the Pomeranchuk theorem' in the case in which assumption (iii) is false but the others remain valid, so that $\bar{\sigma}(\infty)$ and $\sigma(\infty)$ may be finite but unequal. (This terminology is unfortunate, since only the hypothesis of the theorem can be violated, and not the theorem itself.) In this case, our result shows that the ratios of the real to imaginary parts of the amplitudes grow logarithmically, with coefficients which are uniquely determined by (4.43); in particular, these ratios have opposite signs for the amplitudes A and $\bar{A}$.

It is interesting to note that in the case of violation of the Pomeranchuk theorem the forward diffraction peak must necessarily attain its maximally allowed rate of shrinkage (see section 4.5). To see this, we note that in this case

$$|A(\omega)| \sim \text{const } \omega \log \omega \sim \text{const } s \log s \qquad (4.44)$$

so that

$$(d\sigma/d|t|)_{t=0} \sim (16\pi/s^2) |A(\omega)|^2 \sim \text{const } \log^2 s \qquad (4.45)$$

Since $\sigma_{\text{el}} = \int (d\sigma/d|t|) \, dt \leqslant \sigma \sim \text{const}$, the width of the forward peak must satisfy the bound

$$\Delta t \lesssim \text{const}/\log^2 s \qquad (4.46)$$

Thus, the lower bound on Δt given by (4.36) must be reached.

The version of the Pomeranchuk theorem given above can be generalised in various ways to remove the restriction of asymptotically constant cross sections. For example, if σ and $\bar{\sigma}$ are assumed to have the more general asymptotic behaviours $\sigma_{\pm}(\omega) \sim C_{\pm}\omega^{\alpha}(\log \omega)^{\beta}$, where $C_{\pm}, \alpha$ and β are constants, then by inserting this form into the dispersion relation we find that the dominant term in the real part gives

$$\text{Re}A_{\pm}(\omega) \sim \pm\text{const}(C_- - C_+)\omega^{\alpha+1}(\log \omega)^{\beta+1} \qquad (4.47)$$

Thus, if it is assumed that the ratios $\text{Re}A_{\pm}(\omega)/\text{Im}A_{\pm}(\omega)$ do not grow like $\log \omega$, we must have $\sigma_+(\omega)/\sigma_-(\omega) \to 1$ as $\omega \to \infty$. However, the difference of the cross sections $\sigma_-(\omega) - \sigma_+(\omega)$ need not approach zero in general.

4.8. Phase relations

It is often convenient to work with amplitudes which have definite symmetry properties with respect to crossing. In this connection, it is important to note that any amplitude $A(v)$ (considering t fixed and suppressing the t variable) can be written as a sum of crossing-symmetric (crossing-even) and crossing-antisymmetric (crossing-odd) parts in the form

$$A(v) = A^{(+)}(v) + A^{(-)}(v) \qquad (4.48)$$

where

$$A^{(\pm)}(v) \equiv \tfrac{1}{2}[A(v) \pm \bar{A}(v)] = \pm A^{(\pm)}(-v) \qquad (4.49)$$

for any (complex) v. As an example, the symmetric and antisymmetric parts of the $\pi^+ p$ scattering amplitude are given by half the sum and difference of the $\pi^+ p$ and $\pi^- p$ amplitudes.

For amplitudes (or components of amplitudes) $A^{(\pm)}(v)$ which are either crossing-symmetric or crossing-antisymmetric, the requirement of analyticity in the complex v-plane leads to simple asymptotic relations between the real and imaginary parts or, what is equivalent, to relations between the asymptotic forms of the modulus and phase.

Consider, for example, an antisymmetric amplitude $A^{(-)}$ for which, as $v \to \infty$, we have

$$|A^{(-)}(v)| \sim \text{const } v^{\alpha}$$

for some real α. In particular, suppose that

$$A^{(-)}(v)/v^\alpha \to M \exp(i\theta) \qquad \text{as} \qquad v \to \infty \qquad (4.50)$$

where M and θ are real constants. Since $A^{(-)}(v)$ is analytic and polynomially bounded at infinity, it must have identical limits along the top of the left-hand and right-hand cuts (see section 2.5). Thus

$$A^{(-)}[v \exp(i\pi)]/v^\alpha \exp(i\pi\alpha) \to M \exp(i\theta) \qquad \text{as} \qquad v \to \infty \qquad (4.51)$$

The antisymmetry property and the Schwarz reflection principle together require that

$$A^{(-)}[v \exp(i\pi)] = -A^{(-)*}(v) \qquad (4.52)$$

Equating the asymptotic limits of the two sides of the relation (4.52) as given by (4.50) and (4.51), we have

$$M \exp(i\pi\alpha)\exp(i\theta)v^\alpha = -M \exp(-i\theta)v^\alpha$$

which in turn implies that θ must have the value

$$\theta = (n + \tfrac{1}{2})\pi - \tfrac{1}{2}\pi\alpha$$

where n is an integer. Thus, as $v \to \infty$

$$A^{(-)}(v) \sim M \exp(i\theta)v^\alpha = \pm iMv^\alpha \exp(-\tfrac{1}{2}i\pi\alpha)$$

Defining $C = \pm M \cos \tfrac{1}{2}\pi\alpha$, we can then write the amplitude in the form

$$A^{(-)}(v) \sim C[i + \tan \tfrac{1}{2}\pi\alpha]v^\alpha \qquad (4.53)$$

where C is real.

For a crossing-symmetric amplitude $A^{(+)}(v)$, the symmetry property and the Schwarz reflection principle give instead

$$A^{(+)}[v \exp(i\pi)] = +A^{(+)*}(v) \qquad (4.54)$$

The analogous argument then leads to the general form

$$A^{(+)}(v) \sim C[i - \cot \tfrac{1}{2}\pi\alpha]v^\alpha \qquad (4.55)$$

where C is again a real constant.

These asymptotic forms are especially important in Regge pole theory (see section 8.3). The complex factors which give the phase often appear in the literature in apparently different (but equivalent) forms; these alternative forms can be derived by using simple trigonometric identities. We quote the results here

$$i + \tan \tfrac{1}{2}\pi\alpha = \frac{1 - \exp(-i\pi\alpha)}{\sin \pi\alpha} = \frac{i}{\cos \tfrac{1}{2}\pi\alpha} \exp(-\tfrac{1}{2}i\pi\alpha) \qquad (4.56)$$

$$i - \cot \tfrac{1}{2}\pi\alpha = \frac{-1 - \exp(-i\pi\alpha)}{\sin \pi\alpha} = -\frac{1}{\sin \tfrac{1}{2}\pi\alpha} \exp(-\tfrac{1}{2}i\pi\alpha) \qquad (4.57)$$

References

1. H. Lehmann, *Nuovo Cimento*, **10** (1958), 579
2. A. Martin, *Nuovo Cimento*, **42** (1966), 930
3. H. Epstein, V. Glaser, and A. Martin, *Commun. Math. Phys.*, **13** (1969), 257
4. I. Ya. Pomeranchuk, *ZhETF*, **34** (1958), 725: English translation, *Soviet Phys. JETP*, **7** (1958), 499

Further reading

A review of the analyticity properties of amplitudes which have been rigorously established in quantum field theory can be found in the following reference.

1. G. Sommer, *Fortschritte der Physik*, **18** (1970), 577

The following references contain reviews of asymptotic bounds.

2. A. Martin, in *Strong Interactions and High Energy Physics*, ed. R. G. Moorhouse, Oliver & Boyd, Edinburgh, 1964, p. 105
3. A. Martin, in *High-Energy Physics and Elementary Particles*, IAEA, Vienna, 1965, p. 155
4. R. J. Eden, in *Particle Interactions at High Energies*, ed. T. W. Preist and L. L. J. Vick, Oliver & Boyd, Edinburgh, 1967, p. 1
5. R. J. Eden, *High Energy Collisions of Elementary Particles*, Cambridge University Press, 1967, Chapters 6–8
6. R. J. Eden, *Rev. Mod. Phys.*, **43** (1971), 15
7. S. M. Roy, *Phys. Reports*, **5C** (1972), 125
8. F. J. Ynduráin, *Rev. Mod. Phys.*, **44** (1972), 645

CHAPTER 5

Fixed-t dispersion relations for πN scattering

5.1. Lorentz-invariant description of πN scattering

Because of the existence of extremely accurate and abundant experimental data on πN scattering and the relatively simple structure of the amplitude for this process, particularly for forward scattering, the most successful applications of dispersion relations at fixed momentum transfer have been made for πN scattering.

So far, we have considered only scattering processes involving spinless particles. We must now allow for the fact that the spin of the nucleon is equal to $\frac{1}{2}$. Since a given pion–nucleon scattering process can take place with or without spin flip, two independent amplitudes are required for its description. The relevant formalism will be summarized briefly in this section; for complete derivations, we refer the reader to the more detailed reviews cited in the Further reading section.

It is conventional to define amplitudes $T_{\pm}$ for elastic $\pi^{\pm} p$ scattering such that the differential cross section in the c.m.s. is given by

$$\mathrm{d}\sigma_{\pm}/\mathrm{d}\Omega = (M/4\pi W)^2 \sum |\bar{u}_f T_{\pm} u_i|^2 \tag{5.1}$$

where M (as used throughout this chapter) is the nucleon mass, $W = \sqrt{s}$ is the usual c.m. energy variable, u_i and u_f are Dirac (4-component) spinors describing the initial and final spin states of the nucleon, and Σ denotes the appropriate average over the spin states (an average over the initial and sum over the final spin states in the case of scattering by unpolarized nucleons). If charge independence is assumed, then the amplitudes for all pion–nucleon processes, including the charge-exchange reaction, can be expressed in terms of the $T_{\pm}$, since there are only two isospin states of the πN system ($I = \frac{1}{2}, \frac{3}{2}$).

The most general form for $T_{\pm}$ consistent with Lorentz invariance and parity conservation can be written

$$T_{\pm} = -A_{\pm} + \tfrac{1}{2}\mathrm{i}\gamma^{\mu}(q_i + q_f)_{\mu} B_{\pm} \tag{5.2}$$

where γ^{μ} are the Dirac matrices, q_i and q_f are the initial and final 4-momenta of the pion, and $A_{\pm}$ and $B_{\pm}$ are Lorentz-invariant amplitudes. Only the term containing $B_{\pm}$ in the expression for $T_{\pm}$ depends on the nucleon spin. The numerical coefficients in (5.2) define the conventional normalisation.

Being Lorentz invariants, the amplitudes $A_\pm$ and $B_\pm$ can be written as functions of the usual kinematic invariants s, t and u. These amplitudes are assumed to have simple analyticity properties analogous to those of the single invariant amplitude for the case of spinless particles and therefore play an analogous role in the theory.

We shall now relate the invariant amplitudes $A_\pm$ and $B_\pm$ to the amplitudes which are commonly used in the non-relativistic description of πN scattering, omitting the subscripts $\pm$ for brevity.

Using Pauli (2-component) spinors $|i\rangle$ and $|f\rangle$ to describe the initial and final spin states of the nucleon, the differential cross section is given by

$$d\sigma/d\Omega = \sum |\langle f| M |i\rangle|^2 \qquad (5.3)$$

where the phase of the matrix element is conventionally defined such that

$$\langle f| M |i\rangle = -(M/4\pi W)\bar{u}_f T u_i \qquad (5.4)$$

In terms of helicity amplitudes, one finds the representation

$$M = f_1(\theta) + (1/q^2)(\sigma \cdot \mathbf{q}_i)(\sigma \cdot \mathbf{q}_f)f_2(\theta) \qquad (5.5)$$

where θ is the c.m. scattering angle, σ is the Pauli spin matrix, $\mathbf{q}_i$ and $\mathbf{q}_f$ are the initial and final c.m. 3-momenta of the pion, and $q = |\mathbf{q}_i| = |\mathbf{q}_f|$.

Since there are only two independent amplitudes for a given πN scattering process, it is possible to express f_1 and f_2 in terms of A and B and vice versa. The relations turn out to be

$$f_1 = [(E + M)/8\pi W][A + (W - M)B] \qquad (5.6a)$$

$$f_2 = [(E - M)/6\pi W][-A + (W + M)B] \qquad (5.6b)$$

and

$$A/4\pi = [(W + M)/(E + M)]f_1 - [(W - M)/(E - M)]f_2 \qquad (5.7a)$$

$$B/4\pi = [1/(E + M)]f_1 + [1/(E - M)]f_2 \qquad (5.7b)$$

where $E = \sqrt{(q^2 + M^2)}$ is the c.m. energy of the nucleon.

Another representation which is sometimes used is

$$M = f(\theta) + (\sigma \cdot \mathbf{n})g(\theta) \qquad (5.8)$$

where $\mathbf{n}$ is the normal to the plane of scattering in the direction of $\mathbf{q}_i \times \mathbf{q}_f$ and $f(\theta)$ and $g(\theta)$ are the non-spin-flip and spin-flip amplitudes respectively, given by

$$f(\theta) = f_1(\theta) + f_2(\theta)\cos \theta \qquad (5.9a)$$

$$g(\theta) = 1f_2(\theta)\sin \theta \qquad (5.9b)$$

The amplitudes f_1 and f_2 have the partial-wave expansions

$$f_1(\theta) = \sum_{l=0}^{\infty} f_{l+} P'_{l+1}(x) - \sum_{l=2}^{\infty} f_{l-} P'_{l-1}(x) \qquad (5.10a)$$

$$f_2(\theta) = \sum_{l=1}^{\infty} [f_{l-} - f_{l+}]P'_l(x) \qquad (5.10b)$$

where $P'_l(x) \equiv dP_l(x)/dx$, $x = \cos \theta$, and $f_{l\pm}$ are the partial-wave amplitudes for scattering in the states with total angular momenta $j = l \pm \frac{1}{2}$. The partial-wave amplitudes are expressible in terms of phase shifts in the usual form

$$f_{l\pm} = (1/2i\delta)[\exp(2i\delta_{l\pm}) - 1] \tag{5.11}$$

the phase shifts $\delta_{l\pm}$ being real below the inelastic threshold. In practice, the partial-wave expansion is written for the combinations of amplitudes which correspond to scattering in definite isospin states.

5.2. Crossing and analyticity properties of the amplitudes

Crossing (see sections 3.2 and 3.4) may be applied separately to each of the two independent terms in the expression (5.2) for the amplitudes $T_{\pm}$. The change of sign of the 4-momenta in the coefficient of $B_{\pm}$ in crossing from the s-channel to the u-channel leads to a minus sign in the crossing relations for $B_{\pm}$. Thus

$$A_{\pm}(-v, t) = A_{\mp}(v, t) \tag{5.12a}$$
$$B_{\pm}(-v, t) = -B_{\mp}(v, t) \tag{5.12b}$$

where v is the energy variable introduced in section 3.4. It is convenient to define the combinations of amplitudes

$$A^{(\pm)} = \tfrac{1}{2}(A_- \pm A_+) \tag{5.13a}$$
$$B^{(\pm)} = \tfrac{1}{2}(B_- \pm B_+) \tag{5.13b}$$

for which the crossing relations read

$$A^{(\pm)}(-v, t) = \pm A^{(\pm)}(v, t) \tag{5.14a}$$
$$B^{(\pm)}(-v, t) = \mp B^{(\pm)}(v, t) \tag{5.14b}$$

Thus, $A^{(+)}$ and $B^{(-)}$ are crossing-symmetric, while $A^{(-)}$ and $B^{(+)}$ are crossing-antisymmetric.

The amplitudes $A_{\pm}$ and $B_{\pm}$ are assumed to satisfy the Mandelstam representation and, in particular, the usual fixed-variable dispersion relations (with an appropriate number of subtractions). Before writing down the fixed-t dispersion relations, however, we require the specific form of the neutron pole term in the $\pi^- p$ scattering amplitude.

We shall express the residue of the nucleon pole in terms of the rationalised, renormalised, pseudoscalar πNN coupling constant g, defined for the $\pi^0 pp$ vertex

$$g \equiv g_{\pi^0 pp}$$

Isospin invariance requires that

$$g_{\pi^- pn} = \sqrt{2} g_{\pi^0 pp} \tag{5.15}$$

There is considerable confusion in the literature regarding the distinction between rationalised and unrationalised coupling constants. The unrationalised coupling constant G is related to the rationalised one by

$$g = \sqrt{(4\pi)G} \qquad (5.16)$$

When numerical values of coupling constants are quoted, values of G^2 or (equivalently) $g^2/4\pi$ are normally given.

The form of the neutron pole term in the $\pi^- p$ invariant amplitude turns out to be (neglecting the small n–p mass difference)

$$A_-^{(\text{pole})}(s, t) = 0 \qquad (5.17a)$$

$$B_-^{(\text{pole})}(s, t) = 2g^2/(M^2 - s) \qquad (5.17b)$$

where the factor 2 in (5.17b) arises from the fact that we express the result in terms of the $\pi^0 pp$ instead of the $\pi^- pn$ coupling constant. Note that the pole term is completely absent in the amplitude A_-.

Using the relation (see section 3.4)

$$s = 2Mv + M^2 + \mu^2 - \tfrac{1}{2}t \qquad (5.18)$$

(we shall use μ for the pion mass throughout this chapter), we find that in the variable v the pole term takes the form

$$B_-^{(\text{pole})}(v, t) = \frac{g^2}{M} \frac{1}{v_N - v} \qquad (5.19)$$

where v_N is the value of v corresponding to $s = M^2$, namely

$$v_N = -(\mu^2/2M) + (t/4M) \qquad (5.20)$$

Crossing implies that the amplitude $B_+(v, t)$ has a similar pole (with the opposite sign of the residue) at $v = -v_N$.

Assuming that the amplitudes $A_\pm$ and $B_\pm$ have the pole terms specified above and the usual unitarity cuts for $s \geqslant (M + \mu)^2$, the dispersion relations for these amplitudes are easily written down. Actually, there is a short unphysical cut below the $\pi^- p$ threshold due to the charge-exchange process $\pi^- p \to \pi^0 n$. We shall neglect this cut, assuming that the masses of the $\pi^- p$ and $\pi^0 n$ systems are equal. The dispersion integrals over the left-hand cuts can be related to integrals involving the crossed amplitudes on their right-hand cuts, as in section 3.5. The dispersion relations take a simpler form, however, when written for the amplitudes $A^{(\pm)}$ and $B^{(\pm)}$, which are related to themselves by crossing. Ignoring for the moment the possible need for subtractions, the resulting dispersion relations have the form

$$\text{Re}A^{(\pm)}(v, t) = \frac{1}{\pi} P \int_{\mu + t/4M}^{\infty} \text{Im}A^{(\pm)}(v', t) \left[\frac{1}{v' - v} \pm \frac{1}{v' + v} \right] dv' \qquad (5.21a)$$

$$\text{Re}B^{(\pm)}(v, t) = \frac{g^2}{2M} \left(\frac{1}{v_N - v} \mp \frac{1}{v_N + v} \right)$$

$$+ \frac{1}{\pi} P \int_{\mu + t/4M}^{\infty} \text{Im}B^{(\pm)}(v', t) \left[\frac{1}{v' - v} \mp \frac{1}{v' + v} \right] dv' \qquad (5.21b)$$

Information on the asymptotic behaviour must be used to determine the minimum number of subtractions required for the validity of such dispersion relations. In some discussions of this problem in the literature, it has been argued that $A^{(+)}$ may require one subtraction, while $A^{(-)}$ and $B^{(\pm)}$ require no subtraction, although these conclusions are based on certain assumptions and cannot be regarded as firmly established.

Dispersion relations for $B_{\pm}$ have been useful in determining the coupling constant, using information from phase-shift analyses at low energies as input data. However, it is simpler in practice to make use of dispersion relations for the forward scattering amplitudes $F_{\pm}(\omega)$, whose imaginary parts are related in the usual way to the total cross sections via the optical theorem

$$\text{Im} F_{\pm}(\omega) = (k/4\pi)\sigma_{\pm}(\omega) = \sqrt{(\omega^2 - \mu^2)}\sigma_{\pm}(\omega)/4\pi \qquad (5.22)$$

One finds that the forward scattering amplitudes in the laboratory system are related to the invariant amplitudes by

$$F_{\pm}(\omega) = (1/4\pi)[A_{\pm}(\nu, 0) + \nu B_{\pm}(\nu, 0)] \qquad (5.23)$$

(using ω instead of ν as the energy variable in the case of $F_{\pm}$). It follows from this that the amplitudes $F_{\pm}(\omega)$ satisfy the crossing relations

$$F_{\pm}(-\omega) = F_{\mp}(\omega) \qquad (5.24)$$

and possess analyticity properties similar to those of $A_{\pm}$ and $B_{\pm}$. In particular, the nucleon pole terms are

$$F_{\pm}^{\text{(pole)}}(\omega) = \frac{g^2}{4\pi} \frac{\omega_N}{M} \frac{1}{\omega_N \pm \omega} \qquad (5.25)$$

where $\omega_N = -\mu^2/2M$.

It has become conventional, in analyses of the forward πN dispersion relations, to use an equivalent pseudovector coupling constant f defined by

$$f = (4\pi)^{-1/2}(\tfrac{1}{2}\mu/M)g \qquad (5.26)$$

In the following sections, we shall therefore write the pole terms in the dispersion relations in terms of f instead of g. In particular

$$F_{\pm}^{\text{(pole)}}(\omega) = -2f^2/(\omega_N \pm \omega) \qquad (5.27)$$

5.3. Twice-subtracted forward dispersion relations

We showed in section 4.4 that two subtractions are certainly sufficient for the fixed-t dispersion relations in the case of spinless particles. We shall assume, as can indeed be shown to be the case, that this result remains valid for the forward scattering amplitude for particles with spin.

In the case of the forward πN dispersion relations, the two subtractions are normally made at the threshold energies $\omega = \pm\mu$. These subtractions can be carried out by writing unsubtracted dispersion relations for the functions

$$G_\pm(\omega) = F_\pm(\omega)/(\omega - \mu)(\omega + \mu) \tag{5.28}$$

From the general form of the unsubtracted dispersion relation (see section 3.5) and the specific form of the pole term given in the preceding section, we find

$$\frac{\mathrm{Re}F_\pm(\omega)}{\omega^2 - \mu^2} = \frac{2f^2}{(\omega_N \pm \omega)(\mu^2 - \omega_N^2)} + \frac{F_\pm(\mu)}{2\mu(\omega - \mu)} - \frac{F_\pm(-\mu)}{2\mu(\omega + \mu)}$$
$$+ \frac{1}{\pi} P \int_\mu^\infty \left[\frac{\mathrm{Im}F_\pm(\omega')}{(\omega'^2 - \mu^2)(\omega' - \omega)} + \frac{\mathrm{Im}F_\mp(\omega')}{(\omega'^2 - \mu^2)(\omega' + \omega)} \right] d\omega'$$

$$\tag{5.29}$$

The second and third terms on the right-hand side of this dispersion relation (the subtraction terms) come from the poles of $G_\pm(\omega)$ due to the denominator in (5.28).

Applying the optical theorem and the crossing relations in the form

$$F_\pm(-\mu) = F_\mp(\mu)$$

we now obtain the conventional form of the dispersion relations for forward $\pi^\pm p$ scattering

$$\mathrm{Re}F_\pm(\omega) = \frac{2k^2 f^2}{(\mu^2 - \omega_N^2)(\omega_N \pm \omega)} + \frac{\omega + \mu}{2\mu} F_\pm(\mu) - \frac{\omega - \mu}{2\mu} F_\mp(\mu)$$
$$+ \frac{k^2}{4\pi^2} P \int_\mu^\infty \frac{1}{k'} \left[\frac{\sigma_\pm(\omega')}{\omega' - \omega} + \frac{\sigma_\mp(\omega')}{\omega' + \omega} \right] d\omega' \tag{5.30}$$

The quantities $F_\pm(\mu)$ are real and can be expressed in terms of the πN scattering lengths. In particular, if charge independence is assumed, then

$$F_+(\mu) = \frac{M + \mu}{M} a_3 \qquad F_-(\mu) = \frac{M + \mu}{M} (\tfrac{2}{3}a_1 + \tfrac{1}{3}a_3) \tag{5.31}$$

where a_1 and a_3 are the πN S-wave scattering lengths for the states of isospin $I = \tfrac{1}{2}$ and $I = \tfrac{3}{2}$, respectively. The factor $(M + \mu)/M$ arises in transforming the amplitude at threshold from the c.m. to the laboratory system.

We shall now discuss briefly the way in which such a dispersion relation can be analysed phenomenologically. First of all, let us assume for simplicity that the values of $F_\pm(\mu)$ appearing in the subtraction terms are already known (one way of determining them from another dispersion relation is discussed in the following section). The total cross sections required for the dispersion integrals have been measured experimentally with great accuracy over the very wide energy range accessible to accelerators, and an extrapolation based on a Regge model, for example, may be used to estimate the unknown asymptotic contribution (which, in any case, is effectively suppressed by the energy de-nominators when ω is not too large). Data on $\mathrm{Re}F_\pm(\omega)$ are available at low energies from phase-shift analyses and at higher energies from direct measurements of the small-angle differential cross sections. However, $\text{Re}F_{\pm}(\omega)$ have been measured at only a limited number of energies and, unlike $\text{Im}F_{\pm}(\omega)$, cannot be regarded as experimentally known over the entire energy range.

At energies at which phase-shift analyses are not available, many values of $|\text{Re}F_{\pm}|$ have been determined by extrapolating the measured differential cross section to the forward direction (which gives $|F_{\pm}|^2$) and comparing the result with the value of $(\text{Im}F_{\pm})^2$ given by the optical theorem. The sign of $\text{Re}F_{\pm}$ can in principle be found from an analysis of the Coulomb interference, although this information is sometimes not avaliable.

For each energy at which a value of $\text{Re}F_{+}(\omega)$ or $\text{Re}F_{-}(\omega)$ is known, the dispersion relations can be solved for the pole term, giving a numerical value for f^2. However, the best overall value of f^2 should be determined by a simultaneous least-squares fit to all the available data on $\text{Re}F_{\pm}(\omega)$. Of course, consistency of the many single-energy determinations of f^2 can provide evidence for the validity of the dispersion relations and hence of the various assumptions (such as analyticity) which enter their derivation.

As an example, we quote the numerical results of a typical analysis[1] of the dispersion relation (5.30). In this work, f^2, $\text{Re}F_{+}(\mu)$ and $\text{Re}F_{-}(\mu)$ were treated as adjustable parameters and a least-squares fit was made to 145 $\pi^- p$ data points and 97 $\pi^+ p$ data points. The following parameter values were determined (in units such that $\hbar = c = \mu = 1$)

$$f^2 = 0\cdot082 \pm 0\cdot003$$
$$a_1 = 0\cdot187 \pm 0\cdot009$$
$$a_3 = -0\cdot105 \pm 0\cdot006$$

This value of f^2 corresponds to $g^2/4\pi = 14\cdot9 \pm 0\cdot5$.

Once the strength of the pole term has been determined, the dispersion relations can be used to calculate $\text{Re}F_{\pm}(\omega)$ as a continuous function of energy. The results thus obtained constitute a fit to the experimental data on the real parts of the forward scattering amplitudes and provide a theoretical interpolation of these data in energy regions where the data are scarce. Good agreement with the existing experimental data is generally found in this way.

Such a fit to the data on $\text{Re}F_{\pm}(\omega)$ may be much more accurately determined at a given energy than a typical data point, since the entire data set is used simultaneously in obtaining the fit. The fit may also show considerably more local structure in its energy dependence than can be seen directly from the data. The reason for this is that local structures in the input data on $\sigma_{\pm}(\omega)$ are automatically reflected as corresponding structures in $\text{Re}F_{\pm}(\omega)$. This is due mainly to the term in the dispersion integral whose denominator becomes small when $\omega' \approx \omega$. For example, a Breit–Wigner resonance peak in one of the total cross sections $\sigma_{\pm}(\omega)$ would lead to a rapid variation (decrease) in the corresponding real part $\text{Re}F_{\pm}(\omega)$ near the energy in question. Contributions to $\mathrm{Re}F_\pm(\omega)$ from more distant energies in the dispersion integrals would be expected to provide a more slowly varying background.

The usual proofs of dispersion relations in quantum field theory depend on the assumption of microscopic causality down to infinitesimal distances. There is no well-defined procedure for incorporating a fundamental length in the theory. According to one model,[2] a violation of causality at distances less than some value l would lead to a breakdown of the forward dispersion relations at energies $\omega \gtrsim 1/l$. For example, from the good agreement of the πN forward dispersion relations with experiment up to at least 20 GeV,[3] one can infer that causality is satisfied down to distances of the order of 10^{-15} cm.

5.4. Alternative forms of the dispersion relations

Dispersion relations for a given process can be formulated in many different but mathematically equivalent forms, for example by making the subtractions in different ways. Since the $\pi^\pm p$ forward scattering amplitudes are described by a single analytic function, whose real and imaginary parts are not independent (by virtue of the dispersion relations), it may appear at first sight that nothing can be gained by considering alternative forms of the dispersion relations. This would be so in principle if the input data were known with infinite precision, so that all possible forms of the dispersion relations would necessarily give identical results. However, the experimental data are known only with finite errors, so that dispersion relations which assign different relative weights to various energy regions may yield predictions of the coupling constants or of the real parts of the amplitudes with different accuracies.

Moreover, if the imaginary part of an amplitude is assumed to be known at all energies, while the real part is known at a large number of discrete energies, then the data form an 'overdetermined' set. In this case, a consistency test of the entire set of data may be made by analysing the same data by means of different dispersion relations.

In this section we shall consider two alternative forms of πN dispersion relations, both of which require for their derivation certain additional assumptions about the asymptotic behaviour of the scattering amplitude, but which have certain advantages over the dispersion relations derived in the preceding section. The additional assumptions are quite plausible and have often been made in phenomenological analyses.

We shall assume, in particular, that (i) the total cross sections have finite asymptotic limits $\sigma_\pm(\infty)$ and (ii) $\mathrm{Re}F_\pm(\omega)/\mathrm{Im}F_\pm(\omega) \to 0$ as $\omega \to \infty$. By the Pomeranchuk theorem, these two assumptions also imply the equality (iii) $\sigma_+(\infty) = \sigma_-(\infty)$.

The first dispersion relation which we shall obtain here is derived by considering the function

$$H(\omega) = [F_-(\omega) - F_+(\omega)]/\omega$$

Condition (iii), when combined with the optical theorem and the property

$H(-\omega) = H(\omega)$, implies that $\mathrm{Im}H(\omega) \to 0$ as $\omega \to \pm\infty$, while (ii) then implies that $\mathrm{Re}H(\omega) \to 0$ as $\omega \to \pm\infty$. Because of this asymptotic behaviour and the analyticity properties of $H(\omega)$ which follow from its definition (note that there is no pole in $H(\omega)$ at $\omega = 0$ because of the zero in the numerator), the function $H(\omega)$ satisfies the unsubtracted dispersion relation

$$\mathrm{Re}H(\omega) = \frac{4Mf^2}{\mu^2}\left(\frac{1}{\omega_N - \omega} + \frac{1}{\omega_N + \omega}\right)$$
$$+ \frac{1}{\pi} P \int_\mu^\infty \mathrm{Im}H(\omega')\left[\frac{1}{\omega' - \omega} + \frac{1}{\omega' + \omega}\right] d\omega' \qquad (5.32)$$

Using the definition of $H(\omega)$ and applying the optical theorem, we can write this dispersion relation in the more conventional form

$$\mathrm{Re}[F_-(\omega) - F_+(\omega)] = \frac{4\omega f^2}{\omega^2 - \omega_N^2} + \frac{\omega}{2\pi^2} P \int_\mu^\infty \frac{k'[\sigma_-(\omega') - \sigma_+(\omega')]\,d\omega'}{\omega'^2 - \omega^2}$$
$$(5.33)$$

In the literature this dispersion relation is sometimes formally derived as an unsubtracted dispersion relation for the difference $F_-(\omega) - F_+(\omega)$. Such a derivation, in spite of the fact that it produces the correct result, is actually fallacious, since the difference of amplitudes does not necessarily vanish at infinity (actually, the correctness of the resulting dispersion relation shows a posteriori that the entire integral over a semicircular contour at infinity would give no contribution). Another well-known but fallacious derivation of the same dispersion relation is to take the difference of two unsubtracted (invalid) dispersion relations for the individual amplitudes $F_-(\omega)$ and $F_+(\omega)$. The existence of this formal derivation has led to the term 'sign-subtracted' dispersion relation for equation (5.33).

The dispersion relation (5.33) makes use of the same experimental data as that of the preceding section, but it has the advantage that it contains no subtraction constants. However, it also has the serious drawback that it requires the two real parts $\mathrm{Re}F_\pm(\omega)$ at the same energy, which makes it difficult to utilize all the available experimental data on $\mathrm{Re}F_\pm(\omega)$ in the analysis.

One way of overcoming this defect is to write a dispersion relation for the more general function

$$H(\omega) = [F_-(\omega + \Delta\omega) - F_+(\omega)]/(\omega + \tfrac{1}{2}\Delta\omega) \qquad (5.34)$$

where $\Delta\omega$ is an arbitrary fixed energy difference. Putting $\bar{\omega} = \omega + \Delta\omega$, the resulting dispersion relation takes the form

$$\mathrm{Re}[F_-(\bar{\omega}) - F_+(\omega)]$$
$$= 2(\omega + \bar{\omega})f^2/(\omega + \omega_N)(\bar{\omega} - \omega_N)$$
$$+ \frac{\omega + \bar{\omega}}{4\pi^2} P \int_\mu^\infty k'\left[\frac{\sigma_-(\omega')}{(\omega' + \omega)(\omega' - \bar{\omega})} - \frac{\sigma_+(\omega')}{(\omega' - \omega)(\omega' + \bar{\omega})}\right] d\omega' \qquad (5.35)$$

This dispersion relation is dependent on the two energy parameters ω and $\bar{\omega}$ and is a generalisation of the previous dispersion relation (5.33), which is recovered by setting $\bar{\omega} = \omega$. The energies ω and $\bar{\omega}$ can be specified arbitrarily, thus enabling one to make use of all the available data on $\text{Re}F_\pm(\omega)$ in the analysis of the dispersion relation.

It is worth pointing out that the dispersion relation (5.33), when evaluated at $\omega = \mu$, constitutes a sum rule giving a definite relationship between f^2 and the difference of the scattering lengths $a_1 - a_3$. Another type of πN forward dispersion relation can be derived by considering the functions

$$H_\pm(\omega) = F_\pm(\omega)/(\omega - \omega_0) \tag{5.36}$$

where ω_0 is some subtraction energy. The asymptotic conditions (i), (ii) and (iii) which were used in the derivation of the preceding dispersion relation are again assumed. Conditions (i) and (iii) imply that $\text{Im}H_\pm(\omega) \to C$ as $\omega \to \infty$, where C is a common real constant. Condition (ii) then gives $H_\pm(\omega) \to iC$ as $\omega \to \infty$. Since $H_\pm(\omega)$ does not vanish asymptotically, it may appear at first sight that the dispersion relations for $H_\pm(\omega)$ require a subtraction. However, we shall show that the semicircular contour integral in the derivation of the un-subtracted dispersion relation (see section 2.4) actually vanishes in this case and hence that $H_\pm(\omega)$ satisfy unsubtracted dispersion relations. The contribution to $\text{Re}H_\pm(\omega)$ from the integration over the semicircular contour is given by

$$I_\pm(\omega) = \text{Re}\left[\frac{1}{2\pi i} \int_{S(R)} \frac{H_\pm(\omega')\,d\omega'}{\omega' - \omega}\right] \tag{5.37}$$

where $S(R)$ is the semicircle in the upper half-plane specified by $\omega' = R\exp(i\phi)$, $0 < \phi < \pi$. The Sugawara–Tubis theorem (section 2.5) implies that $H_\pm(\omega)$ have the common asymptotic limit iC in all directions in the upper half-plane. Letting the radius R tend to infinity and replacing $H_\pm(\omega')$ in the integrand by its limiting value, we find

$$\lim_{R\to\infty} I_\pm(\omega) = \lim_{R\to\infty} \text{Re}\left[\frac{C}{2\pi} \int_{S(R)} \frac{d\omega'}{\omega'}\right] = \lim_{R\to\infty} \text{Re}\left[\frac{C}{2\pi} \int_0^\pi \frac{iR\exp(i\phi)\,d\phi}{R\exp(i\phi)}\right] = 0 \tag{5.38}$$

Since the semicircular contour integral does not contribute, the unsubtracted dispersion relations are valid. Using the known form of the nucleon poles at $\omega = \pm\omega_N$ and noting that each of the functions $H_\pm(\omega)$ has an additional pole at $\omega = \omega_0$ with residue $F_\pm(\omega_0)$, the dispersion relations become

$$\frac{\text{Re}F_\pm(\omega)}{\omega - \omega_0} = \frac{\text{Re}F_\pm(\omega_0)}{\omega - \omega_0} \pm \frac{2f^2}{(\omega_N \pm \omega)(\omega_N \pm \omega_0)}$$

$$+ \frac{1}{4\pi^2} P\int_\mu^\infty k'\left[\frac{\sigma_\pm(\omega')}{(\omega' - \omega_0)(\omega' - \omega)} - \frac{\sigma_\mp(\omega')}{(\omega' + \omega_0)(\omega' + \omega)}\right] d\omega' \tag{5.39}$$

Note that the dispersion integrals over σ_+ and σ_- are separately divergent in this case, as well as in the sign-subtracted dispersion relation. The combined integrals converge only because of a cancellation between the two terms in the integrand.

The dispersion relations (5.39) are sometimes derived by the formal (invalid) procedure of taking the difference between the unsubtracted dispersion relation for $F_\pm(\omega)$ and a similar unsubtracted dispersion relation for $F_\pm(\omega_0)$, where ω_0 is another energy. For this reason, the result is sometimes known as an 'energy-subtracted' dispersion relation. Equation (5.39) is also known simply as a once-subtracted dispersion relation.

The sign-subtracted and energy-subtracted dispersion relations were derived in rather different ways. However, contrary to what is commonly believed, they are not actually distinct relations. Thus, if we make the substitutions $\bar{\omega} \to -\omega$, $\omega \to \omega_0$ in (5.35), we arrive at the dispersion relation obtained by taking the upper signs in (5.39); alternatively, making the substitutions $\bar{\omega} \to \omega$, $\omega \to -\omega_0$, we get the dispersion relation corresponding to the lower signs in (5.39).

It is convenient to choose the subtraction point at $\omega_0 = 0$ in the dispersion relations (5.39). The dispersion relations then reduce to the somewhat simpler form

$$\mathrm{Re}F_\pm(\omega) = C - \frac{2f^2}{\omega_N \pm \omega} + \frac{\omega}{4\pi^2} P \int_\mu^\infty \frac{k'}{\omega'}\left[\frac{\sigma_\pm(\omega')}{\omega'-\omega} - \frac{\sigma_\mp(\omega')}{\omega'+\omega}\right] d\omega' \quad (5.40)$$

where $C = F(0) + 2f^2/\omega_N$ and $F(0)$ is the common (real) value of $F_+(0)$ and $F_-(0)$ (which are equal by virtue of crossing).

Note that part of the pole term (the constant part) is included in the definition of the constant C, so that the remaining part (which is written explicitly in equation 5.40) has an energy dependence proportional to $1/\omega$ at large distances from the pole. This facilitates the separation of the two unknown constants (C and f^2) in the analysis of the dispersion relation. If $F(0)$ and f^2 were taken instead as parameters, they would both correspond to asymptotically constant contributions and would therefore be difficult to distinguish.

All the available data on $\mathrm{Re}F_\pm(\omega)$ can be used in the analysis of the dispersion relations (5.40). There are two unknown constants, namely C and f^2. These two constants may be determined by a simultaneous least-squares fit to the entire set of data, each experimental value of $\mathrm{Re}F_\pm(\omega)$ providing one data point to be fitted. Once C and f^2 have been determined, the dispersion relations can be used to calculate $\mathrm{Re}F_\pm(\omega)$ as a function of energy and, in particular, to evaluate the quantities $F_\pm(\mu)$ (or, equivalently, the S-wave scattering lengths a_1 and a_3). A typical analysis of this type,[4] using a total of 90 values of $\mathrm{Re}F_\pm(\omega)$, gave the results (in units such that $\hbar = c = \mu = 1$)

$$C = -0\cdot106 \pm 0\cdot002$$

$$f^2 = 0\cdot076 \pm 0\cdot002$$

$$a_1 + 2a_3 = 0\cdot003 \pm 0\cdot008 \qquad a_1 - a_3 = 0\cdot271 \pm 0\cdot011$$

The combinations of scattering lengths given here are those which are obtained by direct evaluation of the dispersion relation expressions for

$$\mathrm{Re} F_-(\mu) \pm \mathrm{Re} F_+(\mu)$$

respectively.

The direct analysis of the πN scattering data at low energies has not allowed a sufficiently precise determination of the values of a_1 and a_3. Thus, our knowledge of these scattering lengths comes mainly from the dispersion relations.

Some idea of the extent to which the dispersion relations are in agreement with experiment can be gained by comparing the dispersion relation predictions for $\mathrm{Re} F_\pm(\omega)$ (or quantities which depend on these real parts, such as forward differential cross sections) with the existing experimental data. Many such comparisons have been made on the basis of various forms of the dispersion relations. As an example, we shall show some of the results obtained by Ferrari,[5] whose calculations are based on the sign-subtracted dispersion relation (5.33) for the difference of amplitudes $F_-(\omega) - F_+(\omega)$ and an appropriately subtracted dispersion relation for the sum of the amplitudes $F_-(\omega) + F_+(\omega)$, with a careful analysis of the uncertainties due to the errors on the input data. Figures 5.1 and 5.2 show the experimental data on the forward differential

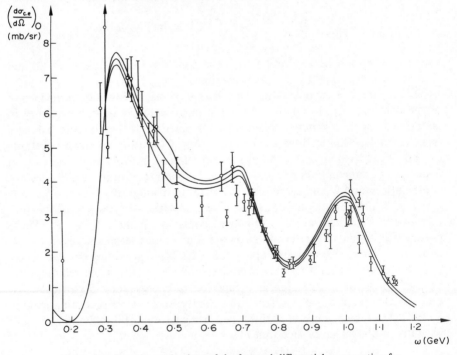

Figure 5.1. Experimental values of the forward differential cross section for πN charge-exchange scattering up to $\omega = 1.2$ GeV. The curves show the theoretical predictions obtained with the aid of dispersion relations, together with their maximum error corridor.

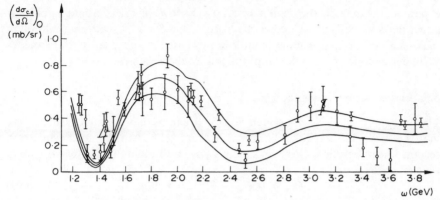

Figure 5.2. The same as in figure 5.1, but in the energy range from 1·2 to 3·9 GeV.

cross section for the charge-exchange process $\pi^- + p \to \pi^0 + n$ in the c.m.s. at relatively low energies, where considerable structure is observed. The corresponding theoretical curves shown in these figures are obtained from the formula

$$(d\sigma_{c.e.}/d\Omega)_0 = \tfrac{1}{2}(q/k)^2 \, |F_-(\omega) - F_+(\omega)|^2$$

which follows from charge independence and the transformation from the laboratory system to the c.m.s.; the required values of $\mathrm{Im}F_\pm(\omega)$ were calculated in terms of experimental data on the $\pi^\pm p$ total cross sections according to the optical theorem, while $\mathrm{Re}[F_-(\omega) - F_+(\omega)]$ was taken from the dispersion relation calculations. Satisfactory agreement is also found at higher energies, although the data become relatively scarce there and exhibit much less structure. As a further example, figure 5.3 shows the dispersion relation predictions for the real part of the $\pi^+ p$ scattering amplitude and their comparison with the

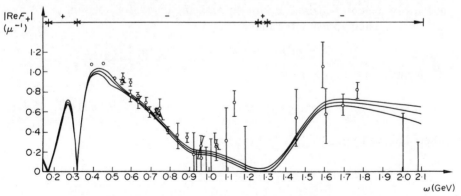

Figure 5.3. Experimental values of $|\mathrm{Re}F_+(\omega)|$ up to 2 GeV. The curves show the dispersion relation predictions and their maximum error corridor; the sign of the predicted real part is indicated at the top of the figure.

experimental data in the region of relatively low energies, where significant structure is again seen. Agreement is also found for $\pi^- p$ scattering, although the quality of the data is much poorer in this case, as well as for both processes at higher energies, where the amplitudes are relatively structureless.

5.5. Linear extrapolation methods

The once-subtracted dispersion relation (5.40) can be reformulated in such a way that the two undetermined constants in it are related to the coefficients of a certain linear function of ω. Specifically, by multiplying (5.40) by $(\omega \pm \omega_N)$, we can write

$$C\omega \pm (C\omega_N - 2f^2) = J_\pm(\omega) \qquad (5.41)$$

where one of the two functions $J_\pm(\omega)$, consisting of all the terms not containing the constants C and f^2, can be evaluated in terms of experimental data at each energy at which a value for $\mathrm{Re}F_\pm(\omega)$ is known. The left-hand side of the relation (5.41) shows that the functions $J_\pm(\omega)$ must actually be linear in ω. According to (5.41), the values of C and f^2 can be determined from the slope of these linear functions and their intercepts at the unphysical energy $\omega = 0$. Actually, it is sufficient to deal with only a single function instead of the two functions $J_\pm(\omega)$, since $J_\pm(-\omega) = -J_\mp(\omega)$, as is easily verified from either the left-hand side of (5.41) or the form of the functions $J_\pm(\omega)$ themselves.

This situation is typical of the so-called linear extrapolation methods. In practice, the unknown constants can be determined in a neat way by performing a least-squares linear fit to the known values of $J_\pm(\omega)$. Such a fit is more convenient to make than a least-squares fit to a non-linear functional form, for example the once-subtracted dispersion relation in the form (5.40), since the parameters of a linear fit can be expressed in closed form in terms of the values of the fitted points.

As a further example, we shall outline a linear extrapolation method originally devised by Haber–Schaim.[6] By multiplying the dispersion relation (5.33) by $(\omega^2 - \omega_N^2)/\omega$ and applying the simple identity

$$1/(\omega'^2 - \omega^2) = \omega^2/[\omega'^2(\omega'^2 - \omega^2)] + 1/\omega'^2$$

to the integrand, it follows that

$$L(\omega) = 4f^2 + [(\omega^2 - \omega_N^2)/2\pi^2]\int_\mu^\infty (k'/\omega'^2)[\sigma_-(\omega') - \sigma_+(\omega')]\,d\omega' \qquad (5.42)$$

where $L(\omega)$ is defined by

$$L(\omega) = (\omega^2 - \omega_N^2)\left\{ \frac{\mathrm{Re}[F_-(\omega) - F_+(\omega)]}{\omega} \right.$$
$$\left. - \frac{\omega^2}{2\pi^2}P\int_\mu^\infty \frac{k'[\sigma_-(\omega') - \sigma_+(\omega')]\,d\omega'}{\omega'^2(\omega'^2 - \omega^2)} \right\} \qquad (5.43)$$

If the real parts $\text{Re}F_{\pm}(\omega)$ are known at a particular energy ω, then (5.43) determines the function $L(\omega)$ at that energy in terms of experimental information. On the other hand, (5.42) asserts that $L(\omega)$ must reduce to a linear function of the variable ω^2. Moreover, since $L(\omega_N) = 4f^2$, the πNN coupling constant can be determined by fitting the known values of $L(\omega)$ in the physical region $\omega > \mu$ to a linear function in the variable ω^2 and extrapolating this fit to the point $\omega^2 = \omega_N^2$.

According to (5.42), the slope of the linear function must have the value

$$dL/d(\omega^2) = (1/2\pi^2)\int_{\mu}^{\infty} (k'/\omega'^2)[\sigma_-(\omega') - \sigma_+(\omega')] \, d\omega' \qquad (5.44)$$

This relation makes it possible to carry out a useful consistency test of the input data as a by-product of the analysis, since the slope of the fitted function can be compared with the value of the right-hand side of (5.44) obtained from the experimental total cross section data.

Although the existence of this consistency test is a definite advantage, a serious weakness of the method is the fact that the analysis requires experimental values of $\text{Re}F_+(\omega)$ and $\text{Re}F_-(\omega)$ at the same energies, which are not always available. Another possible disadvantage of both linear extrapolation methods which we have considered so far is that they are based on dispersion relations which require the additional special assumptions of section 5.4 for their validity. Even if these conditions are satisfied, as appears to be the case on the basis of the empirical evidence, the dispersion integrals in (5.41) and (5.42) may be rather slowly convergent (the dispersion integral in (5.43) converges more rapidly, owing to the higher power of ω' in the denominator).

We shall now describe an alternative method[7] which is free of these defects. The method is based on the use of the twice-subtracted dispersion relation (5.30) in the form

$$(\omega + \mu)F_{\pm}(\mu) - (\omega - \mu)F_{\mp}(\mu) = H_{\pm}(\omega) \qquad (5.45)$$

where the functions $H_{\pm}(\omega)$ contain all the dependence on $\text{Re}F_{\pm}(\omega)$, the pole term involving f^2, and the dispersion integrals over $\sigma_{\pm}(\omega)$. The essence of the method is to use experimental data to calculate numerical values of $H_{\pm}(\omega)$ at all the energies at which data on $\text{Re}F_{\pm}(\omega)$ exist. As in the first linear extrapolation method which we have described, it is necessary to deal with only a single function instead of the two functions $H_{\pm}(\omega)$, since $H_{\pm}(-\omega) = H_{\mp}(\omega)$.

Equation (5.45) shows that this function must be linear in ω. Thus, as before, the procedure is to obtain the best linear fit to the experimentally determined values of $H_{\pm}(\omega)$. Since $H_{\pm}(\mu) = 2\mu F_{\pm}(\mu)$, the values of the fitted function at $\omega = \pm \mu$ provide a direct determination of $F_{\pm}(\mu)$ or, equivalently, the $\pi^{\pm}p$ scattering lengths.

A complication of this method is the occurrence of the coupling constant in the expression for $H_{\pm}(\omega)$. One can, of course, simply take the value of f^2 from some other analysis. Alternatively, f^2 can be used as a parameter to be adjusted together with the parameters of the straight line in getting the best fit.

Two of the linear extrapolation methods which we have considered, namely those based on (5.41) and (5.45), yield theoretical fits to the real parts $\mathrm{Re}F_\pm(\omega)$ as a by-product of the analysis, since these equations can be solved explicitly for $\mathrm{Re}F_\pm(\omega)$ once the values of the fitted parameters are known. Such analyses provide a means of correlating all the experimental data to obtain an overall best fit to $\mathrm{Re}F_\pm(\omega)$ and, at the same time, to determine the πNN coupling constant. Of course, the extent to which the relevant functions can actually be fitted by linear forms provides a measure of the consistency of the data with the dispersion relations.

5.6. Dispersion relations for the B amplitudes

We have already pointed out that the amplitudes $A_\pm$ and $B_\pm$ satisfy fixed-t dispersion relations. The dispersion relation for B_+ at $t = 0$ turns out to be particularly suitable for an accurate determination of the πNN coupling constant. To see why this is so, let us write down this relation

$$\mathrm{Re}B_+(\omega) = -\frac{16\pi Mf^2}{\mu^2(\omega + \omega_N)} + \frac{1}{\pi}P\int_\mu^\infty \left[\frac{\mathrm{Im}B_+(\omega')}{\omega' - \omega} - \frac{\mathrm{Im}B_-(\omega')}{\omega' + \omega}\right]d\omega' \quad (5.46)$$

It is assumed that no subtraction is required here.

Now the amplitudes $B_\pm$ are related as follows to the amplitudes B_1 and B_3 for the πN scattering in the states of definite isospin $I = \frac{1}{2}$ and $I = \frac{3}{2}$, respectively

$$B_+ = B_3$$
$$B_- = \tfrac{2}{3}B_1 + \tfrac{1}{3}B_3$$

The amplitude B_+ is known experimentally with great accuracy at low energies, where the dominant contribution is given by the very well-determined N^* (1236) resonance (the so-called 33 resonance) in the P wave with $j = \frac{3}{2}$, $I = \frac{3}{2}$. In this region, the other partial-wave contributions to B_+ are known less accurately but are much less important. Thus, the principal-valued integral involving $\mathrm{Im}B_+(\omega)$ in the dispersion relation (5.46) can be reliably evaluated over the energy region in which the 33 resonance is dominant. Similarly, the left-hand side of (5.46) is well determined in this energy region. The quantity $\mathrm{Im}B_-(\omega')$ appearing in the remaining part of the dispersion integral need not be determined with the same accuracy, since its contribution is suppressed by the energy denominator $(\omega' + \omega)$ which accompanies it. It turns out that, because of the 33 resonance, the overall low-energy contribution to the dispersion integral is so strongly dominant that the details of the amplitudes in the entire energy region $\omega' \gtrsim 350$ MeV are quite unimportant. As a result, an accurate determination of f^2 can be made from the dispersion relation (5.46) when ω is not too large.

As an example, we cite one of the first analyses[8] of the dispersion relation (5.46), which, making use of experimental data for a set of values of ω from threshold up to 325 MeV, resulted in a fitted value for the pole term corresponding to

$$f^2 = 0.081 \pm 0.003$$

One of the earliest and best known applications of πN dispersion relations was the use of (5.46) to resolve the Fermi–Yang ambiguity for πN scattering. This ambiguity refers to the existence of two alternative sets of phase shifts which yield identical predictions for the πN differential cross sections. Although a knowledge of the recoil proton polarisation can easily distinguish between the two sets of phase shifts, this information was not available from experiment when the Fermi–Yang ambiguity was first resolved theoretically by means of dispersion relations.

Specifically, the Fermi–Yang ambiguity in this case is described by a certain transformation $\delta_{1\pm} \leftrightarrow \delta'_{1\pm}$ on the $I = \frac{3}{2}$ P-wave phase shifts δ_{1-} and δ_{1+} for the states with $j = \frac{1}{2}$ and $j = \frac{3}{2}$, respectively, which can be shown to leave the differential cross section invariant. The conventional (Fermi) solution consists of a phase shift δ_{1+} which rises rapidly with energy through the resonant value $\frac{1}{2}\pi$ at the position of the N^* (1236), accompanied by a small non-resonant phase shift δ_{1-}. In the alternative (Yang) solution, the qualitative roles of these phase shifts are interchanged (this solution being somewhat dubious, as it yields a rapidly decreasing phase shift δ_{1-}, suggesting a conflict with the Wigner condition).

We shall now describe the method by which the Fermi–Yang ambiguity was first resolved. The technique is rather similar to the Haber-Schaim linear extrapolation method described in the preceding section, but is based on the dispersion relation for $B_+(\omega)$. By applying the identity

$$1/(\omega' \pm \omega) = 1/\omega' \mp \omega/[\omega'(\omega' \pm \omega)]$$

to the integrand of (5.46), the dispersion relation can be written in the form

$$\mathrm{Re}B_+(\omega) = -\frac{16\pi M f^2}{\mu^2(\omega + \omega_N)} + C + \omega I(\omega) \tag{5.47}$$

where

$$C = \frac{1}{\pi} \int_\mu^\infty \frac{\mathrm{Im}[B_+(\omega') - B_-(\omega')] \, d\omega'}{\omega'} \tag{5.48}$$

is a constant (independent of ω) and

$$I(\omega) = \frac{1}{\pi} P \int_\mu^\infty \left[\frac{\mathrm{Im}B_+(\omega')}{\omega'(\omega' - \omega)} + \frac{\mathrm{Im}B_-(\omega')}{\omega'(\omega' + \omega)} \right] d\omega' \tag{5.49}$$

Because of the additional factor ω' in the denominator, the integral $I(\omega)$ is more rapidly convergent than the original dispersion integral in (5.46). Let us suppose that the low-energy data on $B_\pm(\omega)$ are sufficient to determine $I(\omega)$ but not the more slowly convergent integral (5.48). It is nevertheless possible in this case to make a consistency test of the data on $B_\pm(\omega)$ by determining the

extent to which the relation (5.47) can be fitted with f^2 and C as free parameters.
An elegant way of doing this is as follows. One defines the new variables

$$x(\omega) = -\mu^2(\omega + \omega_N)/16\pi M$$
$$y(\omega) = x(\omega)[\text{Re}B_+(\omega) - \omega I(\omega)]$$

In these variables, equation (5.47) takes the form

$$y = f^2 + Cx \qquad (5.50)$$

Thus, if the values of y evaluated from the phase-shift analyses are plotted as a function of the variable x, the resulting graph should take the form of a straight line, whose intercept at $x = 0$ determines the value of f^2 and whose slope determines the value of the constant C.

Such an analysis was first made[9] using πN phase-shift solutions of both the Fermi and Yang types in the energy region between threshold and $\omega = 440$ MeV. The resulting plots of y as a function of x (figure 5.4) showed a striking difference between the two solutions. The graph of $y(x)$ for the Fermi-type solution was found to be very close to a straight line within the entire energy region considered, in accordance with (5.50), and the extrapolated value of y at $x = 0$ was found to be close to the known value of f^2. The Yang-type solution, on the other hand, led to gross deviations from a linear form at energies near the 33 resonance; moreover, it extrapolated to a negative value for f^2. Thus, the Yang-type solution must be rejected.

Finally, we point out that dispersion relations of the type considered in this section are sometimes known as spin-flip dispersion relations. The reason for

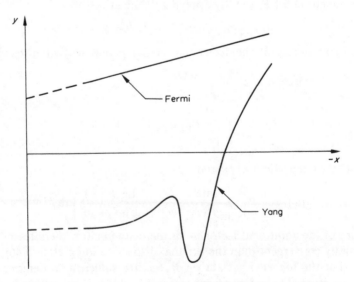

Figure 5.4. The quantity y as a function of x for the Fermi and Yang-type phase-shift solutions.

this is as follows. Equation (5.7b) expresses the B amplitude as a certain linear combination of the amplitudes f_1 and f_2. As can easily be verified, the ratio of the coefficients of f_1 and f_2 in this expression, namely $(E - M)/(E + M)$, is quite small throughout the relevant low-energy region, so that f_2 is dominant in the expression for B. According to (5.9b), the spin-flip amplitude $g(\theta)$ is equal to $if_2(\theta) \sin \theta$. In other words, although $g(\theta)$ vanishes at $\theta = 0$, its small-angle behaviour is governed entirely by f_2, which in turn is directly related to B at low energies.

5.7. Computational problems in the analysis of dispersion relations

In applications of dispersion relations which make use of experimental data, such as those discussed in the preceding sections, one must face the general problem of evaluating dispersion integrals of the type

$$I = \int_a^b h(\omega)\sigma(\omega) \, d\omega \tag{5.51}$$

where $\sigma(\omega)$ is some experimentally measured cross section and $h(\omega)$ is a known function, which we shall call the weight function. In certain cases the weight function $h(\omega)$ contains a factor $(\omega - \omega_0)^{-1}$ and the integral is taken to be principal-valued with respect to the point $\omega = \omega_0$.

Although the precise mathematical form of the weight function $h(\omega)$ is assumed to be known throughout the region of integration, numerical values of the cross section $\sigma(\omega)$ are available from experiment only at a discrete set of points ω_i $(i = 1, 2, \ldots)$. Moreover, each of the measured values $\sigma_i \equiv \sigma(\omega_i)$ must be assumed to have some statistical error (standard deviation) $\delta\sigma_i$. The basic problem is to exploit this information to calculate a value for the integral I, as well as the statistical error δI to be attached to this value.

A reasonable procedure is to adopt a definite interpolation of the cross section $\sigma(\omega)$ between the experimental points. One may, for example, make a linear interpolation between each pair of successive points or a quadratic interpolation between groups of three successive points. Alternatively, the function $h(\omega)\sigma(\omega)$ or some other related function can be interpolated. Still another possibility is to make the interpolation in a different variable, such as the momentum instead of the energy. In any case, once a definite interpolation is adopted, the value of the integral is completely determined and can be found by any of the standard methods of numerical integration.

Although numerical methods for the evaluation of non-singular integrals, such as Simpson's rule, are sufficiently well known, it should be stressed that special care is essential in the evaluation of principal-valued integrals. It is not feasible in practice to carry out the limiting operation by which we have originally defined the principal value of an integral (section 2.1), since the integration over the region on each side of the singularity is separately divergent. However, various methods exist which may be safely used to evaluate principal-valued integrals. As examples, we shall discuss two such methods here.

Let us isolate the factor which gives rise to the singularity by writing the integral to be evaluated in the general form

$$I = P\int_a^b \frac{F(\omega)\,d\omega}{\omega - \omega_0} \tag{5.52}$$

where $a < \omega_0 < b$, and $F(\omega)$ is a function which is assumed to have no singularities and to be known numerically in the interval $a < \omega < b$.

The first method consists in separating the integral into a sum of a singular and a non-singular part in such a way that the former can be evaluated analytically, while the latter can be treated by standard numerical methods. Such a decomposition is achieved, for example, by writing

$$I = P\int_a^b \frac{F(\omega_0)\,d\omega}{\omega - \omega_0} + \int_a^b \frac{[F(\omega) - F(\omega_0)]\,d\omega}{\omega - \omega_0} \tag{5.53}$$

The first integration is easily performed analytically by resorting to the original definition of the principal value. This gives

$$P\int_a^b \frac{F(\omega_0)\,d\omega}{\omega - \omega_0} = F(\omega_0)\log\left(\frac{b - \omega_0}{\omega_0 - a}\right) \tag{5.54}$$

The second integration in (5.53) involves no singularity, since the integrand has a finite limit as $\omega \to \omega_0$ (namely, the derivative $F'(\omega_0)$); the evaluation of this integral is straightforward, although care is required in evaluating the integrand near the point $\omega = \omega_0$

Another practical technique for evaluating a principal-valued integral is to make direct use of some interpolation of the non-singular factors of the integrand. For example, suppose that the function $F(\omega)$ in (5.52) is known at $\omega = \omega_0$ and at two neighbouring points ω_1 and ω_2, with $\omega_1 < \omega_0 < \omega_2$. Let $F_i \equiv F(\omega_i)$ $(i = 0, 1, 2)$. As a specific interpolation between these three points, let us choose a quadratic function $F_Q(\omega) = \alpha\omega^2 + \beta\omega + \gamma$, where the coefficients α, β and γ are chosen so that the three conditions $F_Q(\omega_i) = F_i$ are satisfied. When $F(\omega)$ is replaced by the approximation $F_Q(\omega)$, the part of the integral (5.52) over the range $\omega_1 < \omega < \omega_2$ can be evaluated analytically. The remaining parts, over the ranges $a < \omega < \omega_1$ and $\omega_2 < \omega < b$, are non-singular and can be evaluated without difficulty by standard numerical methods.

The evaluation of the singular part of the integral is straightforward, although the algebra is rather lengthy. Defining

$$J = P\int_{\omega_1}^{\omega_2} \frac{F_Q(\omega)\,d\omega}{\omega - \omega_0}$$

the final result is

$$J = F_0\left[\frac{d^2 - c^2}{2cd} + \log\left(\frac{d}{c}\right)\right] + F_2\left(\frac{c + d}{2d}\right) - F_1\left(\frac{c + d}{2c}\right) \tag{5.55}$$

where $c = \omega_0 - \omega_1$ and $d = \omega_2 - \omega_0$. It is of interest to note that in the special case of equal intervals, that is $c = d$, (5.55) takes the much simpler form

$$J = F_2 - F_1 \tag{5.56}$$

which is independent of the value of F_0 and the size of the interval.

We turn now to the problem of estimating the statistical error on a dispersion integral in terms of the errors on the input data. Let us suppose that the cross section $\sigma(\omega)$ in the dispersion integral (5.51) has been interpolated in some way between the experimental points, as discussed above. It is not necessary to specify the precise nature of the interpolation for our considerations; we shall make only the very general assumption that the interpolated value $\sigma(\omega)$ at any particular value of ω within the range of integration is a known linear combination of some set of data points σ_i.

It is easy to see that the value of the integral (5.51) is then given by a certain linear combination of the entire set of data points σ_i, that is

$$I = \sum_i c_i \sigma_i \tag{5.57}$$

where the coefficients c_i are determined entirely by the weight function $h(\omega)$ and the values ω_i. The linear relationship (5.57) holds for both non-singular and principal-valued integrals, not only for the exact value of the integral I (after the interpolation between the experimental points has been made), but also for the approximate value determined by any of the standard methods of numerical integration. It can be seen, for example, that (5.55) constitutes a linear relationship of this type.

If the errors $\delta\sigma_i$ on the individual data points σ_i are assumed to be statistically independent, it follows at once from (5.57) and the law of propagation of errors that the statistical error to be assigned to the integral is

$$\delta I = \left[\sum_i c_i^2 (\delta\sigma_i)^2 \right]^{1/2} \tag{5.58}$$

In spite of the results which we have obtained, great care is required in certain cases in the numerical evaluation of integrals. It sometimes happens, for example, that, within the errors, one of the data points σ_i is inconsistent with the trend defined by the other neighbouring points and is therefore suspect. If the weight function in the integral is smooth in the energy region in question, a spurious displacement of an individual data point is of little consequence; in fact, random effects of this type will, on the average, tend to compensate each other in the evaluation of the integral. However, if the integral is principal-valued, with the singularity at a point $\omega = \omega_0$ near the suspicious data point, it is clear (see the discussion in section 5.3) that the spurious structure in the input values of $\sigma(\omega)$ will be reflected by a corresponding local structure in the value of the integral as a function of ω_0. We recall that ω_0 usually has the interpretation of the energy at which the dispersion relation is evaluated. Since it is generally

D

unreasonable to interpret a single shifted point as evidence for a structure in the amplitude, it is probably better to reject the suspicious data point and perform the analysis without it.

Another possible procedure is to abandon the direct use of the experimental data and to perform the dispersion integrals instead with the help of some smooth fit to the entire set of data points in a given energy region. In this way, spurious local structures are eliminated. By repeating the calculation using different parametrisations which give an acceptable fit to the experimental data, one can estimate the error on an integral without relying too strongly on any particular parametrisation.

An alternative procedure, which takes a point of view intermediate between those of the two approaches described above, would be to replace only the suspicious points by the values predicted by a fit to the neighbouring points. The (enlarged) errors associated with these points can be taken, for example, to be of the order of the difference between the experimental and fitted values.

Another possible complication in the analysis of dispersion relations is the occurrence of systematic errors. Measurements of the cross sections are often made at a large number of different energies in a single experiment, using the same experimental set-up. In addition to the purely statistical errors on the individual points, there are usually a number of uncertainties which can produce an overall systematic shift in the measured cross sections by approximately the same amount at all the energies. This is the systematic error of the experiment.

The effect of such a systematic error on a dispersion integral such as (5.51) can be estimated by allowing all the points measured in a given experiment to be shifted by their systematic error. However, since the effects due to the systematic errors of different experiments are statistically independent of one another, they should be combined according to the usual law of propagation of (statistical) errors in order to estimate their total effect on the calculated integral.

In the case of a principal-valued integral (5.52), the effect of the systematic error of a particular experiment may be suppressed if the singular point $\omega = \omega_0$ lies well within the energy range covered by the experiment, since there are cancellations due to the change of sign of the singular factor $(\omega - \omega_0)^{-1}$ within the region of integration. In fact, it can be seen from (5.56) that, with the approximation made in deriving that equation, a systematic error produces no effect at all when the singular point lies precisely in the middle of the range of integration.

References

1. N. Sznajder Hald, *Nucl. Phys.*, **B48** (1972), 549. The numerical coefficient in front of the dispersion integral is written incorrectly in this paper.
2. R. Oehme, *Phys. Rev.*, **100** (1955), 1503
3. K. J. Foley *et al.*, *Phys. Rev. Lett.*, **19** (1967), 193

4. V. K. Samaranayake and W. S. Woolcock, *Nucl. Phys.*, **B48** (1972), 205
5. E. Ferrari, *Revista Brasileira de Fisica*, **2** (1972), 225
6. U. Haber-Schaim, *Phys. Rev.*, **104** (1956), 1113
7. H. J. Schnitzer and G. Salzman, *Phys. Rev.*, **113** (1959), 1153
8. J. Hamilton and W. S. Woolcock, *Rev. Mod. Phys.*, **35** (1963), 737
9. W. C. Davidon and M. L. Goldberger, *Phys. Rev.*, **104** (1956), 1119

Further reading

General surveys of various aspects of our knowledge of the πN interaction can be found in the following references.

1. J. Hamilton, in *High Energy Physics*, Vol. 1, ed. by E. H. S. Burhop, Academic Press, New York, 1967, p. 193
2. R. G. Moorhouse, *Ann. Rev. Nucl. Science*, **19** (1969), 301
3. G. Giacomelli, *Rivista del Nuovo Cimento*, **2** (1970), 297

For further details of the formalism for describing πN scattering, see the following references.

4. H. Pilkuhn, *The Interactions of Hadrons*, North-Holland, Amsterdam, 1967, Chapters 3 and 7
5. A. D. Martin and T. D. Spearman, *Elementary Particle Theory*, North-Holland, Amsterdam, 1970, Chapters 5 and 7
6. A. Donnachie, *Reports on Progr. in Phys.*, **36** (1973), 695

Reviews of πN dispersion relations and their applications appear in the following references.

7. J. Hamilton and W. S. Woolcock, *Rev. Mod. Phys.*, **35** (1963), 737
8. J. Hamilton in *Strong Interactions and High Energy Physics*, ed. R. G. Moorhouse, Oliver & Boyd, Edinburgh, 1964, p. 281
9. V. S. Barashenkov, *Fortschritte der Physik*, **14** (1966), 741
10. V. K. Samaranayake and W. S. Woolcock, *Nucl. Phys.*, **B48** (1972), 205

A comprehensive survey of all aspects of the πN interaction can be found in the following book.

11. B. H. Bransden and R. G. Moorhouse, *The Pion–Nucleon System*, Princeton University Press, 1973

CHAPTER 6

Further applications of dispersion relations

6.1. Dispersion relations for KN scattering

The spin structure and analyticity properties of the kaon–nucleon scattering amplitudes are analogous to those for πN scattering, so that kaon–nucleon dispersion relations can be written down at once in analogy with the πN case which we have already considered in chapter 5. There are, however, three significant differences to be taken into account.

(i) The antiparticles of the pions belong to the same isospin multiplet (π^-, π^0, π^+), whereas for kaons the K and $\overline{K}$ multiplets (K^0, K^+) and $(K^-, \overline{K}^0)$ are distinct. The KN and $\overline{K}N$ systems each have two isospin states $(I = 0, 1)$. If charge independence is assumed, there are therefore a total of four independent kaon–nucleon processes (which may be taken to be $K^\pm p$ and $K^\pm n$ elastic scattering), while there are only two independent pion–nucleon processes (for example, $\pi^\pm p$ elastic scattering). A given dispersion relation involves two different processes, related by crossing. Thus, in contrast with the πN case, for kaon–nucleon scattering it is necessary to consider two independent dispersion relations (for example, one for $K^\pm p$ and one for $K^\pm n$ scattering).

(ii) In the kaon–nucleon case there are two pole terms instead of one, corresponding to the Λ and Σ hyperons, both of which couple to the $\overline{K}N$ system. These hyperons have isospin $I = 0$ and $I = 1$, respectively, so that there is one pole term associated with each of the two isospin states of the $\overline{K}N$ system.

(iii) The $\overline{K}N$ scattering amplitudes have cuts extending a significant distance below the threshold for elastic scattering, owing to the existence of the inelastic processes $\overline{K} + N \rightarrow \pi + \Lambda$, $\overline{K} + N \rightarrow \pi + \Sigma$ and $\overline{K} + N \rightarrow \pi + \pi + \Lambda$. The thresholds for these processes are at values of the invariant energy $W = \sqrt{s}$ equal to 1·25, 1·33 and 1·39 GeV, respectively (the $\overline{K}N$ threshold is at $W = 1·43$ GeV). The amplitudes on these cuts (called the unphysical cuts) are not directly accessible from experiment.

We shall now consider in detail the additional complications which arise in the study of the kaon–nucleon dispersion relations because of the special features mentioned above. To be specific, let us consider elastic $K^\pm p$ scattering. In view of points (ii) and (iii) above, the analytic structure of the $K^- p$ forward scattering amplitude is as shown in figure 6.1.

The pole terms in the $K^- p$ invariant amplitudes are found to have the form

$$A_-^{(\text{pole})}(s, t) = \sum_Y \frac{(m_p - m_Y)g_Y^2}{m_Y^2 - s} \tag{6.1a}$$

$$B_-^{(\text{pole})}(s, t) = \sum_Y \frac{g_Y^2}{m_Y^2 - s} \tag{6.1b}$$

where the summation is over the two terms with $Y = \Lambda, \Sigma$ and g_Y is the rationalised, renormalised, pseudoscalar $K^- pY$ coupling constant (analogous to the coupling constant g which we have introduced for πN scattering in chapter 5). Note that, in contrast with the πN case, poles now occur in both of the amplitudes A_- and B_- (the pole term in A_- would vanish if the nucleon and hyperon masses were equal). The factor 2 which occurs in the analogous expression for the pole term in the B_- amplitude of πN scattering, equation (5.17b), is now absent, since the coupling constants are defined here directly for the $K^- pY$ vertex.

Using (6.1), we find that the forward scattering amplitude $F_-(\omega)$ contains the pole terms

$$F_-^{(\text{pole})}(\omega) = \sum_Y \frac{g_Y^2}{4\pi} \frac{m_p - m_Y + \omega_Y}{m_Y^2 - s} \tag{6.2}$$

where $\omega_Y = (m_Y^2 - m_p^2 - m_K^2)/2m_p$. It is usual to write these pole contributions in terms of the variable ω in the form

$$F_-^{(\text{pole})}(\omega) = \sum_Y \frac{X_Y}{\omega_Y - \omega} \tag{6.3}$$

where the pole residues X_Y are given by

$$X_Y = \frac{g_Y^2}{4\pi} \frac{(m_Y - m_p)^2 - m_K^2}{4m_p^2} \tag{6.4}$$

It is now an easy matter to write down the kaon–nucleon dispersion relation of any particular form. For example, the $K^\pm p$ forward dispersion relation

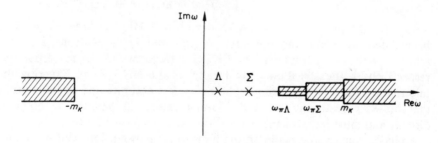

Figure 6.1. The analytic structure of the $K^- p$ forward scattering amplitude.

analogous to the sign-subtracted πN dispersion relation (5.33) is

$$\text{Re}[F_-(\omega) - F_+(\omega)] = \sum_Y \frac{2\omega X_Y}{\omega_Y^2 - \omega^2} + \frac{2\omega}{\pi} \int_{\omega_{\pi\Lambda}}^{m_K} \frac{\text{Im}F_-(\omega')\,d\omega'}{\omega'^2 - \omega^2}$$
$$+ \frac{\omega}{2\pi^2} P \int_{m_K}^{\infty} \frac{k'[\sigma_-(\omega') - \sigma_+(\omega')]\,d\omega'}{\omega'^2 - \omega^2} \qquad (6.5)$$

where $\omega_{\pi\Lambda} = [(m_\pi + m_\Lambda)^2 - m_p^2 - m_K^2]/2m_p$ is the value of ω corresponding to the $\pi\Lambda$ threshold. This dispersion relation, evaluated at the threshold energy $\omega = m_K$, was the first one to be used in practice for a quantitative determination of the KNY coupling constants. The first integral is the dispersion integral over the K^-p unphysical region, where the optical theorem cannot be applied. An exactly analogous dispersion relation holds for the $K^\pm n$ scattering amplitude, except for the form of the pole terms. Isospin invariance requires that

$$g^2_{K^- n\Sigma^-} = 2g^2_{K^- p\Sigma^0}$$

while the Λ pole is absent in the K^-n amplitude, which corresponds to a state of isospin $I = 1$. This means that any dispersion relation for $K^\pm n$ scattering is obtained from the corresponding $K^\pm p$ dispersion relation by inserting a factor 2 in the Σ pole term and omitting the Λ pole term.

Other types of kaon–nucleon dispersion relations can similarly be written down in analogy with the πN case. Apart from the additional integral over the unphysical region below the elastic threshold, the only difference is in the form of the pole terms. In deriving the $K^\pm p$ dispersion relation corresponding to a given $\pi^\pm p$ dispersion relation, each of the two hyperon pole terms is obtained by making the replacements $f^2 \to -\frac{1}{2}X_Y$ and $\omega_N \to \omega_Y$ in the original nucleon pole term.

For example, the $K^\pm p$ dispersion relations analogous to the once-subtracted πN dispersion relations (5.40) have the form

$$\text{Re}F_\pm(\omega) = C + \sum_Y \frac{X_Y}{\omega_Y \pm \omega} - \frac{\omega}{\pi} \int_{\omega_{\pi\Lambda}}^{m_K} \frac{\text{Im}F_-(\omega')\,d\omega'}{\omega'(\omega \pm \omega')}$$
$$- \frac{\omega}{4\pi^2} P \int_{m_K}^{\infty} \frac{k'}{\omega'} \left[\frac{\sigma_\pm(\omega')}{\omega - \omega'} + \frac{\sigma_\mp(\omega')}{\omega + \omega'} \right] d\omega' \qquad (6.6)$$

The Λ and Σ pole terms in the $K^\pm N$ dispersion relations of a given type may be isolated by evaluating the kaon–proton and kaon–neutron dispersion relations in the linear combinations $2(K^\pm p) - (K^\pm n)$ and $(K^\pm n)$, corresponding respectively to the $I = 0$ and $I = 1$ states of the $\overline{K}N$ system. Experimental information on $K^\pm n$ scattering is, however, less accurate and complete than that on $K^\pm p$ scattering, since the former cannot in practice be obtained directly and must be extracted mainly from analyses of $K^\pm d$ interactions.

Analyses can also be made on the basis of $K^\pm p$ dispersion relations alone. Such analyses avoid the use of the much less accurate $K^\pm n$ data, but allow the determination of only a certain effective combination of g_Λ^2 and g_Σ^2. Suppose, for example, that the $K^\pm p$ dispersion relation (6.5) is used. Then, assuming that the energy ω at which it is evaluated is such that $\omega \gg \omega_Y$, the sum of the pole terms in the dispersion relation will be proportional to $X_\Lambda + X_\Sigma$, which in turn is found to depend on the combination $g_\Lambda^2 + 0.84g_\Sigma^2$. The most commonly used dispersion relations of other types generally involve rather similar linear combinations of g_Λ^2 and g_Σ^2.

As in the πN case, the dispersion integrals over the physical region are well determined from total cross section data, although the low-energy contributions can be estimated more accurately by expressing $\sigma_\pm$ in terms of phenomenological parametrisations of the low-energy scattering data. This is particularly important in the case of $K^- N$ scattering, where the cross sections σ_- are known poorly by direct measurement and, in fact, become infinite at threshold with a k^{-1} dependence because of the presence of absorptive processes. In particular, use may be made of global analyses of all the low-energy $K^\pm N$ data, which, as a by-product, yield predictions for $\sigma_\pm$ at low energies. Data on $\text{Re}F_\pm(\omega)$ exist at a large number of energies for $K^\pm p$ scattering but are rather meagre for $K^\pm n$ scattering.

The largest uncertainty in phenomenological analyses of the ordinary kaon-nucleon dispersion relations has been associated with the integral over the unphysical region $\omega_{\pi\Lambda} \leqslant \omega \leqslant m_K$. The numerical value of this integral has usually been estimated by analytically continuing the amplitude $F_-(\omega)$ into this region by means of some low-energy parametrisation based on conventional effective-range theory or an expansion of the multi-channel K-matrix, whose parameter values are determined by fitting experimental data on $K^- p$ interactions in the low-energy physical region.

In the $I = 0$ state, it is found that an important contribution comes from the dispersion integral over the unphysical region, which is dominated by the Y_0^* (1405) resonance occurring in the S-wave amplitude. The various low-energy parametrisations all reproduce this resonance with a reasonable position and width, although the detailed shape and position of the resonance peak can vary considerably from one parametrisation to another. As a result, the dispersion relation predictions for g_Λ^2 are rather model-dependent. Many attempts have been made to resolve this ambiguity by making consistency tests based on comparisons of the results of different dispersion relations and by using carefully chosen dispersion relations which give a relatively small weight to the unphysical region. Nevertheless, there has been a long period of controversy over the favoured value of g_Λ^2 and the accuracy with which it can be determined.

The unphysical region also receives a contribution from another hyperon resonance, the Y_1^* (1385), which occurs in the $I = 1$ $P_{3/2}$ state of the $\bar{K}N$ system. However, this resonance is found to be much less crucial than the Y_0^* (1405). The integral over the unphysical region in the $I = 1$ state turns out to be less important than for $I = 0$. It comes mainly from the non-resonant S

wave, whose energy dependence is quite smooth and which may be more reliably determined by analytic continuation from the physical region. As a result, there is only a small uncertainty in the $KN\Sigma$ coupling constant determined from the forward dispersion relations, all recent analyses giving a value which is rather small in magnitude.

The determination of the KNY coupling constants is of special interest as a test of $SU(3)$ symmetry. According to this symmetry scheme, these coupling constants are related to the πNN coupling constant g by

$$g_\Lambda^2 = \tfrac{1}{3}(1 + 2\alpha)^2 g^2$$
$$g_\Sigma^2 = (1 - 2\alpha)^2 g^2$$

where α is a parameter specifying the fraction of F-type coupling. Since the value of g^2 is known with good accuracy, these equations give a definite relation between g_Λ^2 and g_Σ^2. Unique values of g_Λ^2 and g_Σ^2 are predicted if one makes the stronger assumption of the validity of $SU(6)$ symmetry, which requires $\alpha = 0.4$ (this value is in approximate agreement with estimates of α from analyses of various experimental data within the framework of $SU(3)$ symmetry). This gives, in particular,

$$g_\Sigma^2/g_\Lambda^2 = 1/27$$

The prediction that the $KN\Sigma$ coupling is weak is in agreement with the results obtained from kaon–nucleon forward dispersion relations. The $KN\Lambda$ coupling constant, on the other hand, is predicted by the symmetry scheme to be of the same order of magnitude as the πNN coupling constant. Analyses of the dispersion relations have yielded values of g_Λ^2 ranging from approximately the value expected from $SU(3)$ symmetry down to less than half of this value.

6.2. Phenomenological analysis of forward KN dispersion relations

As we have already pointed out, a major difficulty in the analysis of kaon–nucleon dispersion relations is the need to evaluate dispersion integrals involving the imaginary parts of the $\bar{K}N$ scattering amplitudes in the unphysical energy region $\omega_{\pi\Lambda} < \omega < m_K$, where the optical theorem cannot be applied.

The simplest parametrisation which has been used to analytically continue the $\bar{K}N$ scattering amplitudes into the unphysical region is based on a constant S-wave scattering length A_I for each of the two isospin states $I = 0, 1$, neglecting all contributions from the higher partial waves. Each of the scattering lengths A_I is complex-valued because of the presence of inelastic processes. This parametrisation gives a good fit to the low-energy scattering data within a limited energy region.

It is readily verified that, according to the scattering-length approximation, the forward $\bar{K}N$ scattering amplitudes in the c.m.s. are given by

$$f_I(\omega) = A_I/(1 - iqA_I) \tag{6.7}$$

If A_I has a large negative real part, then (6.7) will exhibit a resonant behaviour at some energy below the physical threshold, owing to the cancellation of the real part of the denominator. For the $I = 0$ state, just such a behaviour is found for all recent analyses of the low-energy data on K^-p interactions which have been made on the basis of the scattering-length parametrisation. For example, according to one analysis[1]

$$A_0 = [(-1\cdot67 \pm 0\cdot04) + i(0\cdot72 \pm 0\cdot04)]fm$$

With this value, the denominator of (6.7) becomes purely imaginary at $q = 118i$ MeV/c, corresponding to a total c.m. energy of the K^-p system equal to 1410 MeV (see equation 1.19). This is in reasonable correspondence with the known position of the $Y_0^*(1405)$ resonance, as determined from production experiments in which the decay of this resonance into the $\pi\Sigma$ channel is seen.

Although the simple scattering-length parametrisation (6.7) appears to give a satisfactory description of the amplitudes at sufficiently low physical energies (in the range corresponding to kaon laboratory momenta $\lesssim 300$ MeV/c), it suffers from certain serious theoretical defects when extended far into the unphysical region. In particular, it is known that the amplitudes have branch points at the thresholds for all coupled channels and are purely real below the lowest threshold ($\pi\Sigma$ for $I = 0$ and $\pi\Lambda$ for $I = 1$). The scattering-length parametrisation incorporates the correct threshold behaviour at the physical threshold ($q = 0$), but not at any of the other thresholds.

This difficulty can be overcome by employing instead the multi-channel K-matrix formalism (section 1.7). A number of analyses of the low-energy $\bar{K}N$ scattering data have been made on the basis of this formalism, both with and without effective-range terms in the expansion of the inverse K-matrix.

It turns out that the width of the $Y_0^*(1405)$ resonance predicted by the K-matrix parametrisation is rather sensitive to small variations in the values of the effective-range terms in the expansion, particularly the off-diagonal terms. Thus, although a parametrisation based on a constant (zero-range) S-wave K-matrix appears to provide a good description of the low-energy $\bar{K}N$ interaction, small effective-range terms may nevertheless have an appreciable influence on the shape of the $Y_0^*(1405)$ resonance. The effective-range terms are difficult to determine from fits to the low-energy data, since the inclusion of a general effective-range matrix in the expansion of the inverse K-matrix leads to a total of twice as many parameters as in the zero-range K-matrix parametrisation. Of course, the inclusion of higher partial waves requires still more parameters. Thus, it is difficult to perform a reliable extrapolation of the scattering amplitude into the unphysical region.

It is perhaps worth mentioning that, using the numerical values of the K-matrix parameters which have been determined from phenomenological fits to the data, one finds that the $Y_0^*(1405)$ resonance does *not* correspond to a pole in the elements of the 2×2 K-matrix for the coupled $\pi\Sigma$ and $\bar{K}N$ channels in the $I = 0$ state (although there is, of course, a pole in the reduced K-matrix for the $\pi\Sigma$ channel). This means that the $Y_0^*(1405)$ has the interpretation of a virtual bound state of the $\overline{K}N$ system (see section 1.7).

An alternative possibility, which is not favoured by the analysis of the experimental data, is that the Y_0^* corresponds to a pole in the full K-matrix; in this case, it would be reasonable to parametrise the K-matrix directly as the sum of a constant matrix (or, more generally, a slowly varying term) and a pole term.

The uncertainty in the shape of the $Y_0^*(1405)$ resonance peak in the imaginary part of the $I = 0$ $\overline{K}N$ amplitude has had a major bearing on the determination of the $KN\Lambda$ coupling constant by means of dispersion relations. To see the reason for this, let us consider for definiteness the linear combination of $K^\pm p$ and $K^\pm n$ dispersion relations of the type (6.5) corresponding to isospin $I = 0$ in the $\overline{K}N$ channel (and containing only the Λ pole term). This combination, when evaluated at the threshold energy $\omega = m_K$, provides what has been the most widely used expression for the $KN\Lambda$ coupling constant. This expression can be regarded essentially as a sum rule relating g_Λ^2 to a dispersion integral over the unphysical region, since the remaining quantities which appear in it, namely $\text{Re}F_\pm(m_K)$ and the dispersion integral over the physical region, are quite well determined.

Specifically, the Λ pole term in this sum rule is of the form

$$4m_K X_\Lambda/(\omega_\Lambda^2 - m_K^2) = (0\cdot 50 \text{ GeV}^{-1})g_\Lambda^2 \tag{6.8}$$

while the contribution to the same side of the equation from the unphysical region is

$$U = \frac{2m_K}{\pi} \int_{\omega_{\pi\Sigma}}^{m_K} \frac{\text{Im}F_-^{(I=0)}(\omega')\,\mathrm{d}\omega'}{\omega'^2 - m_K^2} \tag{6.9}$$

The dominant $Y_0^*(1405)$ resonance gives a positive contribution to $\text{Im}F_-^{(I=0)}$ (see, for example, equation 6.7), so that the value of (6.9) is negative. This is to be compared with the positive value of (6.8). Since the remaining terms in the dispersion relation are determined with good accuracy, there is a strong correlation between the value of the unphysical region contribution U predicted by a particular model and the corresponding calculated value of g_Λ^2. The fact that (6.8) and (6.9) are of opposite sign means that this correlation is such that an increase in the width of the $Y_0^*(1405)$ will lead to an increase in the predicted value of g_Λ^2 (assuming that there is no change in $\text{Re}F_-(m_K)$, which is usually determined from the same parametrisation as that used to estimate the unphysical region contribution).

The sensitivity of g_Λ^2 to the value of the integral U is further enhanced by the fact that, if the dispersion relation is solved explicitly for g_Λ^2 in terms of U and the sum of the remaining contributions involving $\text{Re}F_\pm(m_K)$ and the integrals of $\sigma_\pm(\omega)$, there is a strong cancellation between the contribution from U and the remaining contributions. The existence of a cancellation can be seen from the form of (6.5), using the fact that empirically

$$\mathrm{Re}[F_-(m_K) - F_+(m_K)] < 0$$
$$\sigma_-(\omega) - \sigma_+(\omega) > 0$$

for the combinations of quantities corresponding to the $I = 0$ $\bar{K}N$ state.

It is instructive to examine the actual numerical values of the various contributions. As an illustrative example, we shall quote the results of an analysis[2] of the dispersion relation (6.5) at the near-threshold energy

$$\omega = 498 \text{ MeV} \equiv \omega_0$$

The dispersion relation was expressed in the form of a sum rule

$$g_\Lambda^2/4\pi = L(\bar{K}N) + L(KN) + I + H$$

where $L(\bar{K}N)$ is the low-energy $\bar{K}N$ contribution (defined as the sum of the terms depending on $\mathrm{Re}F_-(\omega_0)$ and the dispersion integral of $\mathrm{Im}F_-(\omega')$ over the unphysical and low-energy region $\omega_{\pi\Sigma} < \omega' < 574 \text{ MeV} \equiv \omega_-$), $L(KN)$ is the low-energy KN contribution (defined as the sum of the terms depending on $\mathrm{Re}F_+(\omega_0)$ and the dispersion integral of $\mathrm{Im}F_+(\omega')$ up to 811 MeV $\equiv \omega_+$), I is the intermediate-energy contribution involving the integrals of $\sigma_\pm(\omega')$ over the ranges $\omega_\pm < \omega' < 20 \text{ GeV}$, and H is the high-energy contribution involving $\sigma_\pm(\omega')$ for $\omega' > 20 \text{ GeV}$.

The values of $\omega_\pm$ were chosen so that the contributions $L(\bar{K}N)$ and $L(KN)$ could be evaluated entirely in terms of certain low-energy parametrisations of the $\bar{K}N$ and KN scattering data which were applicable in the appropriate energy ranges; the quantity I was evaluated directly in terms of experimental total cross section data; finally, H was estimated according to a simple Regge pole model. In this way, it was found that $L(KN) = 8\cdot7$, $I = -13\cdot2$ and $H = -1\cdot3$. Two alternative parametrisations for the low-energy $\bar{K}N$ contribution (based on constant scattering lengths and on a multi-channel effective-range expansion of the inverse K-matrix) gave the values $L(\bar{K}N) = 9\cdot0$ and $L(\bar{K}N) = 19\cdot0$, respectively. The difference between these two values is mainly a reflection of the different widths of the $Y_0^*(1405)$ resonance for the two parametrisations.

When these values were added to the remaining contributions, the final results were $g_\Lambda^2/4\pi = 3\cdot1$ and $g_\Lambda^2/4\pi = 13\cdot1$, respectively (the total statistical error in each case being $\pm 2\cdot7$). These results show that the calculated value of g_Λ^2 is very sensitive to the model which is used to extrapolate the $\bar{K}N$ amplitude into the unphysical region (although the two parametrisations employed here give practically identical predictions in the low-energy physical region). This sensitivity is large in comparison with the total statistical error which is obtained when any one model is used. Most subsequent estimates of $g_\Lambda^2/4\pi$ have been in the range between the two values given above.

There is a similar correlation between the value of the $KN\Sigma$ coupling constant calculated from the $K^\pm n$ forward dispersion relation and the assumed strength of the $Y_1^*(1385)$ resonance in the unphysical region. It turns out that, unlike the $Y_0^*(1405)$, this resonance, being in a P wave, gives a negative contribution to $\mathrm{Im}F_-(\omega)$. As a result, the Σ pole term and the $Y_1^*(1385)$ resonance give contributions of the *same* sign to the dispersion relation.

Although little is known about the shape of the $Y_1^*(1385)$ peak in $\mathrm{Im}F_-(\omega)$, it appears that this resonance is weakly coupled to the $\overline{K}N$ system, so that its effect is not too important in the dispersion relation calculations. In any case, even if no specific assumption is made about this resonance, it is known that it gives a negative contribution to g_Σ^2. This means that in practice one can effectively calculate an upper bound on g_Σ^2. All analyses of the dispersion relations for g_Σ^2 have been consistent with a rather small value of this coupling constant, $g_\Sigma^2/4\pi \lesssim 3$.

The coupling constants can of course also be determined by other types of dispersion relations, including any of those discussed in chapter 5 in connection with πN scattering. Some of the alternative methods yield predictions for the coupling constants which are somewhat less sensitive to the model adopted for the $\overline{K}N$ unphysical region. For example, an analysis has been made[3] of the once-subtracted $K^\pm p$ dispersion relation analogous to (5.40), using the available data on $\mathrm{Re}F_\pm(\omega)$. Using the same scattering-length solution and K-matrix parametrisation as those chosen in the above-mentioned analysis of the charge-subtracted dispersion relation, the values $8 \cdot 0 \pm 1 \cdot 7$ and $10 \cdot 9 \pm 1 \cdot 7$, respectively, were found in this way for the effective coupling strength

$$(g_\Lambda^2 + 0 \cdot 85 g_\Sigma^2)/4\pi$$

A valuable consistency check of the alternative parametrisations can be made by comparing the predictions for the coupling constants according to different dispersion relations which make use of the same input data. Work of this kind has tended to favour those parametrisations which lead to the smaller values of g_Λ^2.

A problem of correlations arises when the dispersion relations are used to calculate the real parts of the scattering amplitudes after the coupling constants have been determined. As we have seen, there are large uncertainties in both the value of g_Λ^2 and the dispersion integral over the unphysical region. However, the uncertainty in g_Λ^2 is associated largely with the model adopted for the unphysical region. These uncertainties should therefore not be treated as statistically independent when evaluating $\mathrm{Re}F_\pm(\omega)$ from the dispersion relations, since this quantity may be determined with greater accuracy than that suggested by some of the individual contributions which are strongly correlated among themselves. Moreover, the statistical error on the value of g_Λ^2 which arises from the statistical errors on the measured total cross sections is clearly not independent of the estimated error on the dispersion integral over the physical region.

The simplest method of taking into account such correlations is to replace g_Λ^2 in the dispersion relation used to evaluate $\mathrm{Re}F_\pm(\omega)$ by the expression for it according to some other dispersion relation which is used to evaluate g_Λ^2. In this way g_Λ^2 is eliminated and we obtain an expression for $\mathrm{Re}F_\pm(\omega)$ in terms of the real parts of the amplitudes at one or more fixed energies and certain dispersion integrals over the imaginary parts. The uncertainty on $\mathrm{Re}F_\pm(\omega)$ can then be estimated by the usual laws of propagation of errors.

A complication in the analysis of low-energy $\overline{K}N$ interactions which we have so far neglected is the inclusion of the Coulomb interaction and the difference $\Delta m \approx 5{\cdot}3$ MeV between the masses of the K^-p and $\overline{K}^0n$ systems (the latter being heavier). The mass difference effect leads, in particular, to a cusp in the K^-p elastic scattering amplitude at the threshold for the charge-exchange reaction $K^- + p \rightarrow \overline{K}^0 + n$.

The electromagnetic effects can be taken into account by introducing appropriate modifications[4] in the formulae for the physical scattering amplitudes. For example, for $\Delta m \neq 0$, the equation

$$f_-(\omega) = \frac{1}{2}\left[\frac{A_0}{1 - iqA_0} + \frac{A_1}{1 - iqA_1}\right] \tag{6.10}$$

for the K^-p elastic scattering amplitude in the c.m.s. according to the scattering-length approximation must be replaced by the more general expression

$$f_-(\omega) = \frac{A_0 + A_1 - 2iq'A_0A_1}{2 - i(q + q')(A_0 + A_1) - 2qq'A_0A_1} \tag{6.11}$$

where q' is the c.m. momentum in the coupled $\overline{K}^0n$ channel. If we assume that $\Delta m = 0$, so that $q' = q$, the formula (6.11) reduces to (6.10).

It has long been debated whether the non-zero value of Δm should be taken into account when using dispersion relations for the strong interactions. Although the effect of the mass difference is included in practice when analysing the experimental data in terms of phenomenological parametrisations, there have been suggestions that it should be neglected in the analysis of dispersion relations. This is possible only if one retains the existing parameters in the corresponding formulae with $\Delta m = 0$ or re-analyses the data according to these modified formulae. It is not obvious that either procedure leads to amplitudes which correctly describe the $\overline{K}N$ interaction with the electromagnetic effects removed, and it may be argued that the most consistent procedure is to employ the amplitudes obtained from fits to the data with the empirical value of the mass difference in the formulae.

6.3. Dispersion relations for NN scattering

The application of dispersion relations for NN scattering is of somewhat greater complexity than for the cases which we have considered so far. Not only is there a large unphysical region here (associated with $\overline{N}N$ scattering), but also a much richer spin structure.

The description of the scattering of two spin-$\frac{1}{2}$ particles requires a total of five independent amplitudes, three of which contribute in the forward direction. We shall not give the full details here.[5] The main point is that in the forward direction there is one particular NN amplitude, which we shall denote by A, for which dispersion relations can be constructed in a straightforward way. This amplitude is related to the total cross section for unpolarised particles by the optical theorem

$$\text{Im}A = k\sigma/4\pi \tag{6.12}$$

and to the corresponding amplitude $\bar{A}$ for $\bar{N}N$ scattering by the crossing relation

$$A(-\omega) = \bar{A}(\omega) \tag{6.13}$$

In the $\bar{N}N$ channel there is an unphysical cut running from the $\pi\pi$ threshold at $\omega = \omega_{\pi\pi} = 2m_\pi^2/m_N - m_N$ to the physical threshold at $\omega = m_N$. There is also a pole term corresponding to the single-particle pion state in the $\bar{N}N$ channel. For $\bar{p}p$ scattering, for example, this pole term (corresponding to the π^0 state) is found to have the form

$$\bar{A}^{(\text{pole})}(\omega) = f^2/2(\omega - \omega_\pi) \tag{6.14}$$

where f is the πNN coupling constant introduced in chapter 5 and

$$\omega_\pi = m_\pi^2/2m_N - m_N$$

Using these results, dispersion relations can be written down at once for the amplitudes $A(\omega)$ and $\bar{A}(\omega)$. For example, the unsubtracted dispersion relation for the pp scattering amplitude $A(\omega)$ takes the form (ignoring here, for simplicity, the need for subtractions)

$$\text{Re}A(\omega) = -\frac{f^2}{2(\omega + \omega_\pi)} + \frac{1}{\pi}\int_{\omega_{2\pi}}^{m_p}\frac{\text{Im}\bar{A}(\omega')\,\text{d}\omega'}{\omega' + \omega}$$

$$+ \frac{1}{4\pi^2}P\int_{m_p}^{\infty}k'\left[\frac{\sigma(\omega')}{\omega' - \omega} + \frac{\bar{\sigma}(\omega')}{\omega' + \omega}\right]\text{d}\omega' \tag{6.15}$$

An analogous dispersion relation can be written for the $\bar{p}p$ scattering amplitude $\bar{A}(\omega)$. Identical dispersion relations also hold for the pn and $\bar{p}n$ scattering amplitudes, apart from an additional factor of 2 in the pole terms, as implied by isospin invariance (5.15). Ample data exist for scattering by both protons and neutrons, the latter being obtained from direct neutron–proton interactions, as well as from the analysis of the interactions of protons with deuterons.

One of the main problems in the analysis of NN dispersion relations is the existence of the large unphysical region in the $\bar{N}N$ channel, extending down to the $\pi\pi$ threshold. Since there are several low-lying meson resonances which appear to couple strongly to the $\bar{N}N$ system, one can expect a significant contribution from the unphysical region.

However, there is at present no means of estimating this contribution by analytic continuation from the $\bar{N}N$ physical region, as in the $\bar{K}N$ case discussed in the preceding sections. The only procedure by which a direct estimate of this contribution can be made is to replace the unphysical continuum by a sum of pole terms[6]

$$\int_{\omega_{2\pi}}^{m_N} \frac{\mathrm{Im}\bar{A}(\omega')\,\mathrm{d}\omega'}{\omega' \pm \omega} \approx \sum_i \frac{R_i}{\omega_i \pm \omega} \tag{6.16}$$

where ω_i is related to the mass m_i of one of the resonances X_i by

$$\omega_i = \tfrac{1}{2}m_i^2/m_N - m_N$$

The residue R_i can be related to the coupling constant for the $X_i NN$ vertex.

The relevant resonances to consider for this purpose are the ρ, ω and η. Certain information on the required coupling constants is available from several sources, for example the comparison of the predictions of one-meson exchange models with the results of phase-shift analyses for the NN interaction at low energies. However, our knowledge of these coupling constants is rather incomplete.

A more convenient procedure, which avoids the need to adopt a specific model for the unphysical region, is to parametrise its effect by means of a small number of adjustable parameters, whose values are determined by obtaining the best fit of the predicted real parts $\mathrm{Re}A(\omega)$ and $\mathrm{Re}\bar{A}(\omega)$ to the available experimental data. If the real parts are fitted only at energies sufficiently distant from the unphysical region, the results are insensitive to the detailed structure of the amplitude on the unphysical cut, which may then be satisfactorily described by a small number of parameters.

One parametrisation which has been suggested[7] is based on an expansion of the integrand of the unphysical region integral in inverse powers of ω; this makes it possible to write, for example

$$\int_{\omega_{2\pi}}^{m_p} \frac{\mathrm{Im}\bar{A}(\omega')\,\mathrm{d}\omega'}{\omega' + \omega} = \frac{C_1}{\omega} + \frac{C_2}{\omega^2} + \cdots \tag{6.17}$$

For sufficiently high energies, for example, $\omega \gtrsim 10$ GeV, the first two terms of such an expansion are sufficient to give a good representation of the effect of the unphysical region. The unknown coefficients of the expansion can be chosen to give the best fit to the entire set of data on the real parts of the amplitudes in this energy region.

An alternative possibility[8] is to replace the unknown integrand in the unphysical region by a truncated series involving a complete set of orthogonal polynomials, whose coefficients are again determined by fitting the experimental real part data.

Although dispersion relation predictions of the real parts of the NN and $\bar{N}N$ scattering amplitudes have generally been in good agreement with the available experimental data, a completely convincing conclusion cannot yet be drawn because of a serious uncertainty in the interpretation of these data. Most of the data have been obtained by analysing the differential cross section near the forward direction in the same way as for πN and KN scattering. However, the differential cross section for NN or $\bar{N}N$ forward scattering actually receives contributions from three independent amplitudes, say A, B and C. Thus, a measurement of the forward differential cross section constitutes a measurement of ReA only if some special assumption is made about the remaining two amplitudes.

Many analyses of the scattering data have been made under the assumption that the amplitude is spin-independent, that is that the three amplitudes which contribute in the forward direction all behave in the same way as functions of s and t. Another proposal, based mainly on the hypothesis of helicity conservation in high-energy diffraction scattering, is that the amplitude A dominates asymptotically. Until the nature of the spin dependence is fully understood, the interpretation of the analyses of dispersion relations for NN scattering must remain subject to some doubt.

6.4. Discrepancy functions

As we have seen, it sometimes happens that a dispersion integral cannot be evaluated in practice because the integrand is not sufficiently well known in some energy region. This is the case, for example, in KN or NN dispersion relations, where there is a significant contribution from an unphysical energy region which is not directly accessible to experiment. Likewise, in a given process, there will always be some energy region above which no experimental data are available.

The analysis of a dispersion relation with an unknown contribution can be carried out either by adopting a specific model for this contribution (such as a low-energy parametrisation for the unphysical region or a Regge model for the asymptotic region) or by taking some more general parametrisation of the unknown contribution involving a certain number of adjustable parameters whose values are fixed by finding the best fit of the dispersion relation predictions to some set of experimental data. If the second course is chosen, the discrepancy function method provides a particularly convenient framework in terms of which to perform the analysis.

The method is perhaps best illustrated by means of an example. For definiteness, let us choose the once-subtracted $K^{\pm}p$ forward dispersion relation (6.6). The discrepancy function, denoted by $\Delta(\omega)$, is defined as the difference between the real part of the amplitude and the sum of all those contributions to the right-hand side of the dispersion relation which can be constructed from experimental data. Thus, we can put

$$\Delta(\omega) = \text{Re}F_-(\omega) + \frac{\omega}{4\pi^2} P \int_{m_K}^{W} \frac{k'}{\omega'}\left[\frac{\sigma_-(\omega')}{\omega - \omega'} + \frac{\sigma_+(\omega')}{\omega + \omega'}\right] d\omega' \qquad (6.18)$$

where W is the highest energy at which the total cross sections $\sigma_{\pm}$ are known. It is sufficient to take the discrepancy function corresponding to only one of the two sets of signs in (6.6), as we have done in (6.18), since the two discrepancy functions $\Delta_\pm(\omega)$ corresponding to the $K^\pm p$ dispersion relations would be simply related by crossing

$$\Delta_\pm(-\omega) = \Delta_\mp(\omega) \tag{6.19}$$

We note that the discrepancy function can be constructed entirely from experimental information, at least at some discrete set of energies. The accuracy with which the total cross sections have been measured experimentally is such that, for the purpose of calculating $\Delta(\omega)$, we may practically assume that $\sigma_\pm(\omega)$ are known as continuous functions of energy over the entire range. This is so because the data on $\sigma_\pm(\omega)$ have generally been measured with high accuracy at closely spaced energies. The real parts of the amplitudes, on the other hand, are often known only at widely spaced energies and with large uncertainties, and the scatter of the data points for $\mathrm{Re}_\pm(\omega)$ is often too great to permit a reliable interpolation between these points. In such cases we must regard $\Delta(\omega)$ as known only at those energies at which the real parts are known, and with errors which arise mainly from the uncertainties in the real parts.

Returning to the original dispersion relation (6.6), we see that the discrepancy function can also be expressed as a sum over the unknown contributions

$$\Delta(\omega) = C + \sum_Y \frac{X_Y}{\omega_Y - \omega} - \frac{\omega}{\pi} \int_{\omega_{\pi\Lambda}}^{m_K} \frac{\mathrm{Im}F_-(\omega')\,d\omega'}{\omega'(\omega - \omega')}$$
$$- \frac{\omega}{4\pi^2} \int_W^\infty \frac{k'}{\omega'} \left[\frac{\sigma_-(\omega')}{\omega - \omega'} + \frac{\sigma_+(\omega')}{\omega + \omega'} \right] d\omega' \tag{6.20}$$

The essence of the discrepancy function method is to parametrise these unknown contributions in some way and to determine the values of the parameters by obtaining the best fit to the experimental values of $\Delta(\omega)$. Note that in constructing the discrepancy function one makes use of all the experimental data on both the real and imaginary parts of the amplitude.

In choosing the parametrisation, we can be guided by the physical nature of the unknown contributions. First of all, the constant C can obviously be chosen as one of the parameters. The form of the pole terms is known exactly, but it would be unrealistic to hope to determine the individual values of g_Λ^2 and g_Σ^2 (unless extremely accurate data exist), since the contributions of both pole terms in (6.20) give approximately the same type of energy dependence; however, one can take as a parameter the effective linear combination of g_Λ^2 and g_Σ^2 which corresponds to the sum of the residues $X_\Lambda + X_\Sigma$.

The contribution of the unphysical region in (6.20) can be parametrised in such a way as to exhibit the known features of $\mathrm{Im}F_-$, for example by including a Breit–Wigner resonance formula to represent the $Y_0^*(1405)$.

A possible parametrisation of the high-energy integral in (6.20) can be constructed by expanding the integral in powers of ω; if most of the fitted values of $\Delta(\omega)$ lie in the range $|\omega| \ll W$, it will suffice to retain only a few terms of this expansion.

The discrepancy function is expected to have relatively little structure in the experimentally accessible energy region, since it is given by a sum over the remaining (unknown) contributions, which are distant from the majority of the fitted data points. Therefore it is possible to fit the discrepancy function in terms of a small number of parameters. The results of such fits provide information about the relative importance of the various unknown contributions. Once a fit to the discrepancy function has been obtained, the equation by which it was originally defined (such as equation 6.18) can be solved for the real part of the amplitude to obtain a fit to the latter.

It should be stressed that the discrepancy function method is of great generality, since it can be applied to dispersion relations of any particular type. In fact, it is even possible to construct a discrepancy function which corresponds to a purely formal dispersion relation containing an insufficient number of subtractions. To do this, it is sufficient to work with the finite-contour form of the dispersion relation, in which, instead of taking the limit as the radius of the semicircular contour in the complex plane tends to infinity (as in section 2.4), one writes the dispersion relation in the form of an integral over the segment of the real axis $-W < \omega < W$ and a contour integral over a semicircle of radius W about the origin in the upper half-plane.

As an example, if the finite-contour form of the dispersion relation is used, the expression for the discrepancy function (6.20) becomes instead

$$\Delta(\omega) = C + \sum_Y \frac{X_Y}{\omega_Y - \omega} - \frac{\omega}{\pi} \int_{\omega_{\pi\Lambda}}^{m_K} \frac{\mathrm{Im} F_-(\omega')\, \mathrm{d}\omega'}{\omega'(\omega - \omega')}$$

$$- \frac{\omega}{\pi} \mathrm{Im} \int_{S(W)} \frac{F_-(\omega')\, \mathrm{d}\omega'}{\omega'(\omega - \omega')} \qquad (6.21)$$

where $S(W)$ is the semicircular contour $|\omega'| = W$ in the upper half-plane. In practice, one can use the same parametrisation of the discrepancy function whichever form is used.

6.5. Backward dispersion relations

So far we have discussed only dispersion relations for scattering amplitudes at fixed t. We shall now examine the case of dispersion relations for backward scattering, considering pion–nucleon scattering for definiteness.

We begin by noting some kinematic relations for backward πN scattering, employing again the notation of chapter 5. The variables s and t are related to the s-channel variables θ and q by

$$s = M^2 + \mu^2 + 2q^2 + 2[(q^2 + M^2)(q^2 + \mu^2)]^{1/2} \qquad (6.22)$$

$$t = -2q^2(1 - \cos\theta) \qquad (6.23)$$

For the special case of backward scattering, (6.23) becomes simply $t = -4q^2$. Backward scattering amplitudes can obviously be specified in terms of the single variable $w = q^2$, and it is conventional to write backward dispersion relations in terms of this variable. (The variable w is usually denoted by v in the literature. We use a different symbol here in order to distinguish it from the variable v which we employ elsewhere to describe scattering at fixed t.)

If we consider s as a function of w, we see from (6.22) that it can be defined on a two-sheeted w-plane, with a branch cut along the segment $-M^2 \leqslant w \leqslant -\mu^2$. It is easy to verify that this cut corresponds to values of s on the circle

$$|s| = M^2 - \mu^2$$

Let us define the first sheet so that $|s| \geqslant M^2 - \mu^2$ and the second sheet so that $|s| \leqslant M^2 - \mu^2$. Then one finds that $|u| \leqslant M^2 - \mu^2$ on the first sheet, while $|u| \geqslant M^2 - \mu^2$ on the second.

If it is assumed as usual that the invariant A and B amplitudes for general s and t have only those singularities required by unitarity in each channel, then the backward scattering amplitudes on the first sheet of the w-plane have cuts for $w \geqslant 0$ (due to the s-channel unitarity cuts for $s \geqslant (M + \mu)^2$) and for $w \leqslant -\mu^2$ (due to the t-channel unitarity cuts for $t \geqslant 4\mu^2$). There are no singularities on the first sheet due to u-channel processes, since $|u| \leqslant M^2 - \mu^2$ on this sheet. The usual nucleon pole term at $s = M^2$, involving the πNN coupling constant f, appears in the amplitude B_- for $\pi^- p$ scattering at

$$w = -\mu^2 + \mu^4/4M^2 \equiv w_N$$

It is customary to work with the amplitudes $A^{(\pm)}$ and $B^{(\pm)}$. Let us introduce the backward amplitudes

$$F^{(+)}(w) = \frac{1}{M} A^{(+)}(w, z = -1) + \frac{\tau}{E} B^{(+)}(w, z = -1) \qquad (6.24a)$$

$$F^{(-)}(w) = \frac{E}{M\tau} A^{(-)}(w, z = -1) + B^{(-)}(w, z = -1) \qquad (6.24b)$$

$$G^{(+)}(w) = \frac{1}{E\tau} B^{(+)}(w, z = -1) \qquad (6.25a)$$

$$G^{(-)}(w) = B^{(-)}(w, z = -1) \qquad (6.25b)$$

where $z = \cos \theta$, and $\tau = (w + \mu^2)^{1/2}$ and $E = (w + M^2)^{1/2}$ are the c.m. energies of the pion and nucleon respectively.

A major advantage of using the amplitudes $F^{(\pm)}(w)$ is that they are directly related to the differential cross sections for the various πN scattering processes in the backward direction

$$\frac{d\sigma}{d\Omega}(\pi^\pm p \to \pi^\pm p)\bigg|_{\theta = \pi} = \frac{M^2 E^2}{(4\pi)^2 s}\left|F^{(+)} \mp \frac{\tau}{E} F^{(-)}\right|^2 \qquad (6.26)$$

$$\frac{d\sigma}{d\Omega}(\pi^- p \to \pi^0 n)\bigg|_{\theta = \pi} = \frac{2M^2 \tau^2}{(4\pi)^2 s}|F^{(-)}|^2 \qquad (6.27)$$

Thus, the errors on the evaluation of $F^{(\pm)}$ are generally much smaller than those on $A^{(\pm)}$ and $B^{(\pm)}$ individually. This is so even if phase-shift analyses are used to evaluate $F^{(\pm)}$, because of correlations among the phase shifts.

It is generally assumed that the behaviour of these backward amplitudes as $|w| \to \infty$ is such that the dispersion relations for them do not require subtractions. This condition is well satisfied in the usual Regge pole model for backward scattering of pions by nucleons.

To write down the dispersion relations, we also require the form of the nucleon pole term

$$B_-^{(\text{pole})}(w) = 16\pi(1 - \mu^2/2M^2)f^2/(w_N - w) \tag{6.28}$$

Then the dispersion relations for the amplitudes $F^{(\pm)}$ become

$$\text{Re}F^{(\pm)}(w) = \frac{R^{(\pm)}}{w_N - w} + \frac{1}{\pi}P\int_0^\infty \frac{\text{Im}F^{(\pm)}(w')\,dw'}{w' - w} + \frac{1}{\pi}\int_{-\infty}^{-\mu^2} \frac{\text{Im}F^{(\pm)}(w')\,dw'}{w' - w}$$

$$\tag{6.29}$$

where

$$R^{(+)} = 4\pi\mu^2 f^2/M^2 \tag{6.30a}$$

$$R^{(-)} = 8\pi(1 - \mu^2/2M^2)f^2 \tag{6.30b}$$

Identical dispersion relations hold for the amplitudes $G^{(\pm)}$, except that the corresponding residues of the pole terms are given by the quantities $S^{(\pm)}$, where

$$S^{(+)} = 16\pi f^2/\mu^2 \tag{6.31a}$$

$$S^{(-)} = 8\pi(1 - \mu^2/2M^2)f^2 \tag{6.31b}$$

The left-hand sides of the dispersion relations (6.29), as well as the low-energy parts of the first dispersion integral, can be evaluated in terms of phase-shift analyses of πN scattering. In addition, the pole terms are known with good accuracy. Since the remaining terms, particularly the contributions from the crossed t-channel cut, are poorly known, phenomenological analyses of πN backward dispersion relations[9] have generally been based on the use of appropriate discrepancy functions.

For example, in analysing the dispersion relations (6.29), one can define the discrepancy functions

$$\Delta^{(\pm)}(w) = \text{Re}F^{(\pm)}(w) - \frac{R^{(\pm)}}{w_N - w} - \frac{1}{\pi}P\int_0^W \frac{\text{Im}F^{(\pm)}(w')\,dw'}{w' - w} \tag{6.32}$$

where W is the highest value of w for which phase-shift analyses are available. These discrepancy functions can be constructed numerically in the range $0 < w < W$ and can then be analysed in terms of both the high-energy contributions to the dispersion integral (for $w > W$) and the contributions from the left-hand cuts. The latter are related to the backward amplitudes for the t-channel process $\pi + \pi \to N + \bar{N}$.

The partial-wave expansions for the t-channel amplitudes are usually expressed in terms of helicity amplitudes $f^J_{\pm}(t)$, where J denotes the total angular momentum and the subscript labels the nucleon helicity state. By the Pauli principle, the even and odd values of J correspond to values of the t-channel isospin $I = 0$ and $I = 1$, respectively. The linear combinations of the $\pi^{\pm} p$ amplitudes which depend on $I = 0$ in the t-channel are $A^{(+)}$ and $B^{(+)}$, while $A^{(-)}$ and $B^{(-)}$ are characterised by $I = 1$ in the t-channel. Thus, separate analyses of the amplitudes $F^{(+)}$ and $F^{(-)}$, for example, can give information on the t-channel helicity amplitudes with even and odd J, respectively. This is, in fact, the main advantage of working with the amplitudes $A^{(\pm)}$ and $B^{(\pm)}$ instead of $A_{\pm}$ and $B_{\pm}$.

It turns out that the partial-wave expansions for $F^{(\pm)}$ in the t-channel contain only the helicity amplitudes f^J_+. Similarly, $G^{(\pm)}$ depend only on f^J_-. If, for example, it is assumed that only the lowest (S-wave) term contributes to the partial-wave expansion, then

$$F^{(+)}(t) = \frac{4\pi}{M(M^2 - t/4)} f^0_+(t) \tag{6.33}$$

Thus, an analysis of the dispersion relation for $F^{(+)}$ can yield information on $f^0_+(t)$ in the low-energy t-channel physical region. Similarly, information on $f^1_+(t)$ and $f^1_-(t)$ can be obtained from analyses of $F^{(-)}$ and $G^{(-)}$, respectively, while the first non-vanishing term in the partial-wave expansion for $G^{(+)}$ turns out to be the D-wave amplitude $f^2_-(t)$.

These helicity amplitudes are in turn closely related to the corresponding partial-wave amplitudes for $\pi\pi$ scattering. It turns out that, below the 4π threshold at $t = 16\mu^2$, where $\pi\pi$ scattering is purely elastic, the phases of the helicity amplitudes for the process $\pi + \pi \to N + \bar{N}$ are equal (modulo π) to the corresponding phases of the partial-wave amplitudes for elastic $\pi\pi$ scattering. To see why this is so, let 1 and 2 denote the coupled $\pi\pi$ and $N\bar{N}$ channels, respectively, and consider the K-matrix equation (see 1.20)

$$T^{-1} = K^{-1} - iq$$

at an energy above the threshold for channel 1 but below the threshold for channel 2. The T-matrix then has the form

$$T^{-1} = \begin{pmatrix} M_{11} - iq_1 & M_{12} \\ M_{12} & M_{22} + |q_2| \end{pmatrix}$$

where the M_{ij} are the (real) elements of the inverse K-matrix. This gives

$$T = \frac{1}{\det(T^{-1})} \begin{pmatrix} M_{22} + |q_2| & -M_{12} \\ -M_{12} & M_{11} - iq_1 \end{pmatrix} \tag{6.34}$$

from which we see that the phases of T_{11} and T_{21} correspond. This result can easily be extended to the case when additional closed channels are present. In practice, it is often assumed that an approximate correspondence of the phases continues to hold in a wider range of energies beyond the 4π threshold (for example, in the range $4\mu^2 \leqslant t \lesssim 50\mu^2$), since there are experimental indications that the coupling of the 2π and 4π channels is weak in this range.

The possibility of extracting information on the $\pi\pi$ interaction in this way from the analysis of backward πN scattering is of great interest, since the pion, being the lightest strongly interacting particle, generates the forces of longest range between other strongly interacting particles and consequently plays a fundamental role in strong-interaction physics.

In analogy with the πN case, studies have also been made of K^+p backward dispersion relations. An advantage of these relations is that they can be used to study the t-channel process $K + \bar{K} \to N + \bar{N}$ (also related to $\pi\pi$ scattering as above) without introducing the complications of simultaneously dealing with the u-channel process $\bar{K} + N \to \bar{K} + N$.

Experimental information on the KN interaction in the isospin state $I = 0$ is rather meagre. Therefore the dispersion relations are written in practice only for the K^+p amplitudes, instead of the combinations $A^{(\pm)}$ and $B^{(\pm)}$ as in the πN case. The price which must be paid for this is that such analyses can give information on only a certain combination of $I = 0$ and $I = 1$ amplitudes in the t-channel.

6.6. Dispersion relations for electromagnetic form factors

The electromagnetic interaction is remarkably well understood on the basis of quantum electrodynamics. Particles which possess only the electromagnetic interaction, such as the electron, can therefore be used as a probe to obtain information about the structure of the strongly interacting particles. One of the ways in which this is possible is through the study of the nucleon electromagnetic form factors deduced from electron–nucleon scattering experiments.

Although it is the electromagnetic structure of nucleons which has been most thoroughly investigated experimentally, owing to the obvious accessibility of nucleon targets, it is simpler to discuss the theory of electromagnetic form factors for the case of pions, in order to avoid the complications due to the nucleon spin. Let us therefore consider electron–pion scattering

$$e^- + \pi \to e^- + \pi$$

To a good approximation, it is sufficient to consider only the contribution of lowest order in the fine structure constant, corresponding to the exchange of a single photon between the electron and pion (figure 6.2).

Quantum electrodynamics alone does not determine the $\gamma\pi\pi$ vertex function, since the pion is a strongly interacting particle. However, by virtue of Lorentz invariance, the invariant scattering amplitude A can depend only on the square of the 4-momentum of the exchanged photon, $p^2 = t$. Hence, without loss of generality, we can write

$$A(t) = \frac{e^2}{t} [1 + tF(t)] \tag{6.35}$$

where $F(t)$ is a scalar function (called the pion electromagnetic form factor) which characterises the modification of the pure Coulomb interaction due to the strong interaction of the pion at the $\gamma\pi\pi$ vertex.

The application of dispersion theory to electromagnetic form factors is based on the fact that $F(t)$ can be shown to be an analytic function in the complex t-plane, with a cut extending to the right along the real axis from the point $t_0 = 4m_\pi^2$ (corresponding to the $\pi\pi$ threshold in the t-channel). The function $F(t)$ is real on the remainder of the real axis and consequently satisfies the Schwarz reflection principle. Thus, $F(t)$ satisfies a dispersion relation (neglecting the possible need for subtractions)

$$F(t) = \frac{1}{\pi} \int_{t_0}^{\infty} \frac{\mathrm{Im}F(t')\,dt'}{t' - t - i\varepsilon} \tag{6.36}$$

The term $-i\varepsilon$ is included in the denominator to show that $F(t)$ in the t-channel physical region is to be evaluated just above the cut.

Little is known theoretically about the asymptotic behaviour of form factors, and it is often assumed that a once-subtracted dispersion relation can be used. The subtraction is conveniently made at the point $t = 0$, giving

$$F(t) = F(0) + \frac{t}{\pi} \int_{t_0}^{\infty} \frac{\mathrm{Im}F(t')\,dt'}{t'(t' - t - i\varepsilon)} \tag{6.37}$$

The physical region of t for electron–pion scattering is $t < 0$, and values of the function $F(t)$ for such t can in principle be determined experimentally by measuring the cross section for this scattering process. On the other hand, in

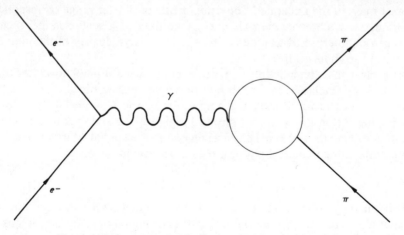

Figure 6.2. Lowest-order diagram for electron–pion scattering.

the range $t > 4m_\pi^2$ the amplitude $A(t)$ describes the crossed t-channel reaction $e^- + e^+ \to \pi + \pi$, that is the process of electron–positron annihilation into two pions. The dispersion relation (6.36) or (6.37) provides an expression of the intimate relationship between these two processes which follows from the fact that their amplitudes are given by the same analytic function.

The dispersion relation is also helpful in elucidating the physical interpretation of the form factor $F(t)$ in terms of the spatial charge distribution of the pion. We recall that $t = -q^2$, where $\mathbf{q}$ is the 3-momentum transfer in the s-channel reaction. Let us introduce the 3-dimensional Fourier transform

$$\tilde{F}(r) = \int F(-q^2)\exp(i\mathbf{q}\cdot\mathbf{r})\,d\mathbf{q} \tag{6.38}$$

Substituting (6.36) into (6.38), we find

$$\tilde{F}(r) = \frac{1}{\pi}\int_{t_0}^{\infty} d(-q'^2)\,\mathrm{Im}F(-q'^2)\int d\mathbf{q}\,\frac{\exp(i\mathbf{q}\cdot\mathbf{r})}{q^2 - q'^2 - i\varepsilon} \tag{6.39}$$

The integration with respect to $\mathbf{q}$ can be evaluated in closed form and gives, after making the substitution $p' = -iq'$

$$\tilde{F}(r) = 2\pi\int_{4m_\pi^2}^{\infty} \mathrm{Im}F(p'^2)\,\frac{\exp(-p'r)}{r}\,d(p'^2) \tag{6.40}$$

The result is well known in connection with the derivation of an expression for the Green's function for the inhomogeneous wave equation. See, for example N. F. Mott and H. S. W. Massey, *The Theory of Atomic Collisions*, 3rd ed., Clarendon Press, Oxford, 1965, chapter 4. This represents a superposition of Yukawa potentials $\exp(-pr)/r$, the components of longest range being determined by the value $t = 4m_\pi^2$, corresponding to the hadron state of lowest mass in the t-channel. The components of shorter range correspond to more massive states in the t-channel. According to a semi-classical picture, $\tilde{F}(r)$ can be interpreted as a description of the charge density of the pion at a distance r from its centre.

It is clear that the function $\tilde{F}(r)$ can be constructed if one knows $\mathrm{Im}F(t)$ for all $t \geqslant 4m_\pi^2$. The latter, in turn, can in principle be determined experimentally either by measuring directly the amplitude for the t-channel process or by measuring $F(t)$ in the s-channel physical region $t < 0$ and making an analytic continuation to the t-channel physical region. It is of special interest to study the amplitude in the t-channel physical region because in the range

$$4m_\pi^2 \leqslant t \leqslant 16m_\pi^2$$

where the only possible hadron state in the t-channel is the two-pion state, this amplitude yields direct information on the $\pi\pi$ interaction. In fact, it was the application of these ideas to the analysis of the electron–nucleon scattering data which historically led to the first theoretical prediction of strong $\pi\pi$ resonances (such resonances were discovered experimentally only later).

For the case of electron–nucleon scattering, the elastic scattering cross section can be expressed in terms of two electromagnetic form factors by the well-known Rosenbluth formula.[10] These form factors are again functions of only the square of the 4-momentum transfer p^2 and can be interpreted loosely in terms of the spatial distributions of electric charge and magnetic moment of the target nucleon. They also individually satisfy dispersion relations similar to the dispersion relation for the pion form factor.

The structure of the Rosenbluth formula is such that, from measurements of the differential cross section for elastic electron–nucleon scattering, it is possible to extract the two form factors of the nucleon. Accurate data on these form factors now exist over a wide range of values of p^2, although there are practical difficulties in the determination of the neutron form factors, owing to the fact that one must use, for example, target neutrons which are bound in the deuteron.

References

1. J. K. Kim, *Phys. Rev. Lett.*, **14** (1965), 29. For a survey of low-energy parameters, see G. Ebel et al., *Nucl. Phys.*, **B33** (1971), 317
2. A. D. Martin, N. M. Queen and G. Violini, *Nucl. Phys.*, **B10** (1969), 481
3. R. Perrin and W. S. Woolcock, *Nucl. Phys.*, **B12** (1969), 26
4. For a full account of the formalism required to do this, see R. H. Dalitz and S. F. Tuan, *Ann. of Phys.*, **8** (1959), 100, and J. D. Jackson and H. W. Wyld, *Nuovo Cimento*, **13** (1959), 85
5. Various representations of the amplitude have been employed for the relativistic description of *NN* scattering. See, for example, D. Amati et al., *Nuovo Cimento*, **17** (1960), 68, and M. L. Goldberger et al., *Phys. Rev.*, **120** (1960), 2250
6. See, for example, P. Söding, *Phys. Lett.*, **8** (1964), 285
7. G. Białkowski and S. Pokorski, *Nuovo Cimento*, **57A** (1968), 219
8. P. Pascual and F. J. Ynduráin, *Nuovo Cimento*, **61A** (1969), 225
9. See, for example, H. Neilsen, J. Lyng Petersen and E. Pietarinen, *Nucl. Phys.*, **B22** (1970), 525, and H. Nielsen and G. C. Oades, *Nucl. Phys.*, **B41** (1972), 525 and **B49** (1972), 586
10. M. N. Rosenbluth, *Phys. Rev.*, **79** (1950), 615

Further Reading

Reviews of KN dispersion relations and their applications appear in the following references.
1. N. M. Queen, M. Restignoli and G. Violini, *Fortschritte der Physik*, **17** (1969), 467 and **21** (1973), 569
2. B. R. Martin, *Springer Tracts in Modern Physics*, **55** (1970), 73

The following reference contains a review of *NN* dispersion relations.

3. V. A. Nikitin, *Problems of Elementary Particle and Atomic Nucleus Physics*, **1** (1970) 7 [in Russian]

Electromagnetic form factors are discussed in the following reviews.

4. R. R. Wilson and J. S. Levinger, *Ann. Rev. Nucl. Science*, **14** (1964), 135
5. T. A. Griffy and L. I. Schiff, in *High Energy Physics*, Vol. I, ed. E. H. S. Burhop, Academic Press, New York, 1967, p. 341
6. P. S. Isaev, *Problems of Elementary Particle and Atomic Nucleus Physics*, **2** (1971), 67 [in Russian]

CHAPTER 7

Modified dispersion relations

7.1. Inverse dispersion relations

From a given scattering amplitude, it is possible to construct many different analytic functions which satisfy dispersion relations. We have already defined several such functions when making various types of subtractions.

Another possibility is to write a dispersion relation for the function $F'(\omega) = iF(\omega)$, where $F(\omega)$ is the scattering amplitude. Since

$$\mathrm{Re}F'(\omega) = -\mathrm{Im}F(\omega) \tag{7.1a}$$

$$\mathrm{Im}F'(\omega) = \mathrm{Re}F(\omega) \tag{7.1b}$$

the dispersion relation for the function $F'(\omega)$ will differ from the usual dispersion relation for $F(\omega)$ in that the roles of $\mathrm{Re}F(\omega)$ and $\mathrm{Im}F(\omega)$ will be interchanged. For this reason, it is called an inverse dispersion relation. In particular, an unsubtracted dispersion relation for $F'(\omega)$ reads

$$-\mathrm{Im}F(\omega) = \frac{1}{\pi} P \int_{-\infty}^{\infty} \frac{\mathrm{Re}F(\omega')\, d\omega'}{\omega' - \omega} \tag{7.2}$$

which is identical with the relation (2.30) which we derived earlier by a different method.

The asymptotic behaviour of the physical scattering amplitudes will not actually ensure the validity of the unsubtracted dispersion relation (7.2). However, subtractions can be made in the usual way to force the contribution from the semicircular contour at infinity to vanish.

It is obvious that the dispersion relations for $F'(\omega)$ and $F(\omega)$ are completely equivalent from a mathematical point of view. However, we recall that a knowledge of both the real and imaginary parts of the scattering amplitude constitutes an overdetermined set of data. We can therefore say that, if, in any particular situation, the simultaneous use of the two dispersion relations for $F'(\omega)$ and $F(\omega)$ is found to give a consistent picture, we can interpret this as evidence of the applicability of dispersion relations to this case, as well as of the overall consistency of the experimental data used in the analysis.

Calculations involving inverse dispersion relations differ in an obvious way from the applications of conventional dispersion relations with which we have been concerned so far. The main experimental information required to evaluate a conventional forward dispersion relation is the total cross section data. These data are known for certain processes with great accuracy, allowing one to estimate the dispersion integrals quite reliably. This is no longer true when one must evaluate a dispersion integral involving the real parts of the amplitudes. The experimental information on the real parts is in general much poorer, being derived from extrapolations of measured differential cross sections to the forward direction or from phase-shift analyses. As a result, there is usually a much larger uncertainty associated with the numerical value of the integral in an inverse dispersion relation.

In practice, inverse dispersion relations have not been applied to physical problems in the form outlined above. The reason for this is as follows. In the conventional dispersion relations there is a certain portion of the real axis of the ω-plane which does not contribute to the dispersion integral because of the vanishing of the imaginary part of the scattering amplitude below the lowest threshold. However, since the real part of the amplitude is in general non-zero over the entire real axis, the integral in the inverse dispersion relation includes a contribution from an appreciable unphysical region. Although it is of course possible in principle to analytically continue the scattering amplitude into this energy region in order to obtain a model for the real part and hence an estimate of the value of the integral, such a procedure proves to be impracticable in many cases.

A more feasible alternative is to replace the scattering amplitude in the inverse dispersion relation by a slightly different function, in order to avoid the use of unphysical real part data. It was first proposed by Gilbert[1] to consider the inverse dispersion relation for the scattering amplitude divided by the laboratory momentum k of the incident particle. This momentum becomes imaginary below the elastic threshold, so that the dispersion integral over the sub-threshold energy region involves $\mathrm{Im}F(\omega)$ instead of $\mathrm{Re}F(\omega)$. Thus, except where unphysical cuts are present, only data from experimentally accessible energy regions will contribute to the dispersion integrals. Moreover, the additional momentum factor has the effect of improving the convergence of the dispersion relation.

As an illustrative example, we quote the form of the inverse dispersion relation for $K^{\pm}p$ scattering obtained by taking $F(\omega) = [F_-(\omega) - F_+(\omega)]/k$ in (7.2), where $F_{\pm}(\omega)$ are the $K^{\pm}p$ forward scattering amplitudes

$$
\frac{\sigma_+(\omega) - \sigma_-(\omega)}{8\omega} = \pi \sum_Y \frac{X_Y}{(\omega_Y^2 - \omega^2)(m_K^2 - m_Y^2)^{1/2}}
$$

$$
+ \int_{W_{\pi\Lambda}}^{m_K} \frac{\mathrm{Im}F_-(\omega')\, d\omega'}{(\omega'^2 - \omega^2)(m_K^2 - \omega'^2)^{1/2}}
$$

$$
+ P\int_{m_K}^{\infty} \frac{\mathrm{Re}[F_-(\omega') - F_+(\omega')]\, d\omega'}{(\omega'^2 - \omega^2)(\omega'^2 - m_K^2)^{1/2}} \tag{7.3}
$$

The notation is that of chapter 6. In deriving (7.3), we have made use of the fact that the function $F(\omega)$ is crossing-symmetric. Note that the correct analytic continuation of the function $k = (\omega^2 - m_K^2)^{1/2}$ into the sub-threshold region is such that k is purely imaginary (with a positive imaginary part) in the range $-m_K < \omega < m_K$ and real (negative) in the range $\omega < -m_K$. The integral involving $\mathrm{Im}F_-(\omega')$ appears on the right-hand side of (7.3) because of the presence of open channels below the elastic threshold.

Because of the problems mentioned earlier, dispersion relations of this type have found only a limited number of applications in phenomenological analyses. They have proved to be useful mainly as consistency tests for certain sets of data, for example in helping to resolve the sign ambiguity which is inherent in the data on the real parts of the amplitudes when these real parts are extracted from differential cross sections without measurements of the Coulomb interference. Since the total cross sections appear on the left-hand side of the inverse dispersion relations, these relations have also been used to obtain theoretical predictions for these cross sections at high energies.

7.2. Weighted dispersion relations

The modification of the scattering amplitude which we introduced in the preceding section, namely its division by a suitable factor, is a particular case of a more general method employed in applications of dispersion relations.

If $F(\omega)$ is an analytic function, one can construct a multitude of other analytic functions by multiplying it by various weight functions $g(\omega)$. The detailed analyticity properties of the product $F(\omega)g(\omega)$ will of course depend on those of both factors, but in many cases it will still be possible to write dispersion relations for the function $F(\omega)g(\omega)$.

The choice of the weight function $g(\omega)$ will depend largely on the particular problem under consideration. As an example, we shall illustrate the application of these ideas to KN scattering.

We saw in chapter 6 that the main uncertainty in the determination of the KNY coupling constants by forward dispersion relations arises from the presence of the Y_0^* (1405) resonance in the unphysical region, so that the parametrisation adopted for this resonance contribution is of crucial importance for the calculation of g_Λ^2. We have also pointed out that simple consistency tests are provided by the requirement that, for a given set of input data, the calculated values of g_Y^2 must not depend on which dispersion relations are used to determine them.

The approach based on weight functions can be applied in the spirit of such consistency tests. If one multiplies the kaon–nucleon scattering amplitude by some weight function $g(\omega)$ and then writes a dispersion relation for the product, the calculated values of the KNY coupling constants must be independent of the choice of $g(\omega)$.

However, by a judicious choice of the function $g(\omega)$ it is possible to suppress the relative importance of the less reliable input information in the dispersion relation. In the case of KN scattering, where the main uncertainty comes from the part of the $\bar{K}N$ unphysical region near the Y_0^* (1405) resonance, it will clearly be convenient to suppress the contribution from this region by choosing a weight function which vanishes there.

The simplest choice of a weight function having this property is obviously

$$g(\omega) = \omega - \omega_0 \tag{7.4}$$

where $\omega_0 = (m_{Y_0^*}^2 - m_K^2 - m_p^2)/2m_p$, taking positive (negative) values of ω to correspond to $\bar{K}N(KN)$ scattering.

A complication which arises when the amplitude $F(\omega)$ is multiplied by the weight function (7.4) is that the asymptotic behaviour of the product contains an additional factor of ω, so that a further subtraction is required. One possible procedure is to compensate for this factor by introducing a similar factor in the denominator, that is to consider instead the function

$$H(\omega) = [(\omega - \omega_0)/(\omega + \bar{\omega})]/F(\omega) \tag{7.5}$$

where $\bar{\omega}$ can be specified arbitrarily. This is equivalent to making a subtraction at the point $\omega = -\bar{\omega}$. If $F(\omega)$ is taken to be the K^-p scattering amplitude $F_-(\omega)$, it is convenient to choose $\bar{\omega}$ to be some energy at which the K^+p scattering amplitude is well known. In evaluating the dispersion relation for the function $H(\omega)$, we will then need to know the residue of $H(\omega)$ at the pole or, equivalently, the value of $\mathrm{Re}F_+(\bar{\omega})$.

Since the function (7.5) has the same asymptotic behaviour as the scattering amplitude itself, the dispersion relation for it still requires a subtraction. One possibility is to make a 'charge subtraction' by writing a dispersion relation for the difference

$$H^{(-)}(\omega) = H(\omega) - H(-\omega)$$

In the notation of chapter 6, the resulting dispersion relation, evaluated at threshold, takes the form

$$\frac{\omega_0 - m_K}{m_K + \bar{\omega}} \mathrm{Re}F_-(m_K) + \frac{\omega_0 + m_K}{m_K - \bar{\omega}} \mathrm{Re}F_+(m_K) + \frac{2m_K(\bar{\omega} + \omega_0)}{\bar{\omega}^2 - m_K^2} \mathrm{Re}F_+(\bar{\omega})$$

$$= 2m_K \sum_Y \frac{(\omega_0 - \omega_Y)X_Y}{(\omega_Y + \bar{\omega})(\omega_Y^2 - m_K^2)} - \frac{2m_K}{\pi} \int_{w_{\pi\Lambda}}^{\infty} \frac{(\omega' - \omega_0)\mathrm{Im}F_-(\omega')\,d\omega'}{(\omega' + \bar{\omega})(\omega'^2 - m_K^2)}$$

$$+ \frac{2m_K}{\pi} \int_{m_K}^{\infty} \frac{(\omega' + \omega_0)\mathrm{Im}F_+(\omega')\,d\omega'}{(\omega' - \bar{\omega})(\omega'^2 - m_K^2)} \tag{7.6}$$

Note that, with this modification of the conventional dispersion relations, it is not necessary to have an accurate knowledge of $\mathrm{Im}F_-(\omega)$ in the unphysical region, owing to the zero of the integrand near the Y_0^* (1405) resonance. However, we require instead one additional piece of information, namely the real part of the K^+p scattering amplitude at the point $\omega = \bar{\omega}$.

An analysis of the $K^{\pm}p$ and $K^{\pm}n$ dispersion relations of type (7.6) led to the results[2]

$$g_{\Lambda}^2/4\pi = 7 \pm 4 \tag{7.7a}$$

from the linear combination of the dispersion relations depending on $I = 0$ in the $\bar{K}N$ channel, and

$$[g_{\Lambda}^2 + \alpha(\bar{\omega})g_{\Sigma}^2]/4\pi = 3{\cdot}75 \pm 1{\cdot}4 \tag{7.7b}$$

from the $K^{\pm}p$ dispersion relation, where $\alpha(\bar{\omega})$ ($\approx 0{\cdot}6$) is a slowly varying function of $\bar{\omega}$ which reflects the difference between the coefficients of g_{Λ}^2 and g_{Σ}^2.

The effectiveness of this method is apparent from the fact that the calculated values of g_{Λ}^2 corresponding to different models for the amplitude in the unphysical region are found to differ by an amount ~ 1, as compared with the much larger variations of up to about 10 which are found when different parametrisations are used in the standard dispersion relations (see section 6.2).

It is also of interest to consider the dispersion relation corresponding to the weight function

$$g(\omega) = 1/\sqrt{(\omega - \omega_1)(\omega - \omega_2)} \tag{7.8}$$

The most striking effect of this choice is not the suppression of the contribution from any particular energy region, but the fact that, owing to the character of the square-root function, the imaginary part of $F(\omega)g(\omega)$ depends on $\mathrm{Re}F(\omega)$ within a limited energy region and on $\mathrm{Im}F(\omega)$ outside this region.

Suppose, for example, that

$$m < \omega_1 < \omega_2 \tag{7.9}$$

Then for $\omega < \omega_1$ the square-root function in (7.8) gives rise to a real factor, so that

$$\mathrm{Im}[F(\omega)g(\omega)] = g(\omega)\mathrm{Im}F(\omega) \tag{7.10}$$

In the interval $\omega_1 < \omega < \omega_2$, on the other hand, $g(\omega)$ is purely imaginary, and

$$\mathrm{Im}[F(\omega)g(\omega)] = -|g(\omega)|\,\mathrm{Re}F(\omega) \tag{7.11}$$

Finally, for $\omega > \omega_2$ we have again the relation (7.10).

Dispersion relations for the scattering amplitude weighted by the function (7.8) are sometimes called 'broad-area subtracted dispersion relations',[3] since they exploit the information on the real part of the scattering amplitude over a finite energy range (7.9), in contrast with the usual once-subtracted dispersion relations, which make use of the real part at only a single subtraction point. Note that, in the limiting case in which $\omega_2 = \omega_1$, the weight function (7.8) reduces to the weight function $1/(\omega - \omega_1)$ which is used in deriving the conventional once-subtracted relation. Modified dispersion relations constructed with the weight function (7.8) turn out to be useful in checking the consistency of phase-shift analyses with dispersion relations, since, by choosing the values of ω_1 and ω_2 appropriately, one can make use of the real part of the amplitude over any particular energy range.

An obvious extension of the method is to take the weight function $g(\omega)$ to be a product of the inverses of several square-root factors such as those appearing in (7.8). In this way, $\text{Im}[F(\omega)g(\omega)]$ can be made to depend on $\text{Re}F(\omega)$ in a number of distinct energy ranges and on $\text{Im}F(\omega)$ elsewhere.

Finally, we shall describe a further generalisation of weighted dispersion relations which makes it possible to utilise data on the real parts of scattering amplitudes when such data are available over a large energy range.

For definiteness, let $F^{(-)}(\omega)$ be the crossing antisymmetric $\pi^{\pm}p$ forward scattering amplitude, and define

$$F'(\omega) = F^{(-)}(\omega)(\omega^2 - \mu^2)^{-\beta} \exp(i\pi\beta) \qquad (7.12)$$

where μ is the pion mass and β is a real parameter. The function $F'(\omega)$ clearly has the same singularities as the amplitude $F^{(-)}(\omega)$ itself. We must, however, carefully specify which branch is to be chosen for the multi-valued function $(\omega^2 - \mu^2)^{-\beta}$. We do this by stipulating that this function be real-valued just above its right-hand cut. The factor $\exp(i\pi\beta)$ is included in the definition of $F'(\omega)$ in order to compensate for the complex phase factor contained in the function $(\omega^2 - \mu^2)^{-\beta}$ in the region $|\omega| < \mu$, where

$$(\omega^2 - \mu^2)^{-\beta} = |\omega^2 - \mu^2|^{-\beta} \exp(-i\pi\beta)$$

Since both the amplitude and the weight function are real in the region $|\omega| < \mu$, we have $\text{Im}F'(\omega) = 0$ there. Moreover, it is readily verified that the function $F'(\omega)$, like the original amplitude, is crossing-antisymmetric.

For appropriate values of the parameter β, $F'(\omega)$ satisfies a convergent dispersion relation, which can be written down in a straightforward way. Because of the presence of the phase factor $\exp(i\pi\beta)$, the dispersion integral involving $\text{Im}F'(\omega)$ will depend on both the real and imaginary parts of the original scattering amplitude $F^{(-)}(\omega)$. Thus, for $\omega > \mu$

$$\text{Im}F'(\omega) = (\omega^2 - \mu^2)^{-\beta}[\cos \pi\beta \, \text{Im}F^{(-)}(\omega) + \sin \pi\beta \, \text{Re}F^{(-)}(\omega)] \quad (7.13)$$

Similarly, $\text{Re}F'(\omega)$ will also depend on both $\text{Re}F^{(-)}(\omega)$ and $\text{Im}F^{(-)}(\omega)$ for $\omega > \mu$.

We shall return once again to the use of weight functions such as that appearing in (7.12) when we come to the discussion of modified sum rules in a later chapter.

7.3. Dispersion relations for the inverse amplitude

If $F(\omega)$ is a scattering amplitude, its inverse

$$[F(\omega)]^{-1} = \frac{F^*(\omega)}{|F(\omega)|^2} \qquad (7.14)$$

will be an analytic function with the same cut structure in the complex ω-plane as $F(\omega)$ itself, but with poles corresponding to the zeros of the original amplitude and with zeros at the original pole positions. It is clear that the function $[F(\omega)]^{-1}$ has all the properties required for the validity of a dispersion relation. In fact, for many physical scattering amplitudes its asymptotic behavior is such that no subtraction is needed in the dispersion relation.

One may, of course, freely introduce subtractions. This can be done without requiring any additional experimental information if the subtraction energies are chosen to be the positions of poles of $F(\omega)$, where $[F(\omega)]^{-1}$ is known to vanish.

Before writing down dispersion relations for the inverse amplitude, we note that

$$\text{Im}[F(\omega)]^{-1} = -\text{Im}F(\omega)/|F(\omega)|^2 \tag{7.15}$$

so that for forward scattering the optical theorem can be used in evaluating the dispersion integral over the physical region, as in the ordinary dispersion relations, provided that $|F(\omega)|^2$ is known. The latter, which is related to the forward differential cross section, is often available from experiment with reasonable accuracy.

Since the roles of the zeros and poles are interchanged when we go over from $F(\omega)$ to $[F(\omega)]^{-1}$, it is essential for the analysis of inverse dispersion relations to know something about the number of zeros of the amplitude and their positions in the complex plane. Unlike the poles of the scattering amplitude, which correspond to physical particles, these zeros are not known a priori.

Apart from the question of zeros, dispersion relations for the function (7.14) utilise essentially the same information as the conventional dispersion relations for $F(\omega)$. However, they assign different relative weights to the various data, so that one can hope that such dispersion relations will be advantageous in certain situations.

Let us now formulate dispersion relations for the inverse amplitude. We consider for definiteness amplitudes $F^{(\pm)}(\omega)$ which are crossing-symmetric or crossing-antisymmetric, so that their left-hand singularities can be expressed in a simple way in terms of their right-hand singularities. Then it is straightforward to verify that the functions

$$h^{(\pm)}(\omega) = [F^{(\pm)}(\omega)]^{-1} \tag{7.16}$$

satisfy dispersion relations of the type below (for simplicity, we assume that all the zeros of $F^{(\pm)}(\omega)$ lie on the real axis. To avoid double-counting, the factor 2 in the pole term of (7.17) must be omitted in the case of a zero at $\omega_j = 0$)

$$\text{Re}h^{(\pm)}(\omega) = \frac{2}{\pi}P\int_{\omega_0}^{\infty} \frac{\omega^{(\pm)}\text{Im}h^{(\pm)}(\omega')\,d\omega'}{\omega'^2 - \omega^2} - \sum_j \frac{2R_j^{(\pm)}}{\omega_j^2 - \omega^2} \tag{7.17}$$

where $\omega^{(+)} = \omega'$ and $\omega^{(-)} = \omega$; ω_j are those positive energies at which

$$F^{(\pm)}(\omega_j) = 0 \tag{7.18}$$

and the quantities $R_j^{(\pm)}$, related to the residues at the poles of $h^{(\pm)}(\omega)$, are given by

$$R_j^{(+)} = \omega_j/[dF^{(+)}/d\omega]_{\omega=\omega_j} \tag{7.19a}$$

$$R_j^{(-)} = \omega/[dF^{(-)}/d\omega]_{\omega=\omega_j} \tag{7.19b}$$

Although the positions of the zeros of the amplitude and the corresponding residues at the poles of the inverse amplitude may be difficult to determine with precision, certain simple constraints on them can sometimes be derived. In certain cases it is possible to infer the presence of a zero of the amplitude in a particular energy region by a simple argument based on the continuity of the amplitude. Consider, for example, $K^{\pm}p$ scattering. Since the two poles corresponding to the Λ and Σ particles are known to have residues of the same sign, the amplitude must change sign somewhere in the interval between these two poles. This argument applies to both the crossing-symmetric and crossing-antisymmetric amplitudes; in each case, there must be a pair of zeros, one for positive and one for negative ω. In the case of the crossing-antisymmetric amplitude, it follows purely from the crossing property $F^{(-)}(-\omega) = -F^{(-)}(\omega)$ that $F^{(-)}(\omega)$ has a third zero at $\omega = 0$.

Similarly, the presence of zeros can sometimes be inferred from a knowledge of the sign of the real part of the scattering amplitude at the lowest threshold. If this sign is identical with that of the residue at the nearest pole, it is possible for the real part to remain of one sign throughout the energy region from that pole to the threshold; if these signs are opposite, however, the amplitude must necessarily have a zero in this interval.

There is also the possibility of zeros off the real axis. Zeros on the imaginary axis must occur in complex conjugate pairs, by virtue of the Schwarz reflection principle. For an amplitude with definite symmetry properties with respect to crossing, zeros which lie on neither the real nor the imaginary axis must occur in symmetric sets of four.

The numerical evaluation of dispersion relations such as (7.17) presents certain difficulties, but these relations have the advantage of good convergence. It is also worth noting that certain amplitudes may be assumed to be purely imaginary, at least at high energies; in this case (7.15) reduces to

$$\text{Im}[F(\omega)]^{-1} = -1/\text{Im}F(\omega) \tag{7.20}$$

In some cases, owing to the good convergence of the dispersion integrals, the analysis of the dispersion relations (7.17) will depend crucially on the positions of the poles of the inverse amplitude.

As an example of the use of such dispersion relations, we shall discuss their application[4] to the inverse of the crossing-antisymmetric $K^{\pm}p$ scattering amplitude $h^{(-)}(\omega) = [F^{(-)}(\omega)]^{-1} = 2[F_-(\omega) - F_+(\omega)]^{-1}$.

The residues at the Λ and Σ poles, in the notation of section 6.1, are given by

$$2X_Y^{-1} = -[dh^{(-)}/d\omega]_{\omega=\omega_Y} \tag{7.21}$$

Substituting the dispersion relation (7.17) into (7.21), we have

$$X_Y^{-1} = -\frac{1}{\pi} \int_{\omega_{\pi\Lambda}}^{\infty} \frac{(\omega'^2 + \omega_Y^2)\mathrm{Im}h^{(-)}(\omega')\,\mathrm{d}\omega'}{(\omega'^2 - \omega_Y^2)^2} + \sum_j \frac{(\omega_j^2 + \omega_Y^2)R_j}{(\omega_j^2 - \omega_Y^2)^2} \quad (7.22)$$

where

$$R_j = 1/[\mathrm{d}F^{(-)}/\mathrm{d}\omega]_{\omega=\omega_j} \quad (7.23)$$

The condition $h^{(-)}(\omega_Y) = 0$ gives, according to (7.17)

$$0 = \frac{1}{\pi} \int_{\omega_{\pi\Lambda}}^{\infty} \frac{\mathrm{Im}h^{(-)}(\omega')\,\mathrm{d}\omega'}{\omega'^2 - \omega_Y^2} - \sum_j \frac{R_j}{\omega_j^2 - \omega_Y^2} \quad (7.24)$$

Adding equations (7.22) and (7.24), we find

$$\frac{1}{X_Y\omega_Y^2} = \frac{2}{\pi} \int_{\omega_{\pi\Lambda}}^{\infty} \frac{\mathrm{Im}F^{(-)}(\omega')\,\mathrm{d}\omega'}{(\omega'^2 - \omega_Y^2)^2\,|F^{(-)}(\omega')|^2} + \sum_j \frac{2R_j}{(\omega_j^2 - \omega_Y^2)^2} \quad (7.25)$$

Now the integral in (7.25) is a slowly varying function of ω_Y in the range $\omega_\Lambda \leqslant \omega_Y \leqslant \omega_\Sigma$, where it may be regarded as a constant. Evaluating (7.25) for both $Y = \Lambda$ and $Y = \Sigma$ and taking the difference of the results, we obtain

$$\frac{1}{X_\Lambda\omega_\Lambda^2} - \frac{1}{X_\Sigma\omega_\Sigma^2} \approx R_0\left[\frac{1}{\omega_\Lambda^4} - \frac{1}{\omega_\Sigma^4}\right] + 2R_1\left[\frac{1}{(\omega_1^2 - \omega_\Lambda^2)^2} - \frac{1}{(\omega_1^2 - \omega_\Sigma^2)^2}\right] \quad (7.26)$$

The absence of the factor 2 in the first term on the right-hand side of (7.26) is explained in the note in brackets just before equation (7.17). The residues R_0 and R_1 in equation (7.26) correspond to the known zeros of $F^{(-)}(\omega)$ at $\omega = 0$ and at some energy $\omega = \omega_1$ such that $\omega_\Lambda < \omega_1 < \omega_\Sigma$. They may be evaluated approximately from (7.23) by retaining only the nearby poles in the conventional dispersion relation (6.5) for the amplitude $F^{(-)}(\omega)$. Moreover, the value of ω_1 may be determined from the condition $F^{(-)}(\omega_1) = 0$. Thus, (7.26) leads to a complicated algebraic equation relating X_Λ and X_Σ, which, when combined with the value of a quantity such as $X_\Lambda + X_\Sigma$ deduced from a conventional dispersion relation, makes it possible to determine the individual values of the $KN\Lambda$ and $KN\Sigma$ coupling constants.

Additional zeros may of course contribute to the right-hand side of (7.26). However, it turns out that calculations based on conventional dispersion relations exclude the possibility of further zeros along the real axis. More distant zeros in the complex plane would not seriously affect the calculation because their contribution to (7.26) would be strongly suppressed by the factors in the denominators.

7.4. Dispersion relations for other functions of amplitudes

So far we have considered only dispersion relations for functions which depend linearly on the amplitude. In certain situations it may be advantageous to utilise dispersion relations for functions of a more general type. Perhaps the simplest such case which has been proposed is that of dispersion relations for the square of an amplitude.[5]

Decomposing the scattering amplitude $F(\omega)$ in the usual way into its real and imaginary parts

$$F(\omega) = \text{Re}F(\omega) + i\,\text{Im}F(\omega) \qquad (7.27)$$

we have for its square

$$F^2(\omega) = \{[\text{Re}F(\omega)]^2 - [\text{Im}F(\omega)]^2\} + i\{2\,\text{Re}F(\omega)\text{Im}F(\omega)\} \qquad (7.28)$$

It is obvious that, if $F(\omega)$ is chosen to be either crossing-symmetric or crossing-antisymmetric, the function $F^2(\omega)$ is crossing-symmetric. We shall assume for simplicity that this condition is satisfied. Then the ordinary (unsubtracted) dispersion relation for the function (7.28) takes the form

$$[\text{Re}F(\omega)]^2 - [\text{Im}F(\omega)]^2 = \frac{4}{\pi}P\int_0^\infty \frac{\omega'\text{Re}F(\omega')\text{Im}F(\omega')\,d\omega'}{\omega'^2 - \omega^2} \qquad (7.29)$$

while the inverse dispersion relation, for the same function becomes

$$\text{Re}F(\omega)\text{Im}F(\omega) = \frac{\omega}{\pi}P\int_0^\infty \frac{\{[\text{Im}F(\omega')]^2 - [\text{Re}F(\omega')]^2\}\,d\omega'}{\omega'^2 - \omega^2} \qquad (7.30)$$

In order to apply (7.29) and (7.30) in practice, we must examine two problems: first, how to treat the contributions from possible pole terms in the amplitude $F(\omega)$, and second, whether subtractions are required to ensure the validity of these new dispersion relations.

A pole in the amplitude will appear as a δ-function singularity in $\text{Im}F(\omega)$ and an explicit pole term in $\text{Re}F(\omega)$. To eliminate this complication, it is convenient to construct the 'finite' amplitude

$$F_F(\omega) = \text{Re}F_F(\omega) + i\,\text{Im}F_F(\omega) \qquad (7.31)$$

by subtracting the pole contributions from (7.27). The dispersion relations (7.29) and (7.30) can then be written for the new function (7.31). This procedure can be justified by the fact that the contributions of a pole term can be shown to satisfy identically the dispersion relations (7.29) and (7.30). In any case, one can simply define an analytic function whose imaginary part coincides with $\text{Im}F(\omega)$ on both the left and right-hand cuts and which vanishes identically on the remainder of the real axis: this leads directly to (7.31), since the quantity $\text{Re}F_F(\omega)$ in (7.31) can be constructed directly from a dispersion relation in terms of $\text{Im}F_F(\omega)$ without ambiguity. Alternatively, one can make use of experimental information on $\text{Re}F(\omega)$ and then subtract off the contribution of the pole terms; in this case, one obviously requires a knowledge of the values of the relevant coupling constants.

We shall henceforth assume for simplicity that there are no pole terms in the amplitude. If pole terms are present, $F(\omega)$ in the equations which follow should be interpreted as $F_F(\omega)$.

It remains to consider the question of subtractions in the dispersion relations. A reasonable assumption about the high-energy behaviour of $F(\omega)$ (or, equivalently, $F_F(\omega)$) is that (see chapter 8)

$$|F^{(+)}(\omega)| \sim \text{const } \omega \qquad |F^{(-)}(\omega)| \sim \text{const } \omega^\alpha \quad (\alpha \approx \tfrac{1}{2}) \qquad (7.32)$$

Under these conditions, subtractions are required. A subtraction would not actually be necessary in the dispersion relation (7.30) if we had $\alpha < \tfrac{1}{2}$. However, such values are not indicated by the data for most amplitudes; moreover, if α were slightly less than $\tfrac{1}{2}$, the convergence would be slow, so that a subtraction would still be desirable.

It is convenient to choose the subtraction point $\omega = \omega_0$ in the cut-free region of the real axis, so that $\text{Im}F(\omega_0) = 0$. Let us exclude the case $\omega_0 = 0$ for the moment, as this would lead to a problem of convergence of the dispersion integral. Thus, the subtracted forms of (7.29) and (7.30) will be

$$[\text{Re}F(\omega)]^2 - [\text{Re}F(\omega_0)]^2 - [\text{Im}F(\omega)]^2$$

$$= \frac{4}{\pi}(\omega^2 - \omega_0^2)P\int_0^\infty \frac{\omega'\text{Re}F(\omega')\text{Im}F(\omega')\,d\omega'}{(\omega'^2 - \omega^2)(\omega'^2 - \omega_0^2)} \qquad (7.33)$$

$$\text{Re}F(\omega)\text{Im}F(\omega) = \frac{\omega}{\pi}(\omega^2 - \omega_0^2)P\int_0^\infty \frac{\{[\text{Im}F(\omega')]^2 - [\text{Re}F(\omega')]^2\}\,d\omega'}{(\omega'^2 - \omega^2)(\omega'^2 - \omega_0^2)} \qquad (7.34)$$

The choice $\omega_0 = 0$ is always possible in (7.33), where the range of integration actually begins at the lowest threshold, since the integrand vanishes identically at lower energies. This choice leads to a simpler form of the dispersion relation. For (7.34), on the other hand, the choice $\omega_0 = 0$ can be made only if $\text{Re}F(\omega)$ is proportional to ω near $\omega = 0$. This will be true if $F(\omega)$ is taken to be a crossing-antisymmetric amplitude.

Let us now consider the possible usefulness of such dispersion relations. These dispersion relations obviously require input data on the real parts of the amplitudes, with their inherent uncertainties. While the direct dispersion relation (7.33) does not appear to offer any major advantage over conventional dispersion relations, the inverse relation (7.34) is of special interest.

We notice, for instance, that the left-hand side of (7.34) vanishes identically below the lowest threshold. Imposing this requirement on the right-hand side, as a function of the energy ω at which (7.34) is evaluated, we obtain a family of sum rules which express a consistency condition on the scattering amplitude. These sum rules may serve as constraints to be used in the determination of low-energy parameters, since the dispersion integrals depend rather heavily on the form assumed for the amplitudes at low energy. In fact, we expect to find not only a very rapid convergence of the integral in (7.34), owing to the ω'^4 behaviour of the denominator, but also a strong cancellation in the numerator of the integrand. In the case of a crossing-antisymmetric amplitude with

$\alpha = \frac{1}{2}$ in (7.32), we would have not only the same power-law behaviour of $\text{Re}F^{(-)}(\omega)$ and $\text{Im}F^{(-)}(\omega)$ at high energies, but also an exact cancellation in the integrand of (7.34) (see equation 4.53).

The remainder of this section will be devoted to modified dispersion relations of a different type, involving the natural logarithm of the scattering amplitude[6]

$$\log F(\omega) = \log |F(\omega)| + i\,\delta(\omega) \tag{7.35}$$

where $\delta(\omega)$ is the phase of the amplitude defined by the relation

$$F(\omega) = |F(\omega)|\exp(i\,\delta(\omega)) \tag{7.36}$$

For simplicity, let us assume that the zeros of $F(\omega)$, if any, all lie on the real axis. Then (7.35) defines an analytic function of ω, for which dispersion relations can be written. These dispersion relations will relate the modulus of the scattering amplitude to its phase. It is most convenient to make use of the inverse dispersion relation, so that the dispersion integral will depend on $|F(\omega)|$, which can be determined experimentally from differential cross section measurements.

Writing such a dispersion relation for the function (7.35) itself, we would have a dispersion integral involving $\log|\text{Re}F(\omega)|$ over the unphysical region of the real axis. This unpleasant complication can be avoided by exploiting the same trick as in the case of the ordinary inverse dispersion relations (see section 7.1), that is by writing instead a dispersion relation for the modified function

$$F'(\omega) = \log F(\omega)/\sqrt{(\omega^2 - m^2)} \tag{7.37}$$

where m is the threshold energy.

General considerations of the asymptotic behaviour lead to the conclusion that $|F'(\omega)| \to 0$ as $\omega \to \infty$, at least in the forward direction, so that no subtractions are required in the dispersion relation for this function.

Defining the value of the square-root function in (7.37) to be positive for $\omega > m$ and taking its correct analytic continuation into the region $\omega < m$, as in section 7.1, the inverse dispersion relation (7.2) for the new function (7.37) reads

$$-\frac{\pi\,\delta(\omega)}{(\omega^2 - m^2)^{1/2}} = P\int_m^\infty \frac{\log|F(\omega')|\,d\omega'}{(\omega' - \omega)(\omega'^2 - m^2)^{1/2}} - \int_{-\infty}^{-m} \frac{\log|F(\omega')|\,d\omega'}{(\omega' - \omega)(\omega'^2 - m^2)^{1/2}}$$

$$+ \int_{-m}^m \frac{\delta(\omega')\,d\omega'}{(\omega' - \omega)(m^2 - \omega'^2)^{1/2}} \tag{7.38}$$

A few remarks should be made regarding the evaluation of the last integral in (7.38). If there are no unphysical cuts in the interval $-m < \omega < m$, so that the amplitude is purely real there, we have $\delta(\omega) = n\pi$ in that region, where n is an integer. The value of n is not in general constant, but can be specified as a function of ω once the positions of the zeros and poles of the amplitude are known. The analyticity of (7.35) requires that, as ω increases, n increases (decreases) by unity whenever ω passes through a simple pole (zero) of the

E*

amplitude. Using this property of $\delta(\omega)$, the integration over the region $-m < \omega < m$ can be performed analytically in closed form.

Dispersion relations of the type (7.38) are of special interest because they completely determine the amplitude in terms of its modulus above the thresholds of the s- and u-channels and the positions of its zeros and poles. This is of particular interest for non-forward scattering, when there is no simple method of experimentally measuring ReF and ImF individually.

7.5. Derivative dispersion relations

As we have already mentioned, a given dispersion relation can provide a consistency test of the input data used for its analysis if one requires that the predictions obtained from it should not depend on the energy at which it is evaluated. For example, one can use a dispersion relation to evaluate the residues of a scattering amplitude at its poles, which in turn are related to certain coupling constants; the calculated value of a particular coupling constant should then not depend on the detailed form of the dispersion relation which is used.

In practice one usually finds that, within the estimated statistical errors, the calculated values of a coupling constant or of some other parameter are indeed compatible with some constant, although the numerical results may suggest some variation with the energy at which a dispersion relation is evaluated. A marked variation of this kind must be viewed with suspicion, even if the total variation over some interval of energies is less than the width of the error corridor; this is so because the calculation makes use of a fixed set of data, so that the results obtained from a given dispersion relation for different values of the energy are actually strongly correlated, particularly for neighbouring energies.

Such considerations can be put on a more quantitative basis by considering so-called derivative dispersion relations.[7] By a derivative dispersion relation we mean a relation which is obtained when a given dispersion relation is solved algebraically for some physical quantity, such as the square of a coupling constant, in terms of all the remaining contributions and the result is then differentiated explicitly with respect to the energy at which the dispersion relation is evaluated or with respect to some other adjustable parameter appearing in the dispersion relation. The sum rule stating that the resulting expression for the derivative must actually vanish can then serve as a consistency test of the data.

Suppose, for example, that $X(\omega)$ represents the predicted value of the residue X at a pole of a scattering amplitude when a particular dispersion relation is evaluated at the energy ω. By differentiating explicitly the expression for $X(\omega)$ provided by the dispersion relation, another expression can be obtained for the derivative $dX(\omega)/d\omega$. Call this expression $X'(\omega)$. Then the consistency requirement is given by the sum rule $X'(\omega) = 0$.

Note that such a sum rule utilises the same input data as the original dispersion relation from which it is derived, but that it does not explicitly involve the value of X itself. The sum rule, even when evaluated at only a single energy, provides a non-trivial consistency test of the data, since it allows one to determine not only the numerical value of the quantity $dX(\omega)/d\omega$, but also the statistical error which is to be assigned to it.

This is in contrast with the analysis of the original dispersion relation, which provides no means of estimating this error. The analysis of a particular dispersion relation of the conventional type can reveal inconsistencies in the data only if it is evaluated over a sufficiently wide range of energies; this is not always possible in practice, for example because of the absence of good data on the real parts of the amplitudes.

In the case in which one differentiates with respect to the energy, the derivation of a derivative dispersion relation from an ordinary dispersion relation requires an explicit expression for the derivative of a principal-valued integral with respect to the position of the pole. Let us therefore turn to the problem of evaluating

$$g(\omega) = \frac{\mathrm{d}}{\mathrm{d}\omega} P \int_{\omega_1}^{\omega_2} \frac{f(\omega')\,\mathrm{d}\omega'}{\omega' - \omega} \qquad (7.39)$$

where $f(\omega)$ is a given function and $\omega_1 < \omega < \omega_2$ (if ω lies outside this range, so that the integral is non-singular, one can simply differentiate directly under the integral sign).

For this purpose we first define the function

$$G(\omega) = \int_{\omega_1}^{\omega_2} \frac{f(\omega')\,\mathrm{d}\omega'}{\omega' - \omega} \qquad (7.40)$$

for all complex ω such that $\mathrm{Im}\,\omega \neq 0$, where the integration runs just above the real axis. The function $G(\omega)$ can be seen to be analytic in the ω-plane, with a cut along the interval $\omega_1 \leqslant \omega \leqslant \omega_2$.

Now $g(\omega)$ is related to $G(\omega)$ as follows

$$g(\omega) = \frac{\mathrm{d}}{\mathrm{d}\omega} \lim_{\varepsilon \to 0} \left[\tfrac{1}{2}G(\omega - \mathrm{i}\varepsilon) + \tfrac{1}{2}G(\omega + \mathrm{i}\varepsilon) \right] \qquad (7.41\mathrm{a})$$

$$= \tfrac{1}{2} \lim_{\varepsilon \to 0} \frac{\mathrm{d}}{\mathrm{d}\omega} \left[G(\omega - \mathrm{i}\varepsilon) + G(\omega + \mathrm{i}\varepsilon) \right] \qquad (7.41\mathrm{b})$$

The analyticity of $G(\omega)$ is sufficient to justify the interchange of the order of the differential and limit operations in (7.41). For ω such that $\mathrm{Im}\,\omega \neq 0$, we have

$$\frac{\mathrm{d}}{\mathrm{d}\omega} G(\omega) = \int_{\omega_1}^{\omega_2} f(\omega') \frac{\mathrm{d}}{\mathrm{d}\omega}\left(\frac{1}{\omega' - \omega}\right) \mathrm{d}\omega' = -\int_{\omega_1}^{\omega_2} f(\omega') \frac{\mathrm{d}}{\mathrm{d}\omega'}\left(\frac{1}{\omega' - \omega}\right) \mathrm{d}\omega' \quad (7.42)$$

Integrating by parts, we find

$$\frac{d}{d\omega} G(\omega) = \frac{f(\omega_1)}{\omega_1 - \omega} - \frac{f(\omega_2)}{\omega_2 - \omega} + \int_{\omega_1}^{\omega_2} \frac{f'(\omega')\,d\omega'}{\omega' - \omega} \tag{7.43}$$

Thus, (7.41b) becomes

$$g(\omega) = \frac{f(\omega_1)}{\omega_1 - \omega} - \frac{f(\omega_2)}{\omega_2 - \omega} + P\int_{\omega_1}^{\omega_2} \frac{f'(\omega')\,d\omega'}{\omega' - \omega} \tag{7.44}$$

where $f'(\omega)$ is the derivative of the function $f(\omega)$. This is the required formula for the derivative of a principal-valued integral.

Using (7.44), the problem of evaluating the derivative of a principal-valued integral is reduced to the evaluation of another principal-valued integral. Once this result is available, it is a straightforward matter to obtain the derivative dispersion relations by differentiating an ordinary dispersion relation term by term. In particular, the derivatives of any non-singular integrals which occur can be found by differentiating explicitly under the integral sign.

It is worth pointing out some difficulties which may arise in the analysis of derivative dispersion relations that are obtained by differentiating conventional dispersion relations with respect to the energy. First, we recall that cusps show up in the scattering amplitude at each threshold, where the derivatives of both the real and imaginary parts may exhibit singularities. Although the resulting singular terms in a derivative dispersion relation must actually cancel at each threshold energy in order to give a finite value for the total derivative, it is convenient for practical purposes to test derivative sum rules at energies at which the amplitudes have a smooth behaviour. Because of the infinite derivative of the amplitude at each threshold cusp, it is also necessary to ensure that equation (7.44) is applied only over an interval $\omega_1 < \omega < \omega_2$ which contains no cusps.

A second difficulty in the analysis of derivative dispersion relations is associated with the fact that the derivatives of the real parts of the scattering amplitudes are relatively more sensitive to the higher partial waves than the amplitudes themselves. The small corrections due to higher partial waves are usually neglected in low-energy parametrisations of the amplitudes. This may have little bearing on the analysis of the ordinary dispersion relations, but it can become important for the derivative relations.

References

1. W. Gilbert, *Phys. Rev.*, **108** (1957), 1078
2. M. Restignoli and G. Violini, *Nuovo Cimento*, **69A** (1970), 691
3. S. L. Adler, *Phys. Rev.*, **137B** (1965), 1022
4. N. Zovko, *Phys. Lett.*, **23** (1966), 143

5. E. Ferrari and G. Violini, *Lettere al Nuovo Cimento*, **5** (1972), 1027
6. R. Odorico, *Nuovo Cimento*, **54A** (1968), 96
7. N. M. Queen, S. Leeman and F. E. Yeomans, *Nucl. Phys.*, **B11** (1969), 115

Further reading

A discussion of several applications of modified dispersion relations to KN scattering may be found in the reference below.

1. N. M. Queen, M. Restignoli and G. Violini, *Fortschritte der Physik*, **21** (1973), 569

CHAPTER 8

Regge theory

8.1. The Sommerfeld–Watson transformation

Scattering amplitudes may have poles in the energy variable, corresponding to bound states and resonances. Each such pole appears in one particular partial-wave amplitude. A familiar occurrence in potential theory for a scattering process involving two spinless particles is a sequence of poles at some energies W_0, W_1, ... corresponding to orbital angular momenta $l = 0, 1, \ldots$. These poles may conceivably have no relation to one another. However, the Regge idea is that they are different manifestations of the same thing, namely a single pole which moves continuously in the complex l-plane as the energy W varies, passing through physical (integral) values of l at certain energies W_l.

Regge[1] showed that in certain cases (namely, for superpositions of Yukawa potentials) the partial-wave amplitude $t_l(W)$ defined by

$$f(W, z) = \frac{1}{q} \sum_{l=0}^{\infty} (2l + 1) t_l(W) P_l(z) \tag{8.1}$$

where $z = \cos \theta$, may, at fixed W, be extended into a well-behaved analytic function of complex l and that moving poles may indeed occur. When regarded as a function of complex l, we shall write $t_l(W)$ as $t(l, W)$. There is some ambiguity in the analytic continuation of $t_l(W)$ from the physical values of l, since one can, for example, replace a given continuation $t(l, W)$ by one of the form $t(l, W) + g(l, W)\sin \pi l$, where g is some analytic function. However, a standard result known as Carlson's theorem implies that, if an interpolation $t(l, W)$ exists, with certain analyticity properties and a reasonable bound as $|l| \to \infty$, then it is unique.

The analytic continuation of $t_l(W)$ away from the positive integral values of l enables one to make the so-called Sommerfeld–Watson transformation of the summation in the partial-wave expansion (8.1) into a certain contour integration in the complex l-plane. As a first step, we show that

$$f(W, z) = \frac{i}{2q} \int_{C_1} (2l + 1)(\sin \pi l)^{-1} t(l, W) P_l(-z) \, dl \tag{8.2}$$

where C_1 is the contour shown in figure 8.1. The contour integral taken in the clockwise direction is equal to $-2\pi i$ times the sum of the residues at the poles enclosed by the contour. The integrand in (8.2) clearly has poles at all the integral values of l. The contour C_1 is chosen to exclude any poles (Regge poles) which

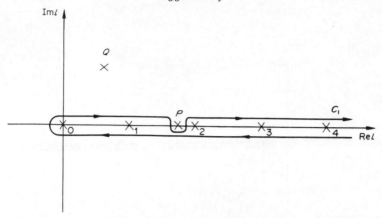

Figure 8.1. The first contour used in making the Sommerfeld–Watson transformation. The points P and Q show typical poles of $t(l, W)$.

arise from the function $t(l, W)$, such as P shown in the figure, so that it encloses only the poles at $l = 0, 1, 2, \ldots$ (we assume for simplicity that there are no poles of $t(l, W)$ at these integral values of l). Using the general relation

$$P_l(-z) = (-1)^l P_l(z) \tag{8.3}$$

the expression (8.2) is found to be equal to

$$f(W, z) = \frac{i}{2q} \sum_{l=0}^{\infty} (2l + 1) t_l(W)(-1)^l P_l(z)(-2\pi i) R_l \tag{8.4}$$

where R_l, the residue of the function $(\sin \pi x)^{-1}$ at $x = l$, is equal to $(-1)^l/\pi$. The summation (8.4) reduces to the original partial-wave expansion (8.1), as required.

The next step is to deform the contour C_1 into the larger contour C_2 shown in figure 8.2 (still excluding the poles of $t(l, W)$). This is possible because it is known from Regge's work that, for a wide class of potentials, the integrand of the contour integral is analytic for $\mathrm{Re}\, l > -\frac{1}{2}$, except for discrete poles. Furthermore, it turns out that, for suitable potentials, $t(l, W)$ approaches zero sufficiently rapidly for large $|l|$ that the integration over the semicircular part of the contour gives no contribution in the limit as its radius becomes infinite. In this case, the contour integral (8.2) becomes

$$f(W, z) = \frac{i}{2q} \int_{-(1/2)-i\infty}^{-(1/2)+i\infty} (2l + 1)(\sin \pi l)^{-1} t(l, W) P_l(-z)\, dl + \frac{i}{2q}(2\pi i) \sum_n T_n \tag{8.5}$$

where T_n ($n = 1, 2, \ldots$) is the residue of the integrand at one of the Regge poles, that is a pole of the function $t(l, W)$. The integral along the line $\mathrm{Re}\, l = -\frac{1}{2}$ is called the background term, for reasons which will become

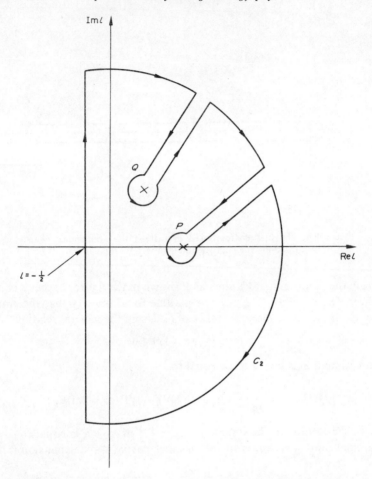

Figure 8.2. The second contour used in making the Sommerfeld–Watson transformation.

apparent later. If the poles of the function $t(l, W)$ are at $l = \alpha_n(W)$, with residues $\gamma_n(W)$, then

$$f(W, z) = \text{background} - \frac{\pi}{q} \sum_n (2\alpha_n + 1)(\sin \pi\alpha_n)^{-1}\gamma_n P_{\alpha_n}^{(-z)} \qquad (8.6)$$

This representation of $f(W, z)$ is valid in a much larger domain of the complex z-plane than the original partial-wave expansion, which converges only inside the Lehmann ellipse with foci at $z = \pm 1$. The new representation holds for all z except real values $|z| \geqslant 1$. This extension was in fact the original aim of Regge's work. Although the representation (8.6) has been derived rigorously only for potential scattering, we shall postulate that it is also valid relativistically and proceed to investigate its consequences.

To study the effects of moving poles in the complex l-plane, let us isolate the contribution from a single Regge pole

$$f(W, z) = -\frac{\pi}{q}(2\alpha + 1)(\sin \pi\alpha)^{-1}\gamma P_\alpha(-z) + \cdots \tag{8.7}$$

Projecting out from the partial-wave expansion the contribution to a particular partial-wave amplitude $t_l(W)$ (here l is some fixed integer), we get

$$t_l(W) = \tfrac{1}{2}q\int_{-1}^{1} f(W, z)P_l(z)\, \mathrm{d}z \tag{8.8}$$

Substituting (8.7) in (8.8), one finds

$$t_l(W) = -\frac{(2\alpha + 1)\gamma}{(\alpha - l)(\alpha + l + 1)} + \cdots \tag{8.9}$$

If $\alpha(W) \approx l$ for some range of energies W, the small denominator gives a large contribution which varies rapidly with W compared with the background term and the sum of the other Regge pole terms. Expanding $\alpha(W)$ in a Taylor series about W_0, the energy at which $\mathrm{Re}\,\alpha(W_0) = l$ (assuming that there is such an energy), we have

$$\alpha(W) = l + i\,\mathrm{Im}\,\alpha(W_0) + (W - W_0)[\mathrm{d}\,\mathrm{Re}\,\alpha(W)/\mathrm{d}W]_{W=W_0} + \cdots \tag{8.10}$$

It is assumed here that $\mathrm{Im}\,\alpha$ remains small in the relevant range of energies, so that higher terms in $\mathrm{Im}\,\alpha$ are not required in (8.10). Hence, for $W \approx W_0$

$$t_l(W) \approx \frac{K(W)}{(W - W_0)[\mathrm{d}\,\mathrm{Re}\,\alpha(W)/\mathrm{d}W]_{W=W_0} + i\,\mathrm{Im}\,\alpha(W_0)} \tag{8.11}$$

where $K(W)$ includes various energy-dependent factors (which are expected to be slowly varying in comparison with the denominator). Equation (8.11) corresponds to a Breit–Wigner resonance formula with a half-width

$$\tfrac{1}{2}\Gamma = [\mathrm{Im}\,\alpha(W_0)]/[\mathrm{d}\,\mathrm{Re}\,\alpha(W)/\mathrm{d}W]_{W=W_0} \tag{8.12}$$

For energies W below the physical threshold, it can be shown directly from the Schroedinger equation that $\mathrm{Im}\,\alpha(W) = 0$ and hence $\Gamma = 0$, which corresponds to a stable particle. Moreover, the residue at the pole is real in this case. On the other hand, when W is above threshold, it is found that $\mathrm{Im}\,\alpha(W) > 0$. Hence there is a resonance ($\Gamma > 0$) only if $\mathrm{d}\,\mathrm{Re}\,\alpha(W)/\mathrm{d}W > 0$. There is no resonance if $\mathrm{Re}\,\alpha(W)$ decreases through an integral value.

We say that a moving pole $\alpha(W)$ traces out a Regge trajectory. To show the various stable particles and resonances which lie on such a trajectory, it is customary to plot $\mathrm{Re}\,\alpha(W)$ as a function of W. Such a graph is known as a Chew–Frautschi plot. An example of a Chew–Frautschi plot for a trajectory connecting four resonances at energies W_0, W_1, W_2, W_3 is shown in figure 8.3. The sequence of resonances terminates at $l = 4$ in this example, since $\mathrm{Re}\,\alpha(W)$ then begins to decrease.

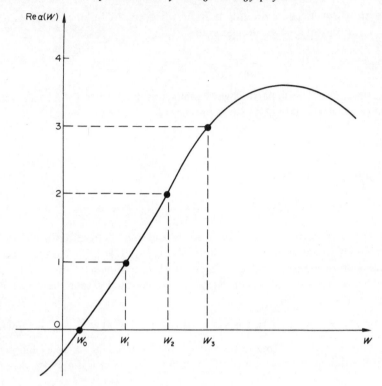

Figure 8.3. A typical Chew–Frautschi plot. The circles indicate the positions
of resonances.

8.2. Regge poles in potential scattering

Potential scattering models can give some insight into the properties of Regge
poles. The simplest exactly soluble model is that of the Coulomb potential
$V(r) = -e^2/r$, Subtracting off the infinite Coulomb phase, the exact S-matrix
for this case is found to be

$$2it(l, E) + 1 = \Gamma[l + 1 - ie^2(M/2E)^{1/2}]/\Gamma[l + 1 + ie^2(M/2E)^{1/2}] \quad (8.13)$$

The Γ-function has no zeros in the complex plane but has simple poles at 0,
$-1, -2, \ldots$. Therefore the only singularities in the l-plane in (8.13) are those
due to the poles of the numerator; these are the Regge poles.

The positions of the Regge poles $\alpha_n(E)$ $(n = 0, 1, 2, \ldots)$ are determined by the
condition

$$\alpha_n(E) + 1 - ie^2(M/2E)^{1/2} = -n \quad (n = 0, 1, 2, \ldots)$$

Thus, all the poles move in step with one another as E varies. By appropriately defining the physical sheet in the cut E-plane, we can choose

$$(-E)^{1/2} = +i|\sqrt{E}|$$

for $E > 0$. Then as $E \to -\infty$, we have $\alpha_n(E) \to -n - 1$, while $\alpha_n(E) \to +\infty$ as $E \to 0^-$. We find that $\alpha_n(E)$ crosses the physical values $l = 0, 1, 2, \ldots$ at the energies

$$E = -Me^4/2(l + n + 1)^2 \equiv E_{n,l}$$

which are just the energy levels of the Bohr atom. For positive energies, $\alpha_n(E) \to +i\infty$ as $E \to 0^+$, while $\alpha_n(E) \to -n - 1$ as $E \to +\infty$. The trajectory of $\alpha_n(E)$ is shown in figure 8.4 for both an attractive and a repulsive Coulomb potential. For a repulsive potential $V(r) = +e^2/r$, there are still an infinite number of Regge poles, but they give no bound states.

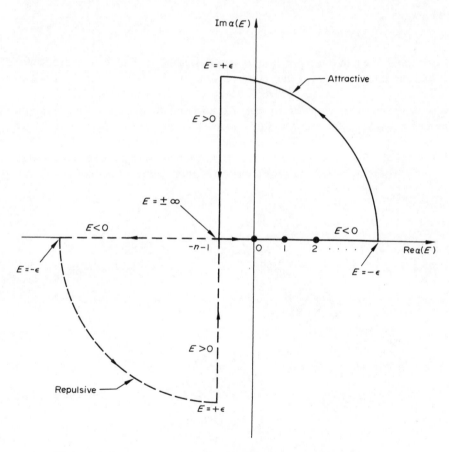

Figure 8.4. Trajectories for the Coulomb potential. The circles indicate the positions of bound states.

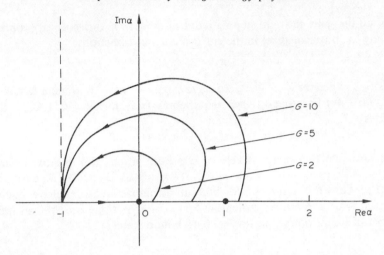

Figure 8.5. A Regge trajectory for the Yukawa potential.

Although the Coulomb potential is exactly soluble, it is of little relevance for the strong interactions. It is therefore of some interest to consider the Yukawa potential $V(r) = -Ge^{-r}/r$. There is no exact solution in closed form for this case, but Regge trajectories for the Yukawa potential have been computed numerically. In figure 8.5 we show the behaviour of one particular Regge trajectory as a function of the coupling parameter G. The associated Chew–Frautschi plot is given in figure 8.6. These trajectories, which turn around within the finite complex plane, are characteristic of short-range potentials in general.

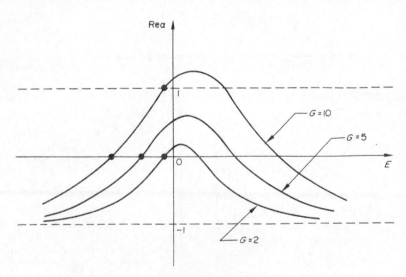

Figure 8.6. The Chew–Frautschi plot corresponding to figure 8.5.

So far we have not allowed for the existence of exchange forces. If exchange forces are present, the interaction may be different in states of even and odd l, so that there are two different analytic continuations, one starting from the physical partial-wave amplitudes of even l and one from those of odd l. We can allow for this possibility by splitting the amplitude f into its even and odd parts with respect to z and making the Sommerfeld–Watson transformation on each part separately.

This decomposition is accomplished by writing

$$P_l(z) = \tfrac{1}{2}[P_l(z) + P_l(-z)] + \tfrac{1}{2}[P_l(z) - P_l(-z)] \tag{8.14}$$

in the original partial-wave expansion (8.1). Since $P_l(z)$ is an even (odd) function of z for even (odd) integers l, the first term on the right-hand side of (8.14) vanishes for odd l, while the second vanishes for even l. After carrying out the Sommerfeld–Watson transformation, one finds Regge pole expansions for the even and odd parts of the amplitude separately. These expansions are identical to (8.6), but with the replacements

$$P_\alpha(-z) \to \tfrac{1}{2}[P_\alpha(-z) \pm P_\alpha(z)] \tag{8.15}$$

This expression has zeros when α passes through odd (even) integers l, if we choose the plus (minus) sign. This means that the Regge poles of each part of the amplitude lie on trajectories which give non-zero residues in the amplitude only at alternate crossings of integral values of l. We say that the trajectories corresponding to the plus (minus) sign in (8.15) have even (odd) signature.

8.3. Regge poles in high-energy scattering

Let us consider a two-body scattering process $A + B \to C + D$, which we call the s-channel. We shall show that under certain circumstances high-energy scattering in the s-channel is dominated by Regge poles in the crossed t-channel.

The kinematics will be characterised by the usual invariants s, t and u. We recall that in the s-channel the variable s is interpreted as the square of the c.m. energy W_s, while t is the momentum transfer variable; for the t-channel process $A + \bar{C} \to \bar{B} + D$, their roles are reversed. Assuming for simplicity that the particles are of equal mass m, we can express s and t in terms of t-channel quantities as follows

$$s = -2q_t^2(1 - \cos\theta_t) \tag{8.16}$$

$$t = W_t^2 = 4(q_t^2 + m^2) \tag{8.17}$$

We now wish to concentrate our attention upon the region of high-energy scattering in the s-channel ($s \gg m^2$) at small physical momentum transfers ($t \leqslant 0$). Since (8.16) and (8.17) imply that

$$z_t \equiv \cos\theta_t = (t - 4m^2 + 2s)/(t - 4m^2) \tag{8.18}$$

we conclude that, in terms of quantities appropriate for describing t-channel scattering, the kinematic region which we have selected corresponds to large (unphysical) values $|z_t| \gg 1$ and small t-channel energies W_t.

Let us consider the Regge representation of the scattering amplitude in the t-channel (since we shall apply crossing, we take the invariant amplitude A for this purpose)

$$A(W_t, z_t) = \text{background} - \frac{\pi W_t}{2q_t} \sum_n \frac{\gamma_n(2\alpha_n + 1)}{\sin \pi\alpha_n} \{\tfrac{1}{2}[P_{\alpha_n}(-z_t) \pm P_{\alpha_n}(z_t)]\} \quad (8.19)$$

where the $(\pm)$ sign depends on the signature of the Regge trajectory in question. We wish to consider the behaviour of the expansion (8.19) in the limit as $|z_t| \to \infty$ for fixed W_t. For this purpose, we exploit the fact that the Legendre functions have the property

$$P_\alpha(z) \sim \text{const } z^\alpha \qquad \text{as } |z| \to \infty \tag{8.20}$$

for any $\alpha > -\tfrac{1}{2}$ (the relevant values of α are real here, since the energy W_t lies below the t-channel threshold).

Regge showed that, for a superposition of Yukawa potentials, there are only a finite number of poles in the right-hand half of the complex l-plane. We shall assume that this property also holds for relativistic scattering. Then it follows from the property (8.20) that as $|z_t| \to \infty$ the amplitude $A(W_t, z_t)$ is dominated by a single Regge pole, namely the one with the largest value of α (the background term cannot give the dominant contribution, since it behaves like const $z_t^{-(1/2)}$).

We can now apply crossing to (8.19) to write down the asymptotic form of the s-channel amplitude as $s \to \infty$ at fixed t. Using (8.18) and (8.20), together with the fact that $(-s)^\alpha = \exp(-i\pi\alpha)s^\alpha$, we find from (8.19) the high-energy behaviour

$$A(s, t) \sim \beta(t)\{1 \pm \exp[-i\pi\alpha_1(t)]\}s^{\alpha_1(t)} \tag{8.21}$$

where $\alpha_1(t)$ (known as the trajectory function) is the position of the Regge pole which lies furthest to the right in the complex l-plane (the so-called leading pole). The quantity $\beta(t)$ (known as the residue function) contains the remaining t-dependent factors in the Regge pole term. The quantity in the curly brackets is sometimes called the signature factor.

It is worth pointing out that, at a particular value of t, the contribution from a Regge pole with trajectory function $\alpha(t)$ gives the same s-dependence as the contribution from the exchange of a particle whose spin is equal to $\alpha(t)$. In fact, we say that the Regge pole is exchanged in the t-channel.

A more accurate representation of the amplitude would be obtained by extending the sum over more Regge pole terms, if any, each term having a similar form. Such a representation is valid for scattering near the forward direction, that is for small $|t|$. Since scattering near the backward direction corresponds to small $|u|$, backward scattering at high energy is expected to be dominated by Regge poles in the u-channel in an analogous manner.

8.4. Basic properties of Regge poles

We shall now consider some elementary consequences of the one-pole model, equation (8.21), for high-energy scattering. The differential cross section for small $|t|$ is given by

$$\frac{d\sigma}{d\,|t|} \sim \frac{16\pi}{s^2} |A(s, t)|^2 \sim H(t)s^{2\alpha_1(t)-2} \tag{8.22}$$

for some function $H(t)$. As a first approximation, let us assume that the trajectory $\alpha_1(t)$ is a straight line (which is reasonable if we consider a sufficiently small interval in t). Then

$$\alpha_1(t) \approx \alpha_1(0) + t\alpha_1'(0) \tag{8.23}$$

so that

$$\frac{d\sigma}{d\,|t|} \sim H(t)s^{2\alpha_1(0)-2} \exp[2t\alpha_1'(0)\log s] \tag{8.24}$$

It is reasonable to suppose that the factor $H(t)$ is more slowly varying than the exponential. Then the one-pole model predicts an approximately exponential form for the diffraction peak at high energies, as is indeed observed experimentally. Moreover, the width of this peak is

$$\Delta t \sim [2\alpha_1'(0)\log s]^{-1} \tag{8.25}$$

Thus, we have the prediction that the width of the diffraction peak shrinks logarithmically as the energy increases. This corresponds to the somewhat surprising result that the semi-classical interaction radius increases logarithmically with energy. There was great excitement among Regge pole theorists when it was found experimentally that pp scattering has a shrinking diffraction peak. However, it was later discovered that the widths of the $\pi^\pm p$ peaks are approximately constant, while the $\bar{p}p$ peak actually expands with energy. This does not necessarily mean that Regge pole theory is wrong, but possibly only that the one-pole model is still inadequate at the energies which are currently accessible. In fact, it is easy to show that several Regge poles may combine in such a way that they produce an expanding diffraction peak in a restricted energy range before the asymptotic behaviour actually sets in.

The total cross section in the one-pole model is

$$\sigma(s) \sim (16\pi/s)\mathrm{Im}A(s, 0) \sim \mathrm{const}\ s^{\alpha_1(0)-1} \tag{8.26}$$

In order for $\sigma(s)$ to satisfy the Froissart bound $\sigma(s) \leqslant \mathrm{const}(\log s)^2$, the leading trajectory $\alpha_1(t)$ must have an intercept at $t = 0$ satisfying $\alpha_1(0) \leqslant 1$. If all total cross sections tend to constant non-zero limits at high energies, as has traditionally been assumed to be the case on the basis of the conventional interpretation of the experimental data, then each elastic forward scattering amplitude must be dominated by a single trajectory $\alpha_P(t)$ (the so-called Pomeranchuk trajectory) such that

$$\alpha_P(0) = 1 \qquad (8.27)$$

It is an attractive hypothesis that there is some saturation principle which makes the strong interactions as strong as possible, so that this bound is actually attained.

We note also that, if the Pomeranchuk trajectory exists, each elastic scattering cross section satisfies

$$\left[\frac{\mathrm{d}\sigma}{\mathrm{d}\,|t|}\right]_{t=0} \to \text{const} \qquad \text{as } s \to \infty \qquad (8.28)$$

Since the Pomeranchuk trajectory controls all forward elastic scattering amplitudes, it must be associated with the quantum numbers of the vacuum. If all other trajectories lie below the Pomeranchuk trajectory at $t = 0$, then all cross sections which do not have a contribution from the Pomeranchuk trajectory (for example, inelastic ones involving the exchange of any quantum numbers) must vanish as $s \to \infty$. On the other hand, if the Pomeranchuk trajectory contributes to a particular inelastic reaction, its cross section should remain constant as $s \to \infty$.

The existence of the Pomeranchuk trajectory can explain in a neat way not only the asymptotic behaviour of σ and $\mathrm{d}\sigma/\mathrm{d}\,|t|$ for elastic scattering processes, but also the Pomeranchuk theorem. This follows from the fact that the Pomeranchuk pole in the t-channel gives equal contributions to the amplitude for a given process $A + B \to A + B$ (s-channel) and its corresponding crossed processes $\bar{A} + B \to \bar{A} + B$ (u-channel).

To see why these contributions are equal, let us refer to the diagram of figure 8.7, in which the alternative labels represent the s-channel and u-channel processes when the diagram is read from left to right. For either alternative, the

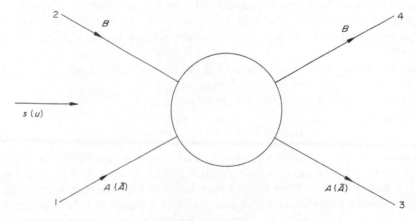

Figure 8.7. Diagram for considering the Pomeranchuk contribution in the t-channel.

same diagram, when read from top to bottom, represents the crossed *t*-channel process $\bar{B} + B \to \bar{A} + A$. Now the *t*-channel c.m. scattering angle θ_t is defined, for example, as the angle between the incoming particle 2 and the outgoing particle 1. For the two alternatives, particle 1 corresponds to the A and $\bar{A}$, which are in fact moving in opposite directions in the c.m.s. in the final state of the reaction $\bar{B} + B \to \bar{A} + A$.

This means that the contribution which a *t*-channel Regge pole makes to the *u*-channel is the same as the contribution which it makes to the *s*-channel, except that $\cos \theta_t$ must be replaced by $-\cos \theta_t$. We recall that, if the Regge pole in question is assumed to have positive (negative) signature, then its contribution is symmetric (antisymmetric) in $\cos \theta_t$. In other words, a Regge pole of positive (negative) signature in the *t*-channel gives contributions to the *s*-channel and *u*-channel of the same (opposite) sign. This general result is known as the line-reversal property of Regge poles.

In the special case of the Pomeranchuk pole, the equality of the total cross sections required by the Pomeranchuk theorem follows at once if it is assumed that this pole has positive signature. In fact, in this case the *s*-channel and *u*-channel processes must also have the same forward values of $d\sigma/d|t|$. The signature of the Pomeranchuk pole cannot be negative, since this would lead to a negative imaginary part for either the *s*-channel or *u*-channel forward amplitude at asymptotic energies, which would in turn imply a negative cross section.

Another consequence of the positive signature of the Pomeranchuk trajectory is that the point $t = 0$ at which $\alpha_P(t) = 1$ does not correspond to a (massless) particle, since particles on a positive-signature trajectory must have even values of spin.

The Regge pole model also makes definite predictions about the phases of amplitudes at high energy. Consider, for example, an elastic scattering amplitude, dominated by the Pomeranchuk pole at high energy. It has the asymptotic form

$$A(s, t) \sim B(t)[\sin \pi\alpha_P(t)]^{-1}\{1 + \exp[-i\pi\alpha_P(t)]\}s^{\alpha_P(t)} \qquad (8.29)$$

where $B(t)$ is a certain function of *t*. We have explicitly extracted the factor $\sin \pi\alpha_P(t)$ from the denominator of (8.19), since this quantity and the factor in the curly brackets in (8.29) both tend to zero as $t \to 0$ in such a way that their ratio has a finite limit. It is easy to verify that

$$\lim_{t \to 0} \frac{1 + \exp[-i\pi\alpha_P(t)]}{\sin \pi\alpha_P(t)} = -i$$

This means that the Pomeranchuk pole gives a purely imaginary contribution to the forward scattering amplitude, so that

$$\frac{\text{Re}A(s, 0)}{\text{Im}A(s, 0)} \to 0 \qquad \text{as } s \to \infty$$

This is a consequence of the positive signature of the Pomeranchuk trajectory; if it had negative signature, the amplitude $A(s, 0)$ would become predominantly real as $s \to \infty$.

Another fundamental property of Regge poles is the condition of factorisation. This means that, when a Regge pole is exchanged in some process, the residue function can be written as a product of two factors, one characteristic of each vertex of an exchange diagram, exactly as for the exchange of an ordinary particle. These two factors can be interpreted as the couplings of the Regge pole to the initial and final states in the t-channel. This restriction leads to definite relations among different processes in which the same Regge pole can be exchanged.

As an example, factorisation requires that the contributions of a given Regge pole to the forward amplitudes for $\pi\pi$, πN and NN scattering must be of the form (see 8.21)

$$F(\pi\pi) = \beta_\pi^2 \xi s^\alpha$$

$$F(\pi N) = \beta_\pi \beta_N \xi s^\alpha$$

$$F(NN) = \beta_N^2 \xi s^\alpha$$

where β_π and β_N are the couplings of the Regge pole at the pion and nucleon vertices, ξ is the signature factor, and α is the trajectory function at $t = 0$. Since all three scattering processes are dominated asymptotically by a single pole (the Pomeranchuk pole), the application of the optical theorem predicts a simple relation among their total cross sections at high energy

$$\sigma(\pi\pi)\sigma(NN) = \sigma^2(\pi N) \tag{8.30}$$

8.5. Simple tests of the Regge pole model

Extensive fits to all the high-energy scattering data for $\pi^\pm p$ and $K^\pm p$ processes have been made within the framework of Regge pole theory. We shall consider the analysis of these processes in greater detail in a subsequent section. Here we merely point out that a minimum of three Regge poles, the P, P' and ρ, are required to explain the $\pi^\pm p$ data, while for $K^\pm p$ scattering, where exchanges of additional quantum numbers are allowed, two more Regge poles, the ω and A_2, are needed (the ρ, ω and A_2 are labelled by the lowest-lying particles on the corresponding trajectories). The parity P, isospin I, signature τ, and approximate values of the $t = 0$ intercepts $\alpha(0)$ of the trajectories of these Regge poles are shown in Table 8.1.

The existence of the secondary Regge pole P' with the vacuum quantum numbers was first predicted by Igi,[2] using a forward dispersion relation for the sum of the $\pi^\pm p$ amplitudes. He noted that this combination of amplitudes, after subtracting from it the contribution of the Pomeranchuk pole, would vanish asymptotically sufficiently fast to satisfy an unsubtracted dispersion relation, provided that no other contributing trajectories have intercepts $\alpha(0) \geqslant 0$.

TABLE 8.1
Properties of the Regge poles required to explain the main features of
$\pi^{\pm}p$ and $K^{\pm}p$ scattering at high energies

Poles	P	I	τ	$\alpha(0)$
P, P'	$+$	0	$+$	$1\cdot0, \sim0\cdot5$
ρ	$-$	1	$-$	$\sim0\cdot6$
ω	$-$	0	$-$	$\sim0\cdot5$
A_2	$+$	1	$+$	$\sim0\cdot3$

This hypothesis is found to be violated, but the discrepancy can be removed by allowing for a P' with intercept $\alpha(0) \approx 0\cdot5$.

Elastic scattering processes such as $\pi^{\pm}p$ and $K^{\pm}p$ scattering require the exchange of so many Regge poles that they do not provide very conclusive tests of the Regge pole model. Elastic NN and $\bar{N}N$ scattering are more complex to analyse than the meson–nucleon processes, since the former have five independent amplitudes, because of spin. To get neat tests of the Regge pole model, it is useful to study reactions in which only particular quantum numbers can be exchanged, thus restricting the number of contributing Regge poles.

A good test is provided by the charge-exchange process $\pi^- + p \to \pi^0 + n$, for which data exist up to rather high energies. Here the only known Regge pole with the appropriate t-channel quantum numbers is the ρ. As predicted by the one-pole model, the diffraction peak is found to shrink for this process. Moreover, the trajectory function $\alpha_\rho(t)$ for small $t < 0$ can be determined directly from the scattering data by analysing the s-dependence of $d\sigma/d|t|$ for fixed t in terms of a power law according to (8.22). The resulting points are found to give approximately a straight line on a Chew–Frautschi plot (see figure 8.8) and, moreover, extrapolate with good accuracy to the correct position of the ρ meson at $\text{Re}\alpha_\rho = 1$.

Another striking prediction of the one-pole model concerning the phase of the amplitude is confirmed experimentally. Since $\alpha_\rho(0) \approx \frac{1}{2}$, the forward scattering amplitude can be approximated by

$$F(s, 0) \sim C(s)[1 - \exp(-\tfrac{1}{2}i\pi)] = C(s)[1 + i]$$

where $C(s)$ is real. This means that the real and imaginary parts of $F(s, 0)$ are approximately equal. It is indeed found experimentally that $d\sigma/d|t|$ at $t = 0$ is about twice the optical limit (that is, the imaginary part of the forward charge-exchange amplitude found by applying the optical theorem to $\pi^{\pm}p$ elastic scattering and using charge independence).

Still another possible application of the one-pole model is to the process $\pi^- + p \to \eta^0 + n$, for which data are available up to high energies. In this case, the A_2 is the only Regge pole which is known to contribute. Shrinking of the diffraction peak is again observed. The trajectory function determined from the scattering data for $t < 0$ appears to have some curvature in this case, but is consistent with an extrapolation to the position of the A_2 meson at $\text{Re}\alpha = 2$.

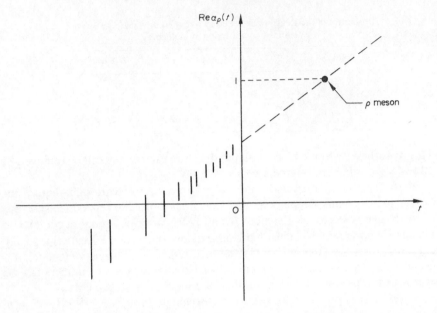

Figure 8.8. The Chew–Frautschi plot for the ρ Regge trajectory.

Although there is again a definite prediction of the phase of the amplitude, it cannot be tested experimentally in a simple way because there is no optical theorem for this process.

The next simplest tests of the Regge pole model are perhaps the charge-exchange reactions $K^+ + n \rightarrow K^0 + p$ and $\bar{K} + p \rightarrow \bar{K}^0 + n$, where both ρ and A_2 are allowed in the t-channel. The predictions for these processes (see section 8.6) are therefore not independent of those for the two cases considered above and provide a valuable consistency check.

8.6. The Regge pole model for πN and KN scattering

Two complications are encountered in constructing Regge pole models for πN and KN scattering: first, several different Regge poles can be exchanged; and second, because of the non-zero spin of the nucleon, there are two independent amplitudes for each specific scattering process. We shall consider these points in turn.

As we have already pointed out, a minimum of three Regge poles, the P, P' and ρ, are required for the description of πN scattering processes at high energy. Essentially, the P would be needed to give (identical) non-zero values of the $\pi^\pm p$ total cross sections at asymptotic energies, while the P' and ρ are required to explain the observed energy variation of the sum and difference of these cross sections. Assuming that no further Regge poles are required, the $\pi^\pm p$ elastic scattering amplitudes take the form

$$F(\pi^{\pm}p) = g_P + g_{P'} \pm g_{\rho} \qquad (8.31)$$

where g_i is the contribution of the Regge pole i to the π^+p scattering amplitude. The signs of the corresponding contributions to the π^-p scattering amplitude are established by applying the line-reversal property of Regge poles, using the signatures τ_i listed in Table 8.1. The fact that the plus sign for g_{ρ} in (8.31) is associated with $F(\pi^+p)$ instead of $F(\pi^-p)$ is purely conventional; the opposite choice is also often adopted in Regge pole phenomenology. Although we are neglecting the complications due to the non-zero spin of the nucleon at this stage, relations such as (8.31) are applicable, for example, to the forward scattering amplitudes.

It follows from charge independence that the amplitude for the charge-exchange process $\pi^- + p \to \pi^0 + n$ is given by

$$F_{c.e}(\pi N) = [F(\pi^+p) - F(\pi^-p)]/\sqrt{2} \qquad (8.32)$$

It is clear from (8.31) and (8.32) that, as already mentioned in section 8.5, the amplitude depends only on the ρ pole.

The description of KN and $\bar{K}N$ scattering is more complicated because of the greater number of contributing Regge poles. The amplitudes for elastic $K^{\pm}p$ and $K^{\pm}n$ scattering are given by

$$F(K^{\pm}p) = h_P + h_{P'} \pm h_{\omega} \pm h_{\rho} + h_{A_2} \qquad (8.33a)$$

$$F(K^{\pm}n) = h_P + h_{P'} \pm h_{\omega} \mp h_{\rho} - h_{A_2} \qquad (8.33b)$$

where, according to our sign convention, the contribution of the Regge pole i to the K^+p scattering amplitude is $+h_i$.

The relation between the upper and lower signs in each of the equations (8.33a) and (8.33b) follows from the line-reversal property, as in the case of πN scattering. The relation between the signs of (8.33a) and the corresponding signs of (8.33b), on the other hand, can be established by charge independence. To see the origin of this relation, consider, for example, the t-channel processes corresponding to elastic K^+p and K^+n scattering, namely $K^+ + K^- \to \bar{p} + p$ and $K^+ + K^- \to \bar{n} + n$, respectively, whose amplitudes we shall denote by F_p and F_n. It turns out that

$$F_p = \tfrac{1}{2}(F^{(0)} + F^{(1)}) \qquad (8.34a)$$

$$F_n = \tfrac{1}{2}(F^{(0)} - F^{(1)}) \qquad (8.34b)$$

where $F^{(I)}$ is the amplitude for the process $K + \bar{K} \to \bar{N} + N$ for isospin I. Equations (8.34) show that t-channel exchanges with $I = 0$ (P, P' and ω) give identical contributions to F_p and F_n, whereas those with $I = 1$ (ρ and A_2) give contributions with opposite signs.

For those poles which are exchanged in both πN and KN scattering, the contributions g_i and h_i involve the same trajectory functions $\alpha_i(t)$, but may of course have different residue functions $\beta_i(t)$, corresponding to different couplings of the Regge poles in question to the $\pi\pi$ and $\bar{K}K$ vertices. Consequently, $h_i(s, t) = q(t)g_i(s, t)$, where $q(t)$ is a t-dependent factor depending on the ratio of the two residue functions.

The KN and $\bar{K}N$ charge-exchange reactions can be discussed in analogy with the πN charge-exchange reaction. Let us denote the amplitudes for the processes $K^+ + n \to K^0 + p$ and $K^- + p \to \bar{K}^0 + n$ by $F_{c.e.}(KN)$ and $F_{c.e.}(\bar{K}N)$, respectively. Charge independence implies that

$$F_{c.e.}(KN) = F(K^+p) - F(K^+n) \tag{8.35a}$$

$$F_{c.e.}(\bar{K}N) = F(K^-p) - F(K^-n) \tag{8.35b}$$

By virtue of (8.33)

$$F_{c.e.}(KN) = 2(h_{A_2} + h_\rho) \tag{8.36a}$$

$$F_{c.e.}(\bar{K}N) = 2(h_{A_2} - h_\rho) \tag{8.36b}$$

Equations (8.36) lead to very simple predictions for the KN and $\bar{K}N$ charge-exchange reactions if we adopt the so-called strong form of exchange degeneracy for the A_2 and ρ trajectories (see section 8.7), which requires both a common trajectory function $\alpha(t)$ and a common residue function $\pm\beta(t)$ for these two trajectories (the sign of the residue function depends on the scattering process in question). In this case, the A_2 and ρ contributions to (8.36) have the form

$$h_{A_2}(s, t) = \beta(t)\{1 + \exp[-i\pi\alpha(t)]\}s^{\alpha(t)} \tag{8.37a}$$

$$h_\rho(s, t) = \beta(t)\{1 - \exp[-i\pi\alpha(t)]\}s^{\alpha(t)} \tag{8.37b}$$

so that

$$F_{c.e.}(KN) = 4\beta(t)s^{\alpha(t)} \tag{8.38a}$$

$$F_{c.e.}(\bar{K}N) = 4\beta(t)s^{\alpha(t)} \exp[-i\pi\alpha(t)] \tag{8.38b}$$

Equation (8.38a) shows that the KN charge-exchange amplitude is expected to be purely real, for $t < 0$ as well as $t = 0$. In particular, the differential cross section in the forward direction is expected to be much greater than the optical value (the value which takes into account only the imaginary part of the amplitude $F_{c.e.}(KN)$ obtained by applying the optical theorem to K^+p and K^+n elastic scattering and making use of charge independence).

On the other hand, since $\alpha(0) \approx \frac{1}{2}$, (8.38b) shows that $F_{c.e.}(\bar{K}N)$ is predominantly imaginary at $t = 0$. This means that the differential cross section for $\bar{K}N$ charge exchange in the forward direction should be approximately equal to the optical value. These predictions are confirmed experimentally.

We next consider the complications arising from the non-zero spin of the nucleon. It is conventional to work with the amplitudes A' and B, where

$$A' = A + \frac{\omega + t/4M}{1 - t/4M^2} B \tag{8.39}$$

Here A and B are the invariant amplitudes introduced in chapter 5, M is the nucleon mass, and the rest of the notation is standard. In terms of these amplitudes, the differential cross section $d\sigma/d|t|$, total cross section σ and polarisation P are given by

$$\frac{d\sigma}{d|t|} = \frac{1}{\pi s}\left(\frac{M}{4q}\right)^2\left[\left(1 - \frac{t}{4M^2}\right)|A'|^2 + \frac{t}{4M^2}\left(\frac{k^2 - st/4M^2}{1 - t/4M^2}\right)|B|^2\right] \quad (8.40)$$

$$\sigma = \frac{1}{k}\text{Im}[A']_{t=0} \quad (8.41)$$

$$\left(\frac{d\sigma}{d|t|}\right)P = -\frac{\sin\theta}{16\pi\sqrt{s}}\text{Im}(A'B^*) \quad (8.42)$$

To obtain a Regge pole representation for the amplitudes A' and B, one assumes that the partial-wave amplitudes in the t-channel can be analytically continued in a suitable manner into the complex j-plane. After applying the Sommerfeld–Watson transformation to each amplitude, we find Regge pole contributions of the form

$$A'(s, t) = C(t)\{1 \pm \exp[-i\pi\alpha(t)]\}s^{\alpha(t)} \quad (8.43a)$$

$$B(s, t) = D(t)\alpha(t)\{1 \pm \exp[-i\pi\alpha(t)]\}s^{\alpha(t)-1} \quad (8.43b)$$

The additional factor $\alpha(t)$ appears for the following reason. The structure of the partial-wave expansions of the t-channel amplitudes from which A' and B are obtained by crossing is such that the Regge form of A' involves the limit of $P_\alpha(-\cos\theta_t)$, while B involves the limit of $P'_\alpha(-\cos\theta_t)$. The former leads to the energy dependence s^α as $s \to \infty$, as in the case of spinless particles. The latter gives

$$\frac{dP_\alpha(-\cos\theta_t)}{d(\cos\theta_t)} \sim \text{const}\frac{d}{ds}s^\alpha = \text{const }\alpha s^{\alpha-1}$$

The effect of this lower power of s is compensated by the higher power of s ($k^2 \sim s^2$) in the coefficient of $|B^2|$ in the expression for $d\sigma/d|t|$. This means that the contributions of A' and B actually have the same s-dependence. Note that the A' and B contributions are also required to have the same phase.

We can now write down the asymptotic forms of (8.40), (8.41) and (8.42) predicted by the simple Regge pole model. If $\alpha_1(t)$ and $\alpha_2(t)$ are the two leading trajectories ($\alpha_1 > \alpha_2$), then

$$\frac{d\sigma}{d|t|}(s, t) \sim \text{const }G(t)s^{2\alpha_1(t)-2} \quad (8.44)$$

$$\sigma(s) \sim \text{const }s^{\alpha_1(0)-1} \quad (8.45)$$

$$P(s, t) \sim \text{const }H(t)s^{\alpha_2(t)-\alpha_1(t)} \quad (8.46)$$

Note that a *single* Regge pole contribution would give $P = 0$, since A' and B have the same phase, so that $\text{Im}(A'B^*) = 0$ in (8.42). Empirically, a non-zero polarisation is found at quite high energies, even for the πN charge-exchange reaction, in which only the ρ quantum numbers can be exchanged in the t-channel. This is generally interpreted as evidence for additional Regge singularities with the quantum numbers of the ρ, for example a secondary (ρ') pole. It turns out that the polarisation may be much more sensitive to such a secondary ρ' pole with a relatively small value of $\alpha_2(t)$ than the cross sections. Thus, the observed non-vanishing polarisation is not incompatible with the fact that the remaining data appear to require only a single ρ pole.

8.7. Regge trajectories and residues

In this section we shall consider several features of the t-dependence of the Regge pole trajectories and residues.

First of all, we note that the trajectories can be classified into two distinct groups with rather different properties: the meson trajectories such as those discussed in the preceding sections, and the baryon trajectories.

We begin with the meson trajectories. It is generally assumed that the trajectory function $\alpha(t)$ satisfies a dispersion relation, and it can be shown that under certain conditions its only singularity is the right-hand cut above the t-channel threshold. The experimental evidence on the spectrum of particles and resonances indicates a remarkable degree of linearity of the Regge trajectories for both mesons and baryons. To allow for the possibility that the trajectories continue to rise indefinitely, as is sometimes conjectured, one can write a dispersion relation for the function $\alpha(t)/t^2$, which takes the form

$$\text{Re}\,\alpha(t) = \alpha(0) + \alpha'(0)t + \frac{t^2}{\pi} \int_{t_0}^{\infty} \frac{\text{Im}\,\alpha(t')\,dt'}{t'^2(t' - t)} \tag{8.47}$$

This is equivalent to making a double subtraction at $t = 0$. Note that the dispersion relation implies that $\text{Re}\,\alpha(t)$ cannot be exactly linear in t.

So far we have considered only meson trajectories. Baryon trajectories in the u-channel are important for the description of backward meson–nucleon scattering, and for this reason we shall employ the variable u instead of t for their description.

Baryon trajectories differ in several important respects from the meson trajectories. Whereas the physical states on the meson trajectories correspond to integral values of the spin J, the physical states on the baryon trajectories have half-integral values of J. Let us now consider, for example, the N^* trajectories containing pion–nucleon resonances. For each value of l in the πN system, the total angular momentum can have either of the two values $j = l \pm \frac{1}{2}$. Since the interaction will in general be different in the two sets of states (corresponding to the presence of a spin-orbit term in potential theory), we must allow for the possibility of different Regge poles of the partial-wave amplitudes $f_{l\pm}$.

It turns out that for certain purposes it is more appropriate to use the variable $W = \sqrt{u}$ for the baryon trajectories than u itself. It can be shown that the baryon partial-wave amplitudes satisfy the so-called MacDowell symmetry property[3]

$$f_{l+}(W) = -f_{(l+1)-}(-W) \tag{8.48}$$

which states that two partial-wave amplitudes with the same j but opposite parities transform into one another when the energy changes sign. This means that a Regge pole in f_{l+} at $\alpha(W)$ would also be a Regge pole in $f_{(l+1)-}$ at $\alpha(-W)$. Since the trajectories on the Chew–Frautschi plot are approximately linear, so that to first order α depends only on $u = W^2$, the baryons occur in parity doublets having approximately the same mass. The trajectories coincide in pairs at $u = 0$. The trajectory functions $\alpha(u)$ are found to be complex in general for $u < 0$, the values of $\alpha(u)$ for the pairs of trajectories being complex conjugates.

It should be mentioned that, as a consequence of the occurrence of pairs of baryon Regge trajectories, there is no analogue of the prediction of the one-pole model (section 8.6) that the polarisation vanishes. In fact, an appreciable polarisation is predicted for backward πN scattering.

For baryon trajectories, the dispersion relation analogous to (8.47) must be written in the variable $W = \sqrt{u}$, since the trajectory function is predicted to be analytic in this variable. There are then two contributing dispersion integrals, corresponding to both positive and negative values of W.

We shall now make a few observations about the general characteristics of the Regge trajectories which are found experimentally. The trajectory functions can be studied experimentally in two independent ways by examining the spectrum of particles and resonances, which gives direct information on the region $t > 0$ (or $u > 0$ in the case of baryon trajectories) of the Chew–Frautschi plot, and by analysing high-energy data for scattering processes which are described by the exchange of Regge poles, in order to investigate the region $t < 0$. As we have seen in section 8.5, the trajectory functions for $t < 0$, when they can be determined experimentally, extrapolate correctly to the lowest-lying physical states in the region $t > 0$.

A general feature of the known trajectories is that all of them (with the possible exception of the Pomeranchuk trajectory) have slopes of the same order of magnitude, namely $d\alpha/dt \approx 1$ GeV^{-2}; this is true for both meson and baryon trajectories.

For unequal-mass kinematics, there are theoretical reasons to expect that, for any particular trajectory $\alpha(t)$ which contributes to the scattering amplitude, there must be another trajectory $\alpha_1(t)$, known as a daughter trajectory, which has the opposite signature and the property $\alpha_1(0) = \alpha(0) - 1$. Since each daughter trajectory in turn has its own daughter, an infinite sequence of such trajectories is predicted. It is not known how the daughter trajectories should behave for $t \neq 0$, and in fact there seems to be little empirical evidence for any resonances contained on such trajectories.

The nature of the Pomeranchuk trajectory has been a subject of much speculation. If the Pomeranchuk trajectory were roughly parallel to the others, we would expect a $J = 2$ particle with the vacuum quantum numbers and a mass of the order of 1 GeV. The identification of the Pomeranchuk trajectory with such a particle is subject to some ambiguity. Moreover, analyses of elastic scattering data indicate that the slope of the Pomeranchuk trajectory in the region $t < 0$ may be much smaller than the common slope of the other trajectories. Arguments have also been put forward that the Pomeranchuk singularity may not be a Regge pole at all, but instead some more complicated type of singularity.

Another remarkable feature of the known trajectories is that certain pairs of trajectories having the same quantum numbers but opposite signature and parity, such as the ρ and A_2, appear to be practically coincident. Thus, the A_2 meson ($J^P = 2^+$, $M^2 = 1.7$ GeV^2) lies almost exactly on the line joining the first two physical states on the ρ trajectory, namely the ρ meson ($J^P = 1^-$, $M^2 = 0.6$ GeV^2) and the g meson ($J^P = 3^-$, $M^2 = 2.8$ GeV^2).

Such a degeneracy would arise from the vanishing of the exchange forces, which contribute differently to the scattering states with even and odd values of l. There are, in fact, grounds for expecting this situation to occur. Thus, the exchange forces in the baryon–antibaryon interaction are generated by dibaryon exchanges and are presumably weaker than the direct forces corresponding to meson exchanges. Likewise, the exchange forces in $K\bar{K}$ interactions are generated by strangeness-2 mesons and should be weaker than the direct forces generated by non-strange mesons. Because of this, we would expect exchange degeneracy to hold in a case like KN scattering.

Now if exchange degeneracy holds for a particular reaction, the trajectories must also be degenerate in any other reaction to which they contribute, although the residues need not in general be degenerate. One often uses the term weak exchange degeneracy to indicate the degeneracy of only the trajectories, and strong exchange degeneracy for the case when both the trajectories and the residues are degenerate. In the case of KN scattering, for example, there is an indication of the validity of strong exchange degeneracy from the flatness of the K^+N total cross sections over a wide energy range, which can be attributed to cancellations of the ρ-A_2 and P'-ω contributions.

Symmetry considerations can imply certain definite relations between different Regge pole residues. For example, since the pion and kaon belong to the same $SU(3)$ multiplet, there is a definite relationship between the $\pi\pi\rho$ and $K\bar{K}\rho$ vertices, which turns out to be

$$\beta_{K\bar{K}\rho} = \tfrac{1}{2}\beta_{\pi\pi\rho} \tag{8.49a}$$

For the same reasons, one also finds

$$\beta_{K\bar{K}A_2} = (\tfrac{3}{2})^{1/2}\beta_{\pi\eta A_2} \tag{8.49b}$$

The relations (8.49) lead directly to a relation between the four reactions

$$\pi^- + p \to \pi^0 + n, \qquad \pi^- + p \to \eta + n, \qquad K^- + p \to \bar{K}^0 + n$$

and $K^- + p \to \eta + \Lambda$, which depend only on ρ and A_2 exchanges. This relation can be tested experimentally and is found to be well satisfied.

We shall now consider some characteristics of the t-dependence of the residue functions. We first point out that certain Regge terms are forced to vanish when the trajectory functions $\alpha(t)$ pass through special values. Consider, for example, the amplitudes A' and B for πN scattering, whose Regge pole contributions are given by (8.43). We see from (8.43b) that the contribution to B from a given Regge pole vanishes when t is such that $\alpha(t) = 0$. Since the πN charge-exchange process is dominated by exchange of the ρ Regge pole, this effect shows up as a dip in the differential cross section for this process near the value of t at which $\alpha_\rho(t) = 0$.

Recalling that there is a factor $(\sin \pi\alpha)^{-1}$ in the Regge pole formula (see, for example, equation 8.19), we observe that a positive-signature amplitude contains a divergent factor when $\alpha(t) = 0$. A divergence of the amplitude for $t < 0$ would be unacceptable, since it would correspond to a t-channel particle with mass squared $m^2 < 0$, that is a 'ghost' state. To eliminate this ghost, the coefficient $C(t)$ in (8.43a) must have a zero at the appropriate value of t.

A further development of this discussion concerns the change of helicity associated with the exchange of a Regge pole at $\alpha(t) = 0$. We define the transition at each vertex of the pole and the external particles as 'sense' ('nonsense') if the helicity change between the external particles is zero (non-zero). Thus, depending on the helicity change at each of the two vertices, three types of Regge amplitudes exist: sense–sense, sense–nonsense and nonsense–nonsense. Let these amplitudes be denoted by A_{ss}, A_{sn} and A_{nn} respectively.

It can be shown that near $\alpha = 0$ these amplitudes behave like

$$A_{ss} \sim \beta_{ss}\xi s^\alpha \tag{8.50a}$$

$$A_{sn} \sim \alpha^{1/2}\beta_{sn}\xi s^\alpha \tag{8.50b}$$

$$A_{nn} \sim \alpha\beta_{nn}\xi s^\alpha \tag{8.50c}$$

where ξ is the signature factor.

Factorisation implies that

$$\beta_{sn}^2 = \beta_{ss}\beta_{nn} \tag{8.51}$$

The presence of the factor $\alpha^{1/2}$ in (8.50b) implies that β_{sn} is proportional to a half-integral power of α, as otherwise A_{sn} would have an unphysical branch-point singularity at the value of t at which $\alpha(t) = 0$. Moreover, the pole in the amplitude must be cancelled if the signature is positive.

Now it follows from (8.51) that either β_{ss} or β_{nn} must contain a factor α. In the first case, the Regge trajectory decouples from the sense states at $\alpha(t) = 0$ and we say that it 'chooses nonsense'. Alternatively, β_{nn} contains a factor α and we say that the trajectory 'chooses sense'; this possibility must be discarded for a positive-signature trajectory with $\alpha(t) = 0$ for $t < 0$, since A_{ss} would then have a ghost state. Other possibilities may also occur; for example, we may assume that β_{sn} contains a factor $\alpha^{3/2}$, which leads to four possible behaviours of β_{ss} and β_{nn}.

Finally, we mention briefly the existence of still another type of constraint which must be imposed on certain Regge amplitudes. Consider, for example, NN scattering in the t-channel. It can be shown that there exist two constraints at $t = 0$ among the five independent t-channel helicity amplitudes. This can be seen from the fact that the value $t = 0$ corresponds to the forward direction in the s-channel, where only three independent amplitudes contribute. The constraint equations relate amplitudes with different quantum numbers in the t-channel, which are dominated by different Regge poles. One way of satisfying such constraints is to impose the necessary conditions on the residue functions themselves; the corresponding behaviour is then known as 'evasion'. Another way of satisfying the constraints, known as 'conspiracy', is to suppose that there exist two or more trajectories with different quantum numbers which together conspire to satisfy the constraints. The mechanism which is actually chosen depends on the particular process in question.

8.8. Further development of the Regge model

In the previous sections we have given an outline of what might be called the classical Regge theory; this is based on the exchange of only Regge poles, with no allowance for any other singularities in the complex angular momentum plane. However, there are strong indications that recent experimental data obtained at the highest accelerator energies at Serpukhov and at Batavia cannot be adequately explained by this simple picture and that more sophisticated models are needed. Unfortunately, the situation becomes rather complicated once we go beyond the simple Regge pole model. Numerous models involving different types of singularities have been proposed, but the nature of the singularities in the complex angular momentum plane remains an open question.

The need for Regge cuts was first suggested by theoretical considerations long before any empirical evidence for them was found. It is now known that, once the existence of Regge poles is accepted, cuts in the angular momentum plane must almost certainly occur as well, as they are generated by the simultaneous exchange of two or more Regge poles.

Ideally, one would like to be able to predict the properties of Regge cuts directly in terms of those of the poles which generate them; in practice this can be done only if some supplementary assumptions are made. There are, however, certain general properties which follow essentially from unitarity arguments and which require no model-dependent assumptions.

The position of the branch point can be determined for the general case of the exchange of any number of Regge poles. We shall confine ourselves here to the discussion of the case of two exchanged Regge poles which are assumed to have linear trajectories $\alpha_i(t) = \alpha_i(0) + t\alpha_i'$ $(i = 1, 2)$. One then finds a cut beginning at a branch point

$$\alpha_c(t) = \alpha_1(0) + \alpha_2(0) - 1 + \frac{\alpha_1'\alpha_2't}{\alpha_1' + \alpha_2'} \tag{8.52}$$

In deriving the Regge representation by means of the Sommerfeld–Watson transformation, an additional contour integral must be taken around each cut in the *l*-plane, from some point $l = b$ on the line $\text{Re}\,l = -\frac{1}{2}$ up to the branch point $l = \alpha_c(t)$. The result will therefore depend on an integral over the discontinuity across the cut, so that the cut has the same effect as a continuous superposition of poles.

We recall that the contribution to the amplitude from a single Regge pole is of the form

$$A(s, t) \sim H(t)s^{\alpha(t)}$$

Consequently, the contribution from a Regge cut with a branch point at $l = \alpha_c(t)$ will be of the form

$$A(s, t) \sim \int_b^{\alpha_c(t)} G(t, l)s^l \, dl \tag{8.53}$$

The type of asymptotic behaviour obtained in this way depends on how $G(t, l)$ behaves as $l \to \alpha_c$. Unfortunately, little is known about the discontinuities across the cuts. For a general power behaviour

$$G(t, l) \sim \text{const}[l - \alpha_c(t)]^{\gamma(t)} \tag{8.54}$$

we have

$$A(s, t) \sim \text{const } s^{\alpha_c(t)}/(\log s)^{\gamma(t) + 1} \tag{8.55}$$

For a logarithmic cut

$$G(t, l) \sim \text{const } \log[l - \alpha_c(t)] \tag{8.56}$$

we have

$$A(s, t) \sim \text{const } s^{\alpha_c(t)}/\log s \tag{8.57}$$

More generally, the behaviour

$$G(t, l) \sim \text{const}\{\log[l - \alpha_c(t)]\}^{\gamma(t)} \tag{8.58}$$

leads to

$$A(s, t) \sim \text{const } s^{\alpha_c(t)}(\log \log s)^{\gamma(t) - 1}/\log s \tag{8.59}$$

We note that in all cases the cut contribution differs from an ordinary pole contribution by logarithmic factors. It would be rather difficult to distinguish between these forms experimentally.

In practice, one usually considers amplitudes $A^{(\pm)}(s, t)$ with definite crossing properties. With minor modifications of the foregoing formulae, the required crossing properties can be incorporated in the expressions for the Regge cut contributions. For this purpose, it is customary to use the energy variable v, which has simple crossing properties (asymptotically, v is proportional to s). The crossing-symmetric variant of (8.55), for example, can be written in the form

$$A^{(+)}(v, t) \sim \text{const}(-iv)^{\alpha_c(t)}(\log v - \tfrac{1}{2}i\pi)^{-\gamma(t) - 1} \qquad (8.60)$$

while the crossing-antisymmetric form is

$$A^{(-)}(v, t) \sim \text{const } i(-iv)^{\alpha_c(t)}(\log v - \tfrac{1}{2}i\pi)^{-\gamma(t) - 1} \qquad (8.61)$$

where the constants are real in both cases.

Let us now consider the effects of Regge cuts generated by the exchange of particular pairs of Regge poles. If both poles are the Pomeranchuk pole, we see from (8.52) that $\alpha_c(0) = 1$, so that for $t = 0$ the s-dependence of the cut differs from that of the Pomeranchuk pole itself by only logarithmic factors. If the Pomeranchuk trajectory is assumed to have a positive slope α'_P, we find that $\alpha_c(t) = 1 + \tfrac{1}{2}t\alpha'_P > \alpha_P(t)$ for $t < 0$. This inequality shows that the effect of the cut must be dominant by a power of the energy for non-forward scattering.

Suppose next that the Pomeranchuk pole is exchanged together with some other lower-lying Regge pole R with $\alpha_R(0) < 1$. Then (8.52) shows that $\alpha_c(0) = \alpha_R(0)$, so that for forward scattering the effect of the cut is a modification of the contribution of the Regge pole R. However, for $t < 0$ we find

$$\alpha_c(t) = \alpha_R(0) + \frac{\alpha'_P \alpha'_R t}{\alpha'_P + \alpha'_R} > \alpha_R(t)$$

Thus, for $t < 0$ the contribution of the cut dominates over that of the pole R by some power of the energy. These considerations show that Regge cuts generated by the exchange of the Pomeranchuk pole and some other pole are likely to become important at very high energies. The dominant cut in any reaction will be that generated by the Pomeranchuk pole together with the leading pole which carries the relevant quantum numbers.

Finally, for the exchange of two Regge poles R_1 and R_2, with $\alpha_{1,2}(0) < 1$, we find that $\alpha_c(0) < \alpha_{1,2}(0)$. Such cuts are therefore expected to have a much weaker effect.

We mention briefly two further properties of Regge cuts. First, the signature of a cut is given by the product of the signatures of the poles which generate it. Second, the factorisation principle does not hold for cuts (this can be seen from the fact that a cut is equivalent to a superposition of poles, while the factorisation principle is a non-linear condition).

Among the other modifications of the simple Regge pole model which have been proposed, there is the suggestion that the meson trajectories could become complex for $t < 0$. This would appear to contradict our previous statement that the trajectory function is real for $t < 0$; however, the latter can be derived only under the assumption that Regge singularities do not collide. We have seen that, if allowance is made for cuts, then at $t = 0$ the cut generated by the Pomeranchuk pole and another Regge pole R has a branch point α_c which coincides with the position of the pole α_R. It turns out that the same also applies to cuts generated by the exchange of the pole R together with any number of Pomeranchuk poles. We must therefore consider the possibility that the trajectories are complex for $t < 0$. If complex trajectories do occur, they must appear in pairs, with complex conjugate trajectories and residues.

The amplitude for such a pair of complex poles is of the general form

$$A(s, t) \sim H(t)s^{\alpha(t)} + H^*(t)s^{\alpha^*(t)} \tag{8.62}$$

It can be verified by explicit calculation of the imaginary part of (8.62) that there is an oscillatory contribution to the energy dependence of the total cross section, although such oscillations would be difficult to detect experimentally because they involve a logarithmic dependence on the energy.

In principle, singularities in the complex angular momentum plane other than simple poles and cuts are also possible, and numerous phenomenological models have been put forward to explain the high-energy scattering data. With our current knowledge, it is not possible to make an unambiguous choice between the many alternatives which are possible.

References

1. T. Regge, *Nuovo Cimento*, **14** (1959), 951
2. K. Igi, *Phys. Rev. Lett.*, **9** (1962), 76 and *Phys. Rev.*, **130** (1963), 820
3. S. W. MacDowell, *Phys. Rev.*, **116** (1959), 774

Further reading

There are many books and review articles devoted to Regge theory, through which the development of the theory and its phenomenological applications can be traced in greater detail. The following list is a selection.

1. S. C. Frautschi, *Regge Poles and S-Matrix Theory*, Benjamin, New York, 1963
2. R. Omnès and M. Froissart, *Mandelstam Theory and Regge Poles*, Benjamin, New York, 1963
3. E. J. Squires, *Complex Angular Momentum and Particle Physics*, Benjamin, New York, 1963
4. R. G. Newton, *The Complex J-Plane*, Benjamin, New York, 1964
5. W. Kummer, *Fortschritte der Physik*, **14** (1966), 429
6. E. Leader, *Rev. Mod. Phys.*, **38** (1966), 476
7. R. L. Omnès, *Ann. Rev. Nucl. Science*, **16** (1966), 263
8. V. Barger, *Rev. Mod. Phys.*, **40** (1968), 129
9. L. Bertocchi, in *Proceedings of the Heidelberg International Conference on Elementary Particles*, ed. H. Filthuth, North-Holland, Amsterdam, 1968, p. 197
10. P. D. B. Collins and E. J. Squires, *Regge Poles in Particle Physics*, Springer, Berlin, 1968
11. W. Drechsler, *Fortschritte der Physik*, **18** (1970), 305
12. D. V. Shirkov, *Usp. Fiz. Nauk*, **102** (1970), 87 [English translation: *Soviet Phys. Uspekhi*, **13** (1971), 599]
13. P. D. B. Collins, *Phys. Reports*, **1C** (1971), 103
14. R. J. Eden, *Reports on Progr. in Phys.*, **34** (1971), 995
15. C. B. Chiu, *Ann. Rev. Nucl. Science*, **22** (1972), 255
16. R. J. N. Phillips, in *Proceedings of the Amsterdam International Conference on Elementary Particles*, ed. A. G. Tenner and M. J. G. Veltman, North-Holland, Amsterdam, 1972, p. 110

CHAPTER 9

Superconvergence relations

9.1. Superconvergent amplitudes

Let $F(v)$ be an amplitude (possibly multiplied by some kinematic factor) which satisfies an unsubtracted dispersion relation

$$\text{Re}F(v) = \sum_n \frac{X_n}{v - v_n} + \frac{1}{\pi} P \int_{\text{cuts}} \frac{\text{Im}F(v')\, dv'}{v' - v} \tag{9.1}$$

If, in addition, $F(v)$ has the asymptotic behaviour

$$|F(v)| \leqslant O(|v|^{-1-\delta}) \qquad \text{as } |v| \to \infty \tag{9.2}$$

for some $\delta > 0$, then an unsubtracted dispersion relation can also be written for the function $vF(v)$

$$v\,\text{Re}F(v) = \sum_n \frac{v_n X_n}{v - v_n} + \frac{1}{\pi} P \int_{\text{cuts}} \frac{v'\,\text{Im}F(v')\, dv'}{v' - v} \tag{9.3}$$

Setting $v = 0$ in (9.3), we have

$$-\sum_n X_n + \frac{1}{\pi} \int_{\text{cuts}} \text{Im}F(v')\, dv' = 0 \tag{9.4}$$

A function $F(v)$ satisfying the condition (9.2) is said to superconverge, and the resulting equation (9.4) is called a superconvergence relation.

It may happen that the function $F(v)$ satisfies an even stronger asymptotic bound of the type

$$|F(v)| \leqslant O(|v|^{-n-\delta}) \qquad \text{as } |v| \to \infty \tag{9.5}$$

with some $\delta > 0$, where n is a positive integer. In this case, unsubtracted dispersion relations can be written for any of the functions $v^m F(v), m = 1, 2, \ldots,$ n. Setting $v = 0$ in these relations, we arrive at the more general set of superconvergence relations (moment conditions)

$$-\sum_n v_n^{m-1} X_n + \frac{1}{\pi} \int_{\text{cuts}} v'^{(m-1)}\text{Im}F(v')\, dv' = 0 \tag{9.6}$$

for $m = 1, 2, \ldots, n$.

If the amplitude $F(v)$ is crossing-symmetric (crossing-antisymmetric), as is often the case in practice, the relations (9.6) with odd (even) moments $(m - 1)$

receive equal contributions from positive and negative energies and can therefore be rewritten purely in terms of the contributions with $v' > 0$.

The Froissart bound on the elastic scattering amplitude for two spinless particles is certainly not sufficient to give superconvergence relations. However, for processes involving particles with higher spins, it turns out that some of the amplitudes necessarily satisfy stronger asymptotic bounds and hence superconvergence relations. It is easy to see how this comes about. Consider, for example, pion–nucleon or kaon–nucleon scattering, for which, as we have seen, there are two independent invariant amplitudes A and B with simple analyticity properties. The expressions for the cross sections involve both A and B, each multiplied by certain kinematic factors (see equations 8.39 to 8.41). At high energies, the coefficient of B is larger than the coefficient of A essentially by an additional factor of the energy. In a Regge pole model, each of these invariant amplitudes, when multiplied by its appropriate kinematic factor, has the same asymptotic behaviour; that is the B amplitude has a lower asymptotic bound than the A amplitude. Similar arguments hold for the invariant amplitudes for particles with higher spins, where some of these amplitudes are multiplied by even higher powers of the energy variable and hence obey stronger bounds.

The use of the invariant amplitudes turns out to be rather cumbersome in the case of higher spins. A more systematic procedure for the construction of superconvergent amplitudes for arbitrary spin can be formulated using the standard helicity formalism.[1]

We shall give a brief outline of the method.[2] Consider a general two-particle (s-channel) reaction $a + b \rightarrow c + d$ and let $F_{cd,ab}(s, t)$ be a helicity amplitude for the corresponding t-channel reaction, where the subscripts denote the helicities of the particles (that is their spin projections in their directions of motion). All the terms in the partial-wave expansion of F contain the common factor

$$f_{\lambda,\mu}(\theta_t) = (\tfrac{1}{2} \cos \theta_t)^{|\lambda+\mu|}(\tfrac{1}{2} \sin \theta_t)^{|\lambda-\mu|} \tag{9.7}$$

where $\lambda = a - b$ and $\mu = c - d$, and it turns out that the function

$$A_{cd,ab} = F_{cd,ab}/f_{\lambda,\mu} \tag{9.8}$$

has simple analyticity properties in the variable s. Using the fact that $\cos \theta_t \sim Cs$ for large s and fixed t, where C is a certain constant (see equation 8.18), it can be shown that

$$|A_{cd,ab}| \sim C |F_{cd,ab}| s^{-n(\lambda,\mu)} \tag{9.9}$$

where $n(\lambda, \mu)$ is defined as the larger of the two values $|\lambda|$ and $|\mu|$.

Bounds on F can be established by relating F to the helicity amplitudes G in the s-channel. The latter are known to satisfy the same high-energy bound $s \log^2 s$ (the Froissart bound) as the amplitude for spinless particles. It can be shown from the crossing relation for helicity amplitudes that all the amplitudes

F for a particular process have the same asymptotic behaviour as $s \to \infty$. The factor $s^{-n(\lambda,\mu)}$ in (9.9) leads to an improved convergence for some of the amplitudes: the higher the helicity flip, the better the convergence. In particular, superconvergent amplitudes are always obtained if the spin of one of the particles is greater than 1.

Many of the processes for which simple superconvergence relations can be derived are not accessible to direct scattering experiments at the present time. In such cases, one may work within the framework of an approximation scheme in which only the contributions from certain resonances are retained in the dispersion integrals. The integrals are then said to be saturated by these resonances. The relevant resonance parameters (positions and widths) are usually known from experimental analyses of production processes in which the resonances show up as peaks in the effective-mass distributions for pairs of final-state particles.

The contribution of each resonance to the appropriate partial-wave amplitude $T_l(v)$ in a given scattering process is represented approximately by a Breit–Wigner formula of the type

$$T_l(v) = \frac{\frac{1}{2}\Gamma_e/q}{M - W - \frac{1}{2}i\Gamma} \tag{9.10}$$

where Γ_e is the elastic width (which is generally less than the total width Γ) and M is the mass of the resonance. When saturating the dispersion integrals of superconvergence relations, it is particularly convenient to take the limit $\Gamma \to 0^+$ in the denominator of (9.10), which gives

$$\mathrm{Im}\,T_l(v) = \frac{\pi\Gamma_e}{2q}\,\delta(W - M) \tag{9.11}$$

This is known as the narrow-width approximation. Moreover, the elastic width Γ_e can be related to the coupling constant of the resonance in question with the particles of the elastic channel.

The virtue of the narrow-width approximation is that the saturation of a superconvergence relation in this way produces simply an algebraic relation among various masses and coupling constants. Such relations are linear in the squares of the coupling constants for elastic scattering (or in products of coupling constants for inelastic reactions), and stable particles and resonant states enter on a completely equal footing.

9.2. Sum rules from Regge asymptotic behaviour

Only a limited number of superconvergence relations can be derived from the general considerations of the preceding section for the processes (with low spins) which are most accessible to experiment. Dynamical models for high-energy scattering, such as the Regge pole model, usually impose bounds on the asymptotic behaviour of amplitudes which are more restrictive than those that follow purely from general principles. These new bounds often lead to additional superconvergence relations.

The importance of superconvergence relations first became widely known when it was pointed out[3] that certain sum rules which had previously been derived as consequences of current algebra actually follow directly from analyticity and suitable asymptotic bounds. This was first noticed for the specific case of forward elastic $\pi\rho$ scattering within the framework of a simple Regge pole model. We shall consider the analysis of this case as a specific example of the derivation and application of superconvergence relations.

The $\pi\rho$ scattering amplitude can be written in terms of four independent invariant amplitudes A, B, C and D, each having simple analyticity properties, in the form

$$T = (\varepsilon_1 P)(\varepsilon_2 P)A + \tfrac{1}{2}[(\varepsilon_1 P)(\varepsilon_2 Q) + (\varepsilon_2 P)(\varepsilon_1 Q)]B$$
$$+ (\varepsilon_1 Q)(\varepsilon_2 Q)C + (\varepsilon_1\varepsilon_2)D \qquad (9.12)$$

where $P = p_\pi + p'_\pi$ and $Q = p_\rho + p'_\rho$ are the sums of the initial and final 4-momenta of the pion and ρ meson, respectively, and ε and ε' are the initial and final polarisation vectors of the ρ meson. If the amplitudes are assumed to be dominated by the exchange of some Regge trajectory $\alpha(t)$ in the t-channel, then at fixed t the amplitudes A, B, C and D will be asymptotically proportional to $v^{\alpha-2}$, $v^{\alpha-1}$, v^α and v^α. Under these conditions, the amplitude A satisfies a superconvergence relation if $\alpha < 1$. Likewise, the somewhat stronger assumption that $\alpha < 0$ leads to an additional superconvergence relation for B.

Consider the $\pi\rho$ scattering amplitudes corresponding to isospin $I = 1$ in the t-channel. The leading Regge pole in this case is the ρ, which has an intercept $\alpha_\rho(0) \approx \tfrac{1}{2}$. Using the fact that the amplitude A_1 is crossing antisymmetric (where the subscript 1 denotes the value of the t-channel isospin), we obtain the superconvergence relation

$$\int_0^\infty \mathrm{Im}A_1(v, t)\, \mathrm{d}v = 0 \qquad (9.13)$$

for $t \leqslant 0$. It should be noted that the $\pi\rho$ amplitudes have pole terms corresponding to the pion state. For simplicity, we do not write the contributions from these pole terms explicitly in the superconvergence relations; they may be taken into account by incorporating appropriate δ-function terms in the imaginary parts of the amplitudes and integrating over the poles as well as the cuts. If, in addition, we adopt the reasonable assumption that no t-channel Regge trajectory with $I = 2$ exists such that $\alpha(0) > 0$ (as is suggested by the absence of low-lying meson states with such quantum numbers), an analogous argument leads to a second superconvergence relation

$$\int_0^\infty \mathrm{Im}B_2(v,t)\, \mathrm{d}v = 0 \qquad (9.14)$$

If the relations (9.13) and (9.14) are saturated by the lowest-lying single-particle states π, ω and ϕ which couple to the $\pi\rho$ system, one finds

$$m_\rho^2(g_{\pi\rho\omega}^2 + g_{\pi\rho\phi}^2) - 4g_{\pi\pi\rho}^2 = 0 \tag{9.15}$$

$$(v_\omega + m_\rho^2)g_{\pi\rho\omega}^2 + (v_\phi + m_\rho^2)g_{\pi\rho\phi}^2 - 4g_{\pi\pi\rho}^2 = 0 \tag{9.16}$$

where

$$v_{\omega,\phi} = \tfrac{1}{2}(m_{\omega,\phi}^2 - m_\rho^2 - m_\pi^2) \tag{9.17}$$

Equations (9.15) and (9.16) together imply that

$$v_\omega g_{\pi\rho\omega}^2 + v_\phi g_{\pi\rho\phi}^2 = 0 \tag{9.18}$$

Since v_ω turns out to be practically zero, the ratio $g_{\pi\rho\phi}^2/g_{\pi\rho\omega}^2$ must be very small. Thus, the two relations (9.15) and (9.16) have the approximate solution

$$g_{\pi\rho\phi}^2 \approx 0 \qquad g_{\pi\rho\omega}^2 \approx 4g_{\pi\pi\rho}^2/m_\rho^2 \tag{9.19}$$

These predictions are well satisfied experimentally. It is also of interest to note that they are identical with the predictions obtained from certain higher symmetry schemes.

With the same assumptions as above, a third superconvergence relation

$$\int_0^\infty v\,\mathrm{Im}A_2(v, t)\,\mathrm{d}v = 0 \tag{9.20}$$

can also be derived (the corresponding relation without the factor v in the integrand is satisfied identically because A_2 is crossing-symmetric). The system of algebraic equations obtained by saturating the enlarged set of superconvergence relations (9.13), (9.14) and (9.20) with the π, ω and ϕ states is found to have only the trivial solution

$$g_{\pi\rho\omega}^2 = g_{\pi\rho\phi}^2 = g_{\pi\pi\rho}^2 = 0 \tag{9.21}$$

This disturbing result, in contrast with the encouraging results obtained by retaining only the two superconvergence relations (9.13) and (9.14), shows that great care is required in selecting the set of superconvergence relations to be used in a simple saturation scheme. Higher-moment sum rules such as (9.20) are, in fact, often less reliable than the zero-moment superconvergence relations. This is so because the former tend to give a larger weight to the region of higher energies and are consequently more sensitive to a greater number of resonances.

As a further example of the application of superconvergence relations, we consider the scattering of pseudoscalar mesons by members of the familiar baryon octet. The earliest applications of superconvergence relations to meson-baryon scattering were made within the framework of $SU(3)$ symmetry. If these processes are dominated by the exchange of a Regge trajectory $\alpha(t)$ in the t-channel, then the usual invariant amplitudes A and B have the asymptotic behaviour

$$A(v, t) \sim \mathrm{const}\ v^{\alpha(t)} \qquad B(v, t) \sim \mathrm{const}\ v^{\alpha(t)-1} \tag{9.22}$$

Thus, the amplitudes for the individual elastic scattering processes are not expected to be superconvergent. However, our knowledge of the meson mass spectrum is consistent with the assumption that any t-channel trajectories associated with the $SU(3)$ 27-plet satisfy $\alpha_{27}(t) < 0$, at least in a range of negative t including $t = 0$. This leads directly to the superconvergence relation

$$\int_0^\infty \text{Im} B_{27}(v, t) \, dv = 0 \tag{9.23}$$

for that part of the B amplitude which corresponds to the exchange of this multiplet. Analogous sum rules can also be constructed for the $SU(3)$ decuplet exchanges, but they are trivially satisfied because of the crossing properties of the amplitudes. The sum rule (9.23) can be applied, for example, to the specific process $\pi^+ + \Sigma^- \to \pi^- + \Sigma^+$, for which good data on the many known Y^* resonances can be used to saturate the integral.

If we make the stronger assumption that the leading Regge trajectory associated with decuplet exchange is such that $\alpha_{10}(0) < -1$, then the amplitude $A'_{10} = A_{10} + vB_{10}$, for example, satisfies the superconvergence relation

$$\int_0^\infty \text{Im} A'_{10}(v, 0) \, dv = 0 \tag{9.24}$$

This result can be written as a sum rule involving the various pion–nucleon and kaon–nucleon scattering processes

$$\int_0^\infty \text{Im}[\Delta_{\pi N}(v) - \Delta_{KN}(v)] \, dv = 0 \tag{9.25}$$

where

$$\Delta_{\pi N} = F(\pi^- p) - F(\pi^+ p) \tag{9.26}$$

$$\Delta_{KN} = F(K^- p) - F(K^+ p) + F(K^+ n) - F(K^- n) \tag{9.27}$$

and the quantities F are the forward scattering amplitudes for the processes indicated. A major advantage of the sum rule (3.26) is that it can be evaluated largely in terms of physically accessible scattering data (total cross sections) and does not require the resonance-saturation approximation. The sum rules (9.23) and (9.25) are found to be well satisfied in practice.

A very great variety of sum rules can be constructed for processes involving particles with higher spins, although their phenomenological analysis depends entirely on the resonance-saturation approximation. The analysis of sum rules for such processes is rather complicated in certain cases, owing to the existence of a large number of independent amplitudes. For example, in the case of elastic scattering of pions by A_2 mesons, one finds that there are nine independent amplitudes. The asymptotic bounds imposed on these amplitudes by general principles lead to five superconvergence relations. Ten additional non-trivial superconvergence relations can be derived if it is assumed that the leading

Regge poles for t-channel isospin $I = 0, 1$ and 2 satisfy $\alpha_P(0) = 1$, $\alpha_\rho(0) \approx \frac{1}{2}$ and $\alpha_2(0) < 0$, respectively.

Sum rules such as those discussed above are generally expected to hold over a range of values of the momentum transfer variable t. A convenient way of expressing this requirement is to differentiate the fixed-t sum rules with respect to t under the integral sign. For example, from the sum rule (9.13) we obtain

$$\int_0^\infty \text{Im}\left[\frac{\partial}{\partial t} A_1(v, t)\right]_{t=0} dv = 0 \tag{9.28}$$

Relations involving higher derivatives can also be constructed. However, care must be exercised in applying such derivative relations in a resonance-saturation scheme, since the derivatives of an amplitude with respect to t are relatively more sensitive to resonances with high spins than the forward scattering amplitude itself. In fact, if a given sum rule is repeatedly differentiated with respect to t at $t = 0$, the contributions to the successive sum rules begin with successively higher partial waves, since $(d^n/dx^n)P_l(x) = 0$ for $n > l$.

9.3. Sum rules for factorised amplitudes

Consider the linear combinations of the elastic pion–nucleon and kaon–nucleon forward scattering amplitudes which depend only on the exchange of the ρ quantum numbers in the t-channel. Since the baryon vertex for this exchange is the same in both cases, it follows from the factorisation principle for the Regge pole residues that the ρ-exchange contributions to the appropriate linear combinations of the A and B amplitudes satisfy the relation $B_{\pi N}/A_{\pi N} = B_{KN}/A_{KN}$. It is therefore reasonable to expect the combination of amplitudes $B_{\pi N}A_{KN} - A_{\pi N}B_{KN}$ to be superconvergent, since the leading (ρ) terms in the Regge expansion cancel and any further Regge singularities corresponding to the same set of exchanged quantum numbers are likely to lie much further to the left in the j-plane.

By applying a somewhat more general form of the factorisation principle[4] to meson–baryon scattering processes, one can derive a class of superconvergent sum rules of the type

$$\int_0^\infty \text{Im}[F_{MB}(v)F'_{M'B'}(v) - F_{M'B}(v)F'_{MB'}(v)] dv = 0 \tag{9.29}$$

where F and F' may be either of the two invariant amplitudes A and B for a particular meson–baryon scattering process, the participating particles being indicated by the subscripts. Likewise, superconvergence relations can be written for certain differences of products of amplitudes for meson–meson and meson–baryon processes, for example

$$\int_0^\infty \text{Im}[M_{\pi\pi}(v)B_{KN}(v) - M_{\pi K}(v)B_{\pi N}(v)] dv = 0 \tag{9.30}$$

where M is the invariant amplitude for the indicated meson–meson scattering process and B is the usual meson–nucleon invariant amplitude. Since several Regge poles normally contribute to a particular scattering process, sum rules such as (9.29) and (9.30) must be written in practice for certain linear combinations of amplitudes which depend on only one particular Regge pole, say the ρ.

The foregoing are typical of a large number of sum rules which can be derived in situations in which different processes are dominated by the exchange of the same Regge pole. Although these sum rules are of great interest from a theoretical point of view, it is exceedingly difficult to establish any convincing saturation scheme for them, since their integrands depend on both the real and imaginary parts of the individual amplitudes which enter the relations. The imaginary part of an amplitude may certainly be dominated by resonance peaks in many situations, but this is not so for the real part (in fact, the Breit–Wigner resonance formula gives a real part which goes through zero at the resonance).

We shall now illustrate a method of avoiding these difficulties by applying the factorisation principle in a different way.[5] Consider the linear combinations of πN, $(KN, \bar{K}N)$ and $(NN, \bar{N}N)$ forward scattering amplitudes $F_{\pi N}^{(\rho)}$, $F_{KN}^{(\rho)}$ and $F_{NN}^{(\rho)}$ corresponding to the exchange of the ρ quantum numbers in the t-channel and assume that each such combination is dominated by a single ρ Regge pole. If the contribution of each Regge pole exchange is written as the product of two factors, one characterising each vertex, one can construct linear combinations of amplitudes for different processes such that the contribution of the dominant Regge pole cancels. This leads to superconvergence relations, which, with an appropriate normalisation of the residues, can be written

$$\int_0^\infty \left[2f_{\rho KK} F_{\pi N}^{(\rho)}(v) + f_{\rho \pi \pi} F_{KN}^{(\rho)}(v) \right] dv = 0 \qquad (9.31)$$

$$\int_0^\infty \left[f_{\rho NN} F_{KN}^{(\rho)}(v) - f_{\rho KK} F_{NN}^{(\rho)}(v) \right] dv = 0 \qquad (9.32)$$

where the quantities f are the factors of the Regge residues referring to the vertices indicated by the subscripts.

If experimental data on the amplitudes are used, each of the relations (9.31) and (9.32) can be solved for the ratio of the two Regge residue factors. An advantage of these sum rules is that they involve only the imaginary parts of the amplitudes. In fact, it is not necessary to saturate the integrals with resonances, since these integrals can be evaluated largely on the basis of experimental data on the total cross sections. There is, of course, some uncertainty from the unphysical regions for $\bar{K}N$ and $\bar{N}N$ scattering, but their contributions to the sum rules are found to be comparatively small, so that the final results are not too sensitive to the models used to evaluate them.

9.4. Sum rules from asymptotic symmetry requirements

We have already seen that, starting from amplitudes which are themselves not superconvergent, one can sometimes construct linear combinations which superconverge, provided that certain additional assumptions are made. One method of doing this is to exploit the relations between different amplitudes which follow from certain symmetry requirements at high energies.

In one of the first examples of sum rules derived from such considerations,[6] it was noted that, if one assumes a Regge pole model in which the residues for different processes are related by $SU(3)$ symmetry (or, alternatively, a quark composite model), then the forward $\pi\pi$ and πK scattering amplitudes corresponding to t-channel isospin $I = 1$ are related to each other at high energies and have a common asymptotic behaviour determined by the intercept of the ρ trajectory

$$M_{\pi\pi}^{(\rho)}(v) \sim 2M_{\pi K}^{(\rho)}(v) \sim \text{const } v^{\alpha_\rho(0)} \tag{9.33}$$

It is therefore reasonable to expect a superconvergence relation to hold

$$\int_0^\infty \text{Im}[M_{\pi\pi}^{(\rho)}(v) - 2M_{\pi K}^{(\rho)}(v)]\,dv = 0 \tag{9.34}$$

If (9.34) is saturated with the important lowest-lying $\pi\pi$ and πK resonances, namely the ρ and $K^*(892)$, one finds an algebraic relation

$$(m_\rho^2 - 4m_\pi^2)g_{\pi\pi\rho}^2 = \left[\frac{(m_{K^*}^2 - m_K^2 + m_\pi^2)^2}{m_{K^*}^2} - 4m_\pi^2\right]g_{\pi KK^*}^2 \tag{9.35}$$

It is interesting to note that (9.35) is found to be identically satisfied if one substitutes into its right-hand side the equalities for the masses and coupling constants which correspond to the limit of exact $SU(3)$ symmetry

$$m_{K^*} = m_\rho \qquad m_K = m_\pi \qquad g_{\pi KK^*}^2 = g_{\pi\pi\rho}^2$$

This is one example out of many in which the evaluation of superconvergence relations in a simple saturation scheme leads to a remarkable agreement with certain symmetry predictions. The relation (9.35) is also well satisfied if the empirical values of the masses and resonance decay widths are used instead.

The application of asymptotic $SU(3)$ symmetry also leads to sum rules for many other processes. A typical sum rule of this type for the invariant amplitudes of meson–baryon scattering is[7]

$$\int_0^\infty \text{Im}[A_{\pi N}^{(\rho)}(v) - 2A_{KN}^{(\rho)}(v)]\,dv = 0 \tag{9.36}$$

where the amplitudes are, as before, those linear combinations which depend on ρ exchange in the t-channel.

Superconvergence relations can also be constructed on the basis of the simple asymptotic relations among total cross sections which follow from the quark model, for example the relation $3\sigma_{\pi N} = 2\sigma_{NN}$ between the average πN and NN total cross sections.

References

1. M. Jacob and G. C. Wick, *Ann. of Phys.*, **7** (1959), 404
2. T. L. Trueman, *Phys. Rev. Lett.*, **17** (1966), 1198
3. V. de Alfaro, S. Fubini, G. Rossetti and G. Furlan, *Phys. Lett.*, **21** (1966), 576
4. G. C. Fox and E. Leader, *Phys. Rev. Lett.*, **18** (1967), 628
5. Y. M. Gupta and A. Rangwala, *Phys. Rev.*, **168** (1968), 1701
6. G. Costa and A. H. Zimerman, *Nuovo Cimento*, **46A** (1966), 198
7. V. P. Seth, M. C. Sharma and B. K. Agarwal, *J. Phys.*, **A3** (1970), 170

Further reading

A comprehensive survey of superconvergence relations and their applications is contained in the following general review of dispersion sum rules.

1. C. Ferro Fontán, N. M. Queen and G. Violini, *Rivista del Nuovo Cimento*, **2** (1972), 357

CHAPTER 10

Finite energy sum rules

10.1. Derivation of the sum rules

The sum rules known as finite energy sum rules constitute a generalisation of superconvergence relations, in the sense that they specify relations between high-energy parameters and dispersion integrals over the amplitudes at low energies; however, they can be written even when the conditions which lead to superconvergence relations are not fulfilled. As we have already noted, scattering amplitudes do not in general decrease sufficiently fast at asymptotic energies to give superconvergence relations. Nevertheless, if a definite asymptotic behaviour of an amplitude is known or assumed, one can exploit this information together with a knowledge of its analyticity properties to derive sum rules.

The basic ideas which originally led to the formulation of finite energy sum rules can be traced back to two sources. One of them, already mentioned in section 8.5, was the sum rule of Igi,[1] which gave the first indication of the presence of a secondary vacuum Regge singularity; this sum rule was obtained by considering a dispersion relation for the difference between the crossing-symmetric πN forward scattering amplitude and the contribution to it from the Pomeranchuk pole. The second significant idea[2] was that, by assuming that beyond a certain energy both the real and imaginary parts of the scattering amplitude have attained their asymptotic form, one can impose the condition that the real part given by a conventional dispersion relation coincides with its asymptotic representation at some sufficiently high energy. Alternatively, the real part can be expressed in terms of a finite-contour dispersion relation (see section 6.4) obtained by applying Cauchy's integral formula to a finite contour (figure 10.1) similar to that used in the derivation of the ordinary dispersion relation in section 2.4, but without taking the limit as the radius of the semicircular part tends to infinity. In this case the integral over the semicircle can be calculated in terms of whatever representation of the amplitude is assumed to be valid at high energies. Following either procedure, one obtains a sum rule which relates a certain function of the high-energy parameters to a dispersion integral depending on the amplitude over a finite range of energies.

Consider, for example, the πN crossing-symmetric scattering amplitude

$$F^{(+)}(\omega) = \tfrac{1}{2}[F_+(\omega) + F_-(\omega)] \tag{10.1}$$

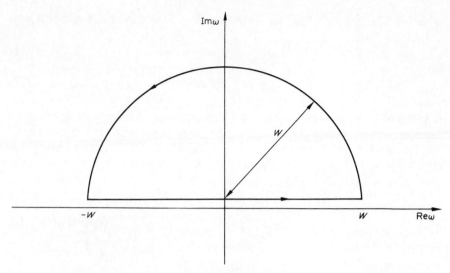

Figure 10.1. The contour used in the derivation of a finite-contour dispersion relation.

for which we can write the finite-contour dispersion relation

$$\mathrm{Re}F^{(+)}(\mu) = \frac{2}{\pi} \int_0^W \frac{\omega \, \mathrm{Im}F^{(+)}(\omega) \, d\omega}{\omega^2 - \mu^2} + \frac{2}{\pi} \, \mathrm{Im} \int_{S(W)} \frac{\omega F^{(+)}(\omega) \, d\omega}{\omega^2 - \mu^2} \qquad (10.2)$$

where $S(W)$ is the semicircle of radius W in the upper half of the ω-plane. If W is chosen to be sufficiently large, we may replace $F^{(+)}(\omega)$ by its asymptotic expansion, as given, for example, by the simple Regge pole model

$$F_{\mathrm{as}}^{(+)}(\omega) = i\beta_P\omega + \beta_{P'}(i - \cot \tfrac{1}{2}\pi\alpha_{P'})\omega^{\alpha_{P'}} \qquad (10.3)$$

The second integral in (10.2) can then be calculated in a straightforward way, giving

$$\frac{2}{\pi} \, \mathrm{Im} \int_{S(W)} \frac{F_{\mathrm{as}}^{(+)}(\omega) \, d\omega}{\omega} = -\frac{2\beta_P W}{\pi} - \frac{2\beta_{P'} W^{\alpha_{P'}}}{\pi\alpha_{P'}} \qquad (10.4)$$

Finally, a sum rule is obtained by inserting (10.4) in (10.2). It should be noted that the dispersion relation (10.2) is not convergent when $W \to \infty$, as can be seen, for example, from (10.4); for this reason, the finite-contour form must be used. Of course, other sum rules can be derived by applying the same idea to different dispersion relations.

There is another method of obtaining sum rules for amplitudes which do not satisfy the asymptotic conditions required for the derivation of superconvergence relations. Consider, for example, a scattering amplitude $F(\omega)$ which behaves asymptotically like

$$|F(\omega)| \sim \mathrm{const} \, \omega^\alpha \qquad (10.5)$$

with $-1 \leqslant \alpha \leqslant 1$. Further, let us assume that $F(\omega)$ can be decomposed into a sum

$$F(\omega) = F_{as}(\omega) + F'(\omega) \tag{10.6}$$

where

$$F_{as}(\omega) = \sum_j c_j \xi_j \omega^{\alpha_j} \tag{10.7}$$

is a sum of Regge pole contributions. (These considerations can be extended to asymptotic behaviours corresponding to more sophisticated Regge models; see, for example M. Restignoli, D. Schiff and G. Violini, *Nuovo Cimento*, **7A** (1972), 856.) ξ_j is the signature factor for a Regge pole with $-1 \leqslant \alpha_j \leqslant 1$; the remainder is assumed to satisfy the asymptotic bound

$$|F'(\omega)| \leqslant O(\omega^\beta) \tag{10.8}$$

for some $\beta < -1$. Since the function $F'(\omega)$ satisfies the condition (9.2), we can write for it the superconvergence relation (9.4)

$$-\sum_n X_n + \frac{1}{\pi} \int_{\text{cuts}} \text{Im} F'(\omega) \, d\omega = 0 \tag{10.9}$$

where the pole terms are those of the scattering amplitude $F(\omega)$. The cut structure of $F'(\omega)$ causes no difficulty because we can evaluate separately the contributions to the integral in (10.9) from $F(\omega)$ and $F_{as}(\omega)$; it should be noted that $F_{as}(\omega)$ has a cut extending down to $\omega = 0$.

If we assume that $F(\omega)$ is crossing-antisymmetric and that the dispersion integral can be truncated at some energy W, that is that $\text{Im} F(\omega)$ may be replaced by its asymptotic form $\text{Im} F_{as}(\omega)$ when $\omega \geqslant W$, we obtain from (10.9) the finite energy sum rule

$$\int_0^W \text{Im} F(\omega) \, d\omega = \sum_j \frac{c_j W^{\alpha_j+1}}{\alpha_j + 1} \tag{10.10}$$

where, for simplicity, we have included possible pole terms in the dispersion integral. It is clear that the same result would be obtained by using instead a finite-contour integration, that is by replacing the integral from W to infinity by an integral over the semicircle of radius W in the upper half-plane.

It should be noted that any number of non-leading terms can be included in the asymptotic form $F_{as}(\omega)$, so that the α_j in the sum rule (10.10) may take any values, including values $\alpha_j < -1$.

For a crossing-symmetric amplitude, (10.10) can be modified by inserting a factor ω in the integrand, in order to express the original dispersion integral over the range $-W \leqslant \omega \leqslant W$ in terms of an integral over only positive energies. The right-hand side of the sum rule is then also modified, and the result reads

$$\int_0^W \omega \, \text{Im} F(\omega) \, d\omega = \sum_j \frac{c_j W^{\alpha_j+2}}{\alpha_j + 2} \tag{10.11}$$

Note that the sum rules (10.10) and (10.11) require no particular bound on the high-energy behaviour of $F(\omega)$. In fact, similar sum rules (moment conditions) can be written for the amplitude $F(\omega)$ multiplied by any positive integral power of ω. These are the Dolen–Horn–Schmid[3] sum rules

$$S_n \equiv \frac{1}{W^{n+1}} \int_0^W \omega^n \operatorname{Im} F(\omega) \, d\omega = \sum_j \frac{c_j W^{\alpha_j}}{\alpha_j + n + 1} \tag{10.12}$$

where for later convenience we have divided both sides by W^{n+1}.

The advantage of the finite energy sum rules over the ordinary dispersion relations and superconvergence relations is apparent; the finite energy sum rules provide a neat separation of the low-energy and high-energy information, as they relate dispersion integrals over a finite energy range to simple functions of the Regge parameters.

It is clear from the preceding discussion that the power of ω appearing in the integrand of (10.12) must have a parity opposite to the crossing property of $F(\omega)$. Indeed, the sum rules (10.9), when written for moments giving the same parity as that of $F(\omega)$, turn out to be identically satisfied. It should be mentioned, however, that under certain circumstances it is possible to write the missing sum rules of type (10.12) (wrong-signature sum rules); these additional sum rules are related to other j-plane singularities (fixed poles).

A further generalisation of the sum rules is obtained if the moment is allowed to assume negative values. However, one must then add to the right-hand side of (10.12) the contribution of the (possibly multiple) pole at $\omega = 0$; this requires a knowledge of the amplitude and its derivatives up to order $n - 1$ at that point.

A particularly interesting case arises when it can be assumed that the amplitude is governed asymptotically by a single Regge pole. In that case the ratio of any pair of sum rules is independent of the value of the residue and we obtain the simple relation

$$\frac{S_n}{S_m} = \frac{\alpha + m + 1}{\alpha + n + 1} \tag{10.13}$$

from which the trajectory can be determined on the basis of the low-energy data alone. In particular, a bootstrap scheme can be formulated in the case of self-conjugate reactions such as $\pi + \pi \rightarrow \pi + \pi$, when the s-channel resonances which contribute to the low-energy amplitude can be identified with the states contained on the trajectories of the Regge poles exchanged in the t-channel. By exploiting the identity of the particles exchanged in the various channels in such a situation, one obtains relations among the masses of the particles and their coupling strengths. This idea, which has been further developed in a series of applications, is closely associated with the origins of the Veneziano model.[4]

10.2. Applications to strong and electromagnetic processes

Finite energy sum rules have been widely applied to the phenomenological analysis of various processes. In general, the earliest applications made use of the lowest positive-moment sum rule; subsequently, higher-moment sum rules have also been considered. It should be noted, however, that these sum rules, particularly for higher moments, emphasise the behaviour of the amplitude just below the cut-off energy W, so that to some extent the connection between high-energy and low-energy data is lost. In practice, the information contained in the higher-moment sum rules for the forward scattering amplitude coincides with that given by the total cross sections at the highest energies below the cut-off energy.

For phenomenological purposes one can use finite energy sum rules as powerful constraints on the high-energy parameters, making full use of the associated statistical errors calculated by the methods discussed in section 5.7. Of course, the sum rules can also be used in a less stringent form to provide an indication of the value of some parameter. When several finite energy sum rules are used simultaneously, some care is needed to ensure that one correctly takes into account the correlations associated with the fact that the various sum rules make use of a common set of input data.

Finite energy sum rules for forward scattering have been applied to several processes. A particularly interesting case is KN scattering, for which, as we have seen, there are four independent t-channel amplitudes. By constructing suitable linear combinations of the $K^{\pm}p$ and $K^{\pm}n$ scattering amplitudes and applying (8.33), one can readily isolate the individual t-channel amplitudes, so as to study the various j-plane singularities. Unfortunately, strong cancellations for certain combinations limit the predictive power of the sum rules.

The idea of considering linear combinations of amplitudes can also be applied to other situations. For example, for both πN and KN forward scattering, one can construct amplitudes corresponding to exchange of the ρ quantum numbers in the t-channel, namely

$$F_{\pi}^{(\rho)} = F(\pi^- p) - F(\pi^+ p) \tag{10.14a}$$

$$F_{K}^{(\rho)} = F(K^- p) - F(K^+ p) + F(K^+ n) - F(K^- n) \tag{10.14b}$$

According to $SU(3)$ symmetry, these two amplitudes are related by the condition (8.49a); this leads to the sum rule

$$\int_0^W F_{\pi}^{(\rho)}(\omega)\,d\omega = \int_0^W F_K^{(\rho)}(\omega)\,d\omega \tag{10.15}$$

which is an analogue of the superconvergence relation (9.25). This sum rule is found to be well satisfied experimentally, the violation being small in comparison with the average magnitude of the six contributing integrals.

Other applications of finite energy sum rules for forward scattering have been made, for example, to investigate the possibility of a violation of the Pomeranchuk theorem in πN and KN scattering. Several analyses of this type have favoured models which give amplitudes satisfying the Pomeranchuk theorem.

In addition to the analyses of forward scattering, for which data on the total cross sections can be used, there have been many attempts to apply finite energy sum rules to πN and KN non-forward scattering by employing the results of phase-shift analyses. Phase-shift analyses can also be used to study the finite energy sum rules for the forward A and B amplitudes separately.

The classical work of Dolen, Horn and Schmid on πN scattering, for example, elucidated the dynamical origin of the πN charge-exchange peak near the forward direction. This peak is due to the large value of the ratio $vB^{(-)}(v)/A^{(-)}(v)$, which depends on the fact that the resonances add coherently in $B^{(-)}$, but not in $A^{(-)}$. In a similar way, the dip in πN charge exchange at $t = -0.6\ (\text{GeV/c})^2$ can be traced back to the simultaneous vanishing in $B^{(-)}$ of all the important resonances in the interval $-0.6 < t < -0.4\ (\text{GeV/c})^2$. As is evident from this example, non-forward sum rules can be used to extract information about the location of the zeros of the amplitudes. This may be of special interest in studying the behaviour of the Regge residues at the points where the trajectory vanishes (see section 8.7), since finite energy sum rules provide a useful tool for determining which mechanism is chosen by a particular trajectory.

A special case of non-forward sum rules is the fixed-u finite energy sum rules near the backward direction, where the relevant Regge poles are the baryon poles. It is important to note two differences between the finite energy sum rules for $t \approx 0$ and those for $u \approx 0$. Firstly, the low-energy integrals in the latter receive contributions from s- and t-channel amplitudes which are not related by crossing symmetry; thus, the Regge terms do not average the single-channel amplitude, in contrast with the situation for forward scattering (see section 10.3). The second difference is a consequence of MacDowell symmetry (see section 8.7): for each Regge pole, the sum rules receive contributions from two terms, corresponding to $\pm\sqrt{u}$. Appropriate combinations of the amplitudes may be considered, at least in principle, to isolate the individual contributions. The use of fixed-u finite energy sum rules has shown that the behaviour of the Regge amplitudes as a function of u is compatible with that of the low-energy integrals. Thus, for example, the N Regge amplitude exhibits a zero near the backward direction, but not the N^*; consequently, a dip is observed in the $\pi^+ p$, but not in the $\pi^- p$ backward differential cross section.

Let us now turn briefly to the application of finite energy sum rules to electromagnetic processes. Compton scattering is described by two analytic functions $F_{1,2}(v)$, whose imaginary parts in the forward direction are related to the total cross sections for photons of energy v with a circular polarisation parallel (P) or antiparallel (A) to the spin of the target nucleon

$$\text{Im}F_1 = (v/8\pi)(\sigma_A + \sigma_P) \tag{10.16a}$$

$$\text{Im}F_2 = (v/8\pi)(\sigma_A - \sigma_P) \tag{10.16b}$$

An important difference between strong and electromagnetic processes is that the latter may have fixed poles of either signature; in particular, a right-signature fixed pole at $j = 0$ would not affect the total cross section, although it would modify the real part of the amplitude. For this reason, finite energy sum rules have been used especially to detect the possible presence of such a pole in the amplitude F_1. A contribution has indeed been found, which may be interpreted as a fixed pole and whose magnitude is compatible with the Thomson limit; however, other interpretations of it as a secondary pole are also possible.

Compton scattering in the non-forward direction is rather complicated because of the presence of a large number of amplitudes. Some of them are required to satisfy constraints at $t = 0$ of the type discussed at the end of section 8.7. Finite energy sum rules have made it possible to study the mechanism by which these constraints are satisfied.

10.3. Finite energy sum rules and duality

A major problem of high-energy physics is to find models which give an adequate description of the scattering amplitude. It is often possible to approximate amplitudes at relatively low energies by a sum of resonances. At the highest energies, on the other hand, different models, such as the Regge pole model, are usually employed. It has been an intriguing problem to understand the relationship between these models in the domain of intermediate energies, which can easily be reached by analytic continuation from either the lower or the higher energy region. Finite energy sum rules have made a significant contribution to the understanding of this problem.

Extensive use has been made of the so-called interference model in the intermediate energy region. In this model the scattering amplitude is constructed by summing two components, one given by the sum of direct-channel resonances and the other by the sum of the contributions of the Regge poles which can be exchanged in the t-channel. It is clear that in the limit of low (high) energies, the first (second) component must dominate. Writing the finite energy sum rule (10.10) in the form

$$\int_0^W \mathrm{Im}F(\omega)\,\mathrm{d}\omega = \int_0^W \mathrm{Im}F_{\mathrm{as}}(\omega)\,\mathrm{d}\omega \tag{10.17}$$

we notice that the average of the imaginary part of the asymptotic form of the amplitude is equal to the average of the imaginary part of the amplitude itself. This fact is sometimes called 'global duality'. Thus, the assumption underlying the interference model does not appear to be justified, since the retention of the Regge amplitude as a kind of background at low energies would imply that the resonant amplitude vanishes on the average.

Thus, the resonance and Regge models must be interpreted instead as two aspects of the same reality; each one individually gives an approximate representation of the scattering amplitude, and, depending on the value of the energy in question, it may be more convenient to choose one or the other of them.

Global duality indicates that the interference model should give sensible results when large cancellations occur between nearby resonances or when either amplitude is small in comparison with the other. This has made it possible to understand why the model seems to be adequate in certain cases but not in others.

Finite energy sum rules not only show clearly how either model can give a description of the full amplitude, but they also exhibit the constraints that each model imposes on the other. From (10.13), for example, we see how the resonances in the case of a single Regge pole exchange fix the trajectory, which in turn also fixes the value of the residue function of the pole.

In connection with this discussion, it may be mentioned that, if the partial-wave amplitudes are projected out from the Regge pole amplitude, one finds resonance-like loops in the Argand diagram. However, the interpretation of these loops as resonances ('local duality') is not at all clear. For example, in certain cases loops are found which rotate in the clockwise sense or which appear in channels with no known resonances.

The duality between Regge poles and resonances can be slightly modified, following a suggestion due to Harari,[5] by discussing separately the Pomeranchuk pole and all the remaining Regge poles. Obviously the relation (10.17) is maintained, but if one decomposes the scattering amplitude into its resonance and background components,

$$F(\omega) = F_{\text{res}}(\omega) + F_{\text{back}}(\omega) \tag{10.18}$$

there is evidence that the background component may be considered dual to the Pomeranchuk pole, in the sense that

$$\int_0^W \text{Im} F_{\text{back}}(\omega) \, d\omega = \int_0^W \text{Im} F_P(\omega) \, d\omega \tag{10.19a}$$

while the amplitude built by summing the resonances is dual to the sum of the remaining Regge pole contributions

$$\int_0^W \text{Im} F_{\text{res}}(\omega) \, d\omega = \sum_{j \neq P} \int_0^W \text{Im} F_j(\omega) \, d\omega \tag{10.19b}$$

This approach makes it possible to reformulate the interference model, in the sense that one may add the direct-channel resonances to the contribution of the Pomeranchuk pole as a background amplitude without committing any double-counting.

The distinction which two-component duality makes between the Pomeranchuk pole and all other Regge poles provides an explanation of many empirical features of the strong interactions, such as the qualitatively different behaviours of the K^+N and K^-N total cross sections or the exchange degeneracy relations. More quantitative tests of the sum rules (10.19) have also given encouraging results.

References

1. K. Igi, *Phys. Rev. Lett.*, **9** (1962), 76, and *Phys. Rev.*, **130** (1963) 820
2. L. Sertorio and M. Toller, *Phys. Lett.*, **18** (1965), 191, and M. Restignoli, L. Sertorio and M. Toller, *Phys. Rev.*, **150** (1966), 1389
3. R. Dolen, D. Horn and C. Schmid, *Phys. Rev. Lett.*, **19** (1967), 402 and *Phys. Rev.*, **166** (1968), 1768
4. G. Veneziano, *Nuovo Cimento*, **57A** (1968), 190
5. H. Harari, *Phys. Rev. Lett.*, **20** (1968), 1395

Further reading

Reviews of finite energy sum rules and their phenomenological applications are given in the following references.
1. R. Dolen, D. Horn and C. Schmid, *Phys. Rev.*, **166** (1968), 1768
2. D. Horn, *Acta Physica Austriaca, Supplementum*, **6** (1969), 124
3. C. Ferro Fontán, N. M. Queen and G. Violini, *Rivista del Nuovo Cimento*, **2** (1972), 357

The idea of duality and its experimental consequences are discussed in the following reference.

4. H. Harari and Y. Zarmi, *Phys. Rev.*, **187** (1969), 2230

CHAPTER 11

Modified sum rules

11.1. Continuous moment sum rules

In chapter 7 we showed how to construct modified dispersion relations by multiplying the scattering amplitude by suitable functions of the energy. In an analogous way, one can obtain modified finite energy sum rules for the product of the scattering amplitude and some weight function.

Perhaps the sum rules of this kind which have been most widely discussed in the literature are the so-called continuous moment sum rules. These sum rules bear this name because they are derived with the help of the weight function

$$g(v) = v^\gamma \exp(-\tfrac{1}{2}i\pi\gamma) \tag{11.1}$$

(Variants of this weight function, involving powers of different energy or momentum variables, have also been used. With minor modifications, the discussion of this section holds for all such weight functions.) In equation (11.1) the moment γ is regarded as a real parameter to be varied in a suitable range; the phase factor $\exp(-\tfrac{1}{2}i\pi\gamma)$ is included in order to enforce the crossing property

$$g(-v) = g(v) \tag{11.2}$$

As a consequence of (11.2), the crossing properties of the scattering amplitude $F(v)$ apply also to the product $F(v)g(v)$.

To derive a continuous moment sum rule, we can simply write a finite energy sum rule for the function $F(v)g(v)$; for example

$$\oint \exp(-\tfrac{1}{2}i\pi\gamma)v^\gamma F(v)\, dv = 0 \tag{11.3}$$

where the contour of integration is taken to be any closed curve in the upper half-plane. It is convenient to choose the contour to be a semicircle of radius W about the origin, together with the finite segment of the real axis

$$-W \leqslant v \leqslant W$$

(just above the cuts), where W is sufficiently large that the scattering amplitude can be replaced by its Regge asymptotic form on the semicircle.

An alternative procedure, which can be seen to lead to the same result, is to subtract from $F(v)$ its Regge asymptotic form (compare with section 10.1)

$$F_{\text{Reg}}(v) = \sum_i \frac{\beta_i[1 \pm \exp(-i\pi\alpha_i)]v^{\alpha_i}}{\sin \pi\alpha_i} \tag{11.4}$$

and to write (11.3) for the remainder; the integral over the semicircular contour can then be neglected. Thus, we are left with an equation which states that the integral of $F(v)g(v)$ over the range $-W \leqslant v \leqslant W$ is equal to the integral of $F_{\mathrm{Reg}}(v)g(v)$ over the same range.

To derive the detailed form of the sum rule, let us follow the second procedure and compare the imaginary parts of the calculated integrals. For definiteness, we shall carry out the calculations under the assumption that the scattering amplitude is crossing-antisymmetric; an analogous argument, with minor modifications, can be used to derive the corresponding sum rule for the case of a crossing-symmetric amplitude.

The integral depending on the scattering amplitude gives

$$\mathrm{Im} \int_{-W}^{W} \exp(-\tfrac{1}{2}i\pi\gamma)v^{\gamma}F(v)\,\mathrm{d}v = 2 \int_{0}^{W} v^{\gamma}[\cos \tfrac{1}{2}\pi\gamma \,\mathrm{Im}F(v) - \sin \tfrac{1}{2}\pi\gamma \,\mathrm{Re}F(v)]\,\mathrm{d}v$$

(11.5)

The integral depending on the Regge asymptotic form gives

$$I = \sum_{i} \frac{\beta_i}{\sin \pi\alpha_i} \mathrm{Im}\left[\exp(-\tfrac{1}{2}i\pi\gamma)[1 - \exp(-i\pi\alpha_i)] \int_{-W}^{W} v^{\gamma+\alpha_i}\,\mathrm{d}v \right]$$

and can be evaluated analytically as follows

$$I = \sum_{i} \frac{\beta_i}{\sin \pi\alpha_i} \mathrm{Im}\left\{ \exp(-\tfrac{1}{2}i\pi\gamma)[1 - \exp(-i\pi\alpha_i)]\left[\frac{v^{\gamma+\alpha_i+1}}{\gamma + \alpha_i + 1} \right]_{-W}^{W} \right\}$$

$$= \sum_{i} \frac{\beta_i}{\sin \pi\alpha_i} \mathrm{Im}\left\{ \frac{\exp(-\tfrac{1}{2}i\pi\gamma)[1 - \exp(-i\pi\alpha_i)]W^{\gamma+\alpha_i+1}}{\gamma + \alpha_i + 1} [1 + \exp\{i\pi(\gamma + \alpha_i)\}] \right\}$$

$$= 2 \sum_{i} \frac{\beta_i W^{\gamma+\alpha_i+1}}{(\gamma + \alpha_i + 1)\sin \pi\alpha_i} [-\sin \tfrac{1}{2}\pi\gamma + \sin \pi(\alpha_i + \tfrac{1}{2}\gamma)]$$

$$= 4 \sum_{i} \frac{\beta_i W^{\gamma+\alpha_i+1}}{\gamma + \alpha_i + 1} \frac{\cos \tfrac{1}{2}\pi(\gamma + \alpha_i)\sin \tfrac{1}{2}\pi\alpha_i}{\sin \pi\alpha_i}$$

$$= 2 \sum_{i} \frac{\beta_i W^{\gamma+\alpha_i+1}}{\gamma + \alpha_i + 1} \frac{\sin \tfrac{1}{2}\pi(\gamma + \alpha_i + 1)}{\cos \tfrac{1}{2}\pi\alpha_i} \qquad (11.6)$$

By equating (11.5) and (11.6), we obtain the continuous moment sum rule

$$\int_{0}^{W} v^{\gamma}[\cos \tfrac{1}{2}\pi\gamma \,\mathrm{Im}F(v) - \sin \tfrac{1}{2}\pi\gamma \,\mathrm{Re}F(v)]\,\mathrm{d}v$$

$$= \sum_{i} \frac{\beta_i W^{\gamma+\alpha_i+1}}{\gamma + \alpha_i + 1} \frac{\sin \tfrac{1}{2}\pi(\gamma + \alpha_i + 1)}{\cos \tfrac{1}{2}\pi\alpha_i} \qquad (11.7)$$

Without repeating the details of the derivation, we quote the form of the corresponding sum rule for a crossing-symmetric amplitude

$$\int_0^W v^\gamma[\sin \tfrac{1}{2}\pi\gamma \,\mathrm{Im}F(v) + \cos \tfrac{1}{2}\pi\gamma \,\mathrm{Re}F(v)]\,\mathrm{d}v = -\sum_i \frac{\beta_i W^{\gamma+\alpha_i+1}}{\gamma + \alpha_i + 1} \frac{\sin \tfrac{1}{2}\pi(\gamma + \alpha_i + 1)}{\sin \tfrac{1}{2}\pi\alpha_i}$$

$$(11.8)$$

If the dispersion integrals can be evaluated with reasonable accuracy for some range of the moment γ (for example, with the help of phase-shift analyses of the low-energy data), the sum rules (11.7) and (11.8) provide powerful constraints on the Regge parameters. For example, we show in figure 11.1 a typical form of the right-hand side of (11.7) as a function of γ in the case in which it is assumed that only a single Regge pole contributes. The parameters α and β of this pole can be determined from the shape and normalisation of this curve.

A feature of such continuous moment sum rules is that the relative weights of the contributions to the dispersion integral from different energy regions depend strongly on γ. Thus, by analysing the sum rules for a range of values of γ, it is possible to minimise the effect of uncertainties originating from any particular energy region. Clearly, the highest energies have a relatively large weight for the largest values of γ.

It should be mentioned that a certain lower limit must be set on the allowed range of γ in order to guarantee the convergence of the dispersion integral. The value of this limit depends on the behaviour of $\mathrm{Re}F(v)$ near $v = 0$. For example,

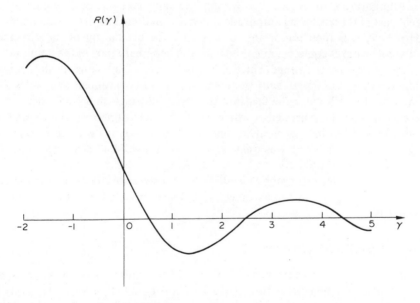

Figure 11.1. A typical Regge pole contribution to the right-hand side of the continuous moment sum rule (11.7) as a function of the moment.

G

in the case of a crossing-antisymmetric amplitude $\mathrm{Re}F(v)$ is proportional to v for small v, which requires $\gamma > -2$. This possible range of γ can be enlarged by introducing a subtraction. For example, by using the function

$$F_1(v) = F(v) - F'(0)v \tag{11.9}$$

in the crossing-antisymmetric case, the allowed range of γ becomes $\gamma > -4$, since $F_1(v)$ will then be proportional to v^3 for small v.

The continuous moment sum rules (11.7) and (11.8) are distinguished from the simple finite energy sum rules in that they contain dispersion integrals involving both the real and imaginary parts of the scattering amplitude. This means that it is no longer possible to employ the optical theorem for a complete determination of the left-hand side of the sum rules for forward scattering. Direct experimental measurements of the real parts of the amplitudes are generally much less accurate than those of the imaginary parts.

There are two possible ways of evaluating the dispersion integrals containing $\mathrm{Re}F(v)$. On the one hand, one can make use of phenomenological phase-shift analyses, which provide direct parametrisations of the complete scattering amplitude. In this case one is generally forced to choose a rather low value for the cut-off energy W, since most phase-shift analyses do not extend beyond energies of about 2–3 GeV. However, it is difficult to justify the use of the high-energy Regge expansion at such energies. Nevertheless, at least in the case of non-forward scattering, this is in practice the only way in which continuous moment sum rules can be used.

Alternatively, for forward scattering one can make use of the values of the real part of the scattering amplitude which are predicted by dispersion relations. However, it is then important to note that the evaluation of the dispersion integral requires some definite model for the imaginary part of the amplitude at energies beyond the range which is actually accessible. Thus, in determining high-energy parameters with the help of continuous moment sum rules, it is important to allow for the fact that the input information actually depends in some way on the parameters which are to be determined. In the earliest applications of continuous moment sum rules it was assumed without justification that this feedback effect was weak. In section 11.3 we shall discuss a method of overcoming this difficulty.

Continuous moment sum rules have been used extensively as phenomenological constraints on the parameters of Regge models for both πN and KN scattering.

11.2. Miscellaneous sum rules

Many modifications and generalisations of the finite energy sum rules and continuous moment sum rules have been proposed. One of the reasons for formulating different sum rules is to overcome certain specific defects of the conventional ones. Firstly, the sum rules which we have considered so far, particularly for high moments, tend to give an undesirably large weight to the input data from the energy region just below the cut-off energy of the integral. Secondly, as we saw in the preceding section, there are problems in determining the real parts of the amplitudes required for the analysis of continuous moment sum rules.

One proposal[1] for reducing the relative importance of the integral containing the real part of the amplitude is to obtain a derivative sum rule from a continuous moment sum rule by differentiating the latter with respect to the moment and then fixing the moment at some suitable value. For example, if we differentiate (11.7) with respect to γ and then set $\gamma = 0$, we obtain the sum rule

$$\int_0^W \log v \, \mathrm{Im}F(v) \, \mathrm{d}v - \tfrac{1}{2}\pi \int_0^W \mathrm{Re}F(v) \, \mathrm{d}v$$

$$= \sum_i \frac{\beta_i W^{\alpha_i+1}}{\alpha_i + 1}\left(\log W - \frac{1}{\alpha_i + 1} - \tfrac{1}{2}\pi \tan \tfrac{1}{2}\pi\alpha_i\right) \quad (11.10)$$

The extra logarithmic factor accompanying $\mathrm{Im}F(v)$ tends to enhance the first integral in (11.10) in comparison with the second integral, at least within a large part of the range of integration, so that by using (11.10) one may hope to reduce the importance of the previously mentioned feedback effect associated with the real part of the amplitude. (Note that the scale factor for the argument of the logarithm is the same as for the Regge pole expansion; for example, $\log(1 \text{ GeV}) = 0$.)

With certain other modifications of the continuous moment sum rules, it is possible to completely eliminate the presence of dispersion integrals containing the real part of the amplitude. One such type of modified sum rule[2] is obtained by multiplying the scattering amplitude by the weight function

$$w(v) = 1/(W^2 - v^2)^\gamma \quad (11.11)$$

As before, the parameter γ in (11.11) is allowed to vary continuously in some appropriate range, while W is some fixed energy. Since $w(v)$ is real for $v < W$, it is convenient to choose W to be the energy at which the dispersion integral is truncated, so that the real part of the scattering amplitude will not enter the sum rule. It turns out that the right-hand side of the sum rule can be expressed in terms of the Euler beta function

$$B(x, y) = \int_0^1 t^{x-1}(1 - t)^{y-1} \, \mathrm{d}t \quad (11.12)$$

For a crossing-antisymmetric amplitude for which the Regge pole representation is assumed to be of the form (11.4), the sum rule reads

$$\int_0^W \frac{\mathrm{Im}F(v) \, \mathrm{d}v}{(W^2 - v^2)^\gamma} = \tfrac{1}{2}\sum_i \beta_i W^{1+\alpha_i - 2\gamma} B(\tfrac{1}{2}[1 + \alpha_i], 1 - \gamma) \quad (11.13a)$$

while for a crossing-symmetric amplitude the corresponding sum rule is

$$\int_0^W \frac{v \, \mathrm{Im}F(v) \, dv}{(W^2 - v^2)^\gamma} = \tfrac{1}{2} \sum_i \beta_i W^{2 + \alpha_i - 2\gamma} B(1 + \tfrac{1}{2}\alpha_i, 1 - \gamma) \qquad (11.13b)$$

The sum rules (11.13) have the additional advantage, when compared with the conventional sum rules, that they do not depend very heavily on the behaviour of the scattering amplitude in the energy region just below the cut-off energy of the dispersion integral. The dispersion integral in (11.13) is actually divergent at its upper limit, but the divergence is integrable, provided that $\gamma < 1$. The contribution from the lower end of the energy range is not damped, as, for example, in the case of the higher-moment finite energy sum rules.

Another reason for constructing modified sum rules is that one would like to find sum rules with a high sensitivity to secondary (lower-lying) Regge contributions; in particular, when two poles are present, one would like to be able to distinguish their effects without the necessity of treating them together as a single effective pole.

One way of constructing a sufficiently general class of sum rules for this purpose is as follows.[3] Let us consider a scattering amplitude $F^{(\pm)}(v)$ with definite crossing properties and construct the difference

$$\Delta^{(\pm)}(v) = F^{(\pm)}(v) - F_{\mathrm{Reg}}^{(\pm)}(v) \qquad (11.14)$$

where $F_{\mathrm{Reg}}^{(\pm)}(v)$ is the Regge asymptotic expansion of $F^{(\pm)}(v)$. If we multiply $\Delta^{(\pm)}(v)$ by a weight function $g(v)$, we obtain the sum rule

$$\int_{-W}^W g(v) \, \Delta^{(\pm)}(v) \, dv = 0 \qquad (11.15)$$

provided that $g(v)$ tends to zero sufficiently rapidly as $|v| \to \infty$. Suppose now that the weight function $g(v)$ is decomposed into its crossing-symmetric and crossing-antisymmetric parts

$$g(v) = g^{(+)}(v) + g^{(-)}(v) \qquad (11.16)$$

Then the sum rule (11.15) can be expressed in the form

$$\int_0^W \mathrm{Re}[g^{(\pm)}(v) \, \Delta^{(\pm)}(v)] \, dv = 0 \qquad (11.17)$$

$$\int_0^W \mathrm{Im}[g^{(\mp)}(v) \, \Delta^{(\pm)}(v)] \, dv = 0 \qquad (11.18)$$

The weight function $g(v)$ may of course depend on some continuous parameter, so that (11.17) and (11.18) actually constitute a family of sum rules.

A particular case of (11.17) which is of special interest is obtained by choosing

$$g^{(+)}(a, v) = a \exp(iav/W)/W \qquad (11.19)$$

In the case of a crossing-symmetric amplitude, the sum rule (11.17) then reads

$$\frac{a}{W} \int_0^W \text{Re}[\exp(iav/W)F^{(+)}(v)] \, dv = -\sum_i \frac{\beta_i W^{\alpha_i}}{a^{\alpha_i} \sin \frac{1}{2}\pi\alpha_i} \text{Im}[\gamma(\alpha_i + 1, ia)] \quad (11.20)$$

where $\gamma(u, v)$ is the incomplete gamma function, defined as

$$\gamma(u, v) = \int_0^v e^{-t} t^{u-1} \, dt \quad (11.21)$$

The sum rule (11.20), which is characterised by an oscillating weight function, has a number of distinct advantages over the ordinary continuous moment sum rules (compare with equation 11.8). First of all, the shape of the function on the right-hand side of (11.20) varies as a function of the α_i; this tends to make the sum rule a more effective tool for determining the Regge parameters. Secondly, the different energy regions tend to give contributions to the dispersion integral on the left-hand side which are of the same order of magnitude; this is true for any value of the parameter a.

The sum rules (11.17) and (11.18) have an obvious interpretation as a generalisation of the conventional sum rules, such as (11.7) and (11.8), which can be expressed in terms of integrals of the general form

$$H(x) = \int_0^W F(v)v^{x-1} \, dv \quad (11.22)$$

where $F(v)$ is a scattering amplitude (or its real or imaginary part). The integral $H(x)$ is called the incomplete Mellin transform of the function $F(v)$ (in analogy with the ordinary Mellin transform, in which the integration extends to infinity).

Another generalisation is obtained by considering different types of incomplete transforms, for example Laplace, Fourier or Hankel transforms. Thus, we may replace the weight function v^{x-1} in (11.22) by one of the functions

$$w_1(v) = \sin[a(W^2 - v^2)^{1/2}] \quad (11.23a)$$
$$w_2(v) = \sinh[a(W^2 - v^2)^{1/2}] \quad (11.23b)$$
$$w_3(v) = J_0[a(W^2 - v^2)^{1/2}] \quad (11.23c)$$
$$w_4(v) = I_0[a(W^2 - v^2)^{1/2}] \quad (11.23d)$$

where $J_0(x)$ and $I_0(x)$ are the usual Bessel functions and a is a real parameter, which is allowed to vary continuously. The sum rules corresponding to such weights, called in general finite-transform sum rules, can be written in the form

$$\int_0^W w_k(v)\text{Im}F(v) \, dv = \int_0^W w_k(v)\text{Im}F_{\text{Reg}}(v) \, dv \quad (11.24)$$

For the case of a crossing-antisymmetric amplitude, the right-hand side of (11.24), using one of the weight functions (11.23), is found to be equal to

$$\int_0^W w_k(v) \mathrm{Im} F_{\mathrm{Reg}}(v)\, \mathrm{d}v = \tfrac{1}{2} \sum_i \beta_i \Gamma[\tfrac{1}{2}(1+\alpha_i)] W^{1+\alpha_i} g_i^{(k)}(W) \qquad (11.25)$$

with

$$g_i^{(1)}(W) = \Gamma(\tfrac{1}{2})(\tfrac{1}{2}aW)^{-(1/2)\alpha_i} J_{1+(1/2)\alpha_i}(aW) \qquad (11.26a)$$

$$g_i^{(2)}(W) = \Gamma(\tfrac{1}{2})(\tfrac{1}{2}aW)^{-(1/2)\alpha_i} I_{1+(1/2)\alpha_i}(aW) \qquad (11.26b)$$

$$g_i^{(3)}(W) = (\tfrac{1}{2}aW)^{-(1/2)(1+\alpha_i)} J_{(1/2)(1+\alpha_i)}(aW) \qquad (11.26c)$$

$$g_i^{(4)}(W) = (\tfrac{1}{2}aW)^{-(1/2)(1+\alpha_i)} I_{(1/2)(1+\alpha_i)}(aW) \qquad (11.26d)$$

With minor modifications, these results are readily generalised to the case of a crossing-symmetric amplitude.

Such finite-transform sum rules, while still containing relatively simple functions, have several advantages over sum rules of the conventional type. Firstly, the dispersion integrals involve only the imaginary part of the amplitude, so that one can avoid the problems associated with the use of the real part. Secondly, the integrand is finite for any value of the parameter a. Finally, no particular part of the region of integration is strongly emphasised. However, it should be noted that for the derivation of these sum rules it is necessary to assume a more rapid convergence of the amplitude $F(v)$ to its asymptotic form $F_{\mathrm{Reg}}(v)$ than in the conventional sum rules based on the usual Mellin transform, in order to ensure that the integral involving $\Delta(v) = F(v) - F_{\mathrm{Reg}}(v)$ over a sufficiently large semicircle in the upper half-plane can be neglected. Whereas for the conventional sum rules one requires only that $\Delta(v)$ tends to zero like some negative power of v, in the case of the finite-transform sum rules $\Delta(v)$ must tend to zero exponentially. This assumption may be difficult to justify.

11.3. Modified sum rules as a superposition of finite energy sum rules

We have seen that certain sum rules contain dispersion integrals involving the real part of the scattering amplitude. As we have already pointed out, a difficulty arises from the fact that the real part of the amplitude can be evaluated by means of dispersion relations only under some assumption about the high-energy behaviour of the amplitude; this high-energy behaviour, in turn, is obviously related to the very parameters which one hopes to determine when using the sum rules as constraints.

One way of overcoming this difficulty is to use instead sum rules such as those discussed in the preceding section, which either give a smaller weight to the dispersion integral over the real part or depend only on the imaginary part. However, there is also the possibility of using a dispersion relation to calculate exactly the contribution which comes from the high-energy input information when data on the real part are required in the conventional sum rules. This contribution can be expressed in terms of the Regge parameters and transferred to the right-hand side of the sum rule, leaving on the left-hand side a dispersion integral which depends only on the experimentally accessible imaginary part. We shall discuss this idea in detail for the case of the conventional continuous moment sum rule, but the following considerations can easily be extended to other types of sum rules.

Let us first consider a crossing-antisymmetric amplitude $F(v)$. We recall that the continuous moment sum rule for this case reads (compare with equation 11.7)

$$\int_0^W v^x [\cos \tfrac{1}{2}\pi x \operatorname{Im}F(v) - \sin \tfrac{1}{2}\pi x \operatorname{Re}F(v)] \, dv$$

$$= \sum_i \frac{\beta_i W^{\alpha_i + x + 1}}{\cos \tfrac{1}{2}\pi \alpha_i} \frac{\sin \tfrac{1}{2}\pi(\alpha_i + x + 1)}{\alpha_i + x + 1} \quad (11.27)$$

To evaluate explicitly the high-energy contribution which is actually contained in the integral of $\operatorname{Re}F(v)$ in (11.27), we shall make use of dispersion relations for the Regge-type functions

$$G_\pm(v) = \frac{\mp 1 - \exp(-i\pi x)}{\sin \pi x} v^x \quad (11.28)$$

These functions have definite crossing properties, as indicated by the subscripts. If x belongs to the interval $-2 < x < 0$ for G_+ or $-1 < x < 1$ for G_-, the functions $G_\pm(v)$ satisfy unsubtracted dispersion relations

$$\operatorname{Re}G_\pm(v) = \frac{2}{\pi} P \int_0^\infty \frac{v_\pm \operatorname{Im}G_\pm(v') \, dv'}{v'^2 - v^2} \quad (11.29)$$

where $v_+ = v'$ and $v_- = v$. The range of positive x for which the dispersion relations are valid can be extended without difficulty by introducing a sufficient number of subtractions in (11.29) at $v = 0$, where all the subtraction constants vanish. The result is simply equivalent to the insertion of a factor $(v/v')^{2(M+1)}$ in the integrand of (11.29); this enlarges the range of x to $2M + 2$ for $G_+(v)$ and to $2M + 3$ for $G_-(v)$.

To eliminate the high-energy contribution on the left-hand side of (11.27), we make use of (11.29) for the function (11.28) whose crossing properties are opposite to those of the scattering amplitude; in the case which we are considering here, this is $G_+(v)$. From (11.29) one easily finds

$$\cos(\tfrac{1}{2}\pi x)v^x = -\frac{2}{\pi} \sin(\tfrac{1}{2}\pi x) P \int_0^\infty \frac{v'^x v' \, dv'}{v'^2 - v^2} \quad (11.30)$$

By substituting (11.30) in (11.27) and interchanging the order of integration in the double integral, we obtain

$$\sin \tfrac{1}{2}\pi x \int_0^\infty dv\, v^x\, \frac{2v}{\pi} P \int_0^W \frac{\mathrm{Im}F(v')\,dv'}{v'^2 - v^2} - \sin \tfrac{1}{2}\pi x \int_0^W v^x\, \mathrm{Re}F(v)\,dv$$

$$= \sum_i \frac{\beta_i W^{\alpha_i + x + 1}}{\cos \tfrac{1}{2}\pi \alpha_i} \frac{\sin \tfrac{1}{2}\pi(\alpha_i + x + 1)}{\alpha_i + x + 1} \quad (11.31)$$

The left-hand side of (11.31) can be replaced by

$$\sin \tfrac{1}{2}\pi x \int_W^\infty dv\, v^x\, \frac{2v}{\pi} \int_0^W \frac{\mathrm{Im}F(v')\,dv'}{v'^2 - v^2} - \sin \tfrac{1}{2}\pi x \int_0^W dv\, v^x\, \frac{2v}{\pi} \int_W^\infty \frac{\mathrm{Im}F(v')\,dv'}{v'^2 - v^2} \quad (11.32)$$

which differs from its original form only by an integral of the function

$$\mathrm{Re}F(v) - \frac{2v}{\pi} P \int_0^\infty \frac{\mathrm{Im}F(v')\,dv'}{v'^2 - v^2} \quad (11.33)$$

which vanishes by virtue of the analyticity of the scattering amplitude.

The new form (11.32) is of interest because it contains only the imaginary part of the scattering amplitude as input. Moreover, we have explicitly separated the contributions from the energy regions $v < W$ and $v > W$. Since we have assumed that the Regge pole expansion provides an adequate representation of $F(v)$ for $v > W$, we can use it to evaluate the second integral in (11.32). To do this, it is convenient to expand the denominator of the integrand in powers of $(v/v')^2$, which enables us to separate the integrals with respect to v' and v. We find, for an individual Regge pole,

$$-\sin \tfrac{1}{2}\pi x \int_0^W dv\, v^x\, \frac{2v}{\pi} \int_W^\infty \frac{\beta v'^\alpha\,dv'}{v'^2 - v^2}$$

$$= -\sin \tfrac{1}{2}\pi x\, \frac{2\beta}{\pi} \sum_{k=0}^\infty \int_0^W dv\, v^{x+1+2k} \int_W^\infty dv'\, v'^{\alpha - 2 - 2k} \quad (11.34)$$

The right-hand side of (11.34) can be integrated to yield

$$\sin \tfrac{1}{2}\pi x\, \frac{2\beta}{\pi} W^{x+\alpha+1} \sum_{k=0}^\infty \frac{1}{(x + 2 + 2k)(\alpha - 2k - 1)} \quad (11.35)$$

which in turn can be expressed in terms of the logarithmic derivative of the gamma function, $\psi(z) = d[\log \Gamma(z)]/dz$, in the form

$$-\frac{1}{\pi} \sin \tfrac{1}{2}\pi x\, \frac{\beta W^{x+\alpha+1}}{x + \alpha + 1} [\psi(1 + \tfrac{1}{2}x) - \psi\{1 - \tfrac{1}{2}(\alpha + 1)\}] \quad (11.36)$$

Now, by making use of (11.27), (11.31), (11.32) and (11.36), together with the well-known relation $\psi(z) - \psi(1 - z) = -\pi \cot \pi z$, we arrive at a sum rule which relates an integral depending only on $\mathrm{Im}F(\nu)$ at low energies to an expression depending only on the Regge parameters

$$
\sin \tfrac{1}{2}\pi x \int_W^\infty \nu^x \, d\nu \, \frac{2\nu}{\pi} \int_0^W \frac{\mathrm{Im}F(\nu') \, d\nu'}{\nu'^2 - \nu^2}
$$

$$
= \frac{1}{\pi} \sin \tfrac{1}{2}\pi x \sum_i \frac{\beta_i W^{x+\alpha_i+1}}{x + \alpha_i + 1} \left[\psi(-\tfrac{1}{2}x) - \psi\{\tfrac{1}{2}(\alpha_i + 1)\} \right] \equiv G(W, x) \quad (11.37)
$$

The sum rule (11.37) solves the problem of enforcing consistency of the parameters used to calculate the real part of the amplitude with those determined by the continuous moment sum rule.

However, we can further modify the left-hand side of (11.37) so as to reveal the intimate connection between the finite energy sum rules and the continuous moment sum rule. By expanding the denominator of the integrand in powers of $(\nu'/\nu)^2$, we achieve a separation of the integrals with respect to ν and ν', the latter being a typical integral of a finite energy sum rule. In this way, (11.37) leads to

$$
-\sin \tfrac{1}{2}\pi x W^{x+1} \frac{2}{\pi} \sum_{k=0}^\infty \frac{S_{2k}(W)}{2k - x} = G(W, x) \quad (11.38)
$$

where $S_{2k}(W)$ is defined by equation (10.12).

It should be noted that this expression, being well-defined and singularity-free for all values of x, actually constitutes the analytic continuation of the original continuous moment sum rule (11.27) to all values of x. When $x = 2k$, it reduces to a standard finite energy sum rule.

From the relationship which we have found between the finite energy sum rules and the continuous moment sum rules, we can conclude that the continuous moment sum rules, when evaluated with $\mathrm{Re}F(\nu)$ given by a dispersion relation, are completely equivalent to the entire set of finite energy sum rules. In phenomenological applications, the first few finite energy sum rules already contain practically all the information and can therefore be used in a fitting procedure. The situation is obviously different if $\mathrm{Re}F(\nu)$ is known from phase-shift analyses; in this case, the conventional form of the continuous moment sum rule can usefully exploit the experimental information on both $\mathrm{Re}F(\nu)$ and $\mathrm{Im}F(\nu)$.

Having discussed the procedure in detail for a crossing-antisymmetric amplitude, we shall now quote the corresponding results for the crossing-symmetric case. Although we cannot write an expression like (11.33) in this case because the amplitude does not satisfy an unsubtracted dispersion relation, by a careful analysis one can nevertheless derive an exact analogue of equations

(11.37) and (11.38), namely

$$-\cos\tfrac{1}{2}\pi x \int_W^\infty v^x\, dv\, \frac{2}{\pi} \int_0^W \frac{v'\, \mathrm{Im} F(v')\, dv'}{v'^2 - v^2}$$

$$= -\frac{1}{\pi}\cos\tfrac{1}{2}\pi x \sum_i \frac{\beta_i W^{x+\alpha_i+1}}{x+\alpha_i+1}\left[\psi\{\tfrac{1}{2}(1-x)\} - \psi(1+\tfrac{1}{2}\alpha_i)\right] \equiv H(W,x) \quad (11.39)$$

$$\cos\tfrac{1}{2}\pi x W^{x+1}\frac{2}{\pi}\sum_{k=0}^\infty \frac{S_{2k+1}(W)}{2k+1-x} = H(W,x) \quad (11.40)$$

As we have already pointed out, the procedure which we have outlined here need not be confined to the standard continuous moment sum rules. As another example, let us consider the sum rule (11.13a) discussed in the preceding section. Expanding its weight function $(W^2 - v^2)^{-x}$ in powers of $(v/W)^2$, we find

$$\int_0^W \frac{\mathrm{Im} F(v)\, dv}{(W^2 - v^2)^x} = W^{1-2x}\sum_{k=0}^\infty C_k^{-x}(-1)^k S_{2k}(W) \quad (11.41)$$

where C_k^{-x} denotes a binomial coefficient. Consequently, the sum rule is equivalent to a superposition of finite energy sum rules

$$\sum_{k=0}^\infty (-1)^k C_k^{-x} S_{2k}(W) = \tfrac{1}{2}\sum_i \beta_i W^{\alpha_i} B(\tfrac{1}{2}[1+\alpha_i], 1-x) \quad (11.42)$$

More generally, any sum rule which makes use of only the imaginary part of the amplitude below a certain energy W can be put into the form

$$\int_0^W \mathrm{Im} F(v)g(v, W, x)\, dv = \sum_{k=0}^\infty c_k(W, x)S_k(W) \quad (11.43)$$

For crossing-antisymmetric (crossing-symmetric) amplitudes, only even (odd) k will contribute to (11.43). The choice of the weight function g can be made on the basis of a criterion of simplicity or of the need to suppress or enhance the contributions from certain energy regions. The criterion of simplicity can apply either to the function g itself or to the coefficients appearing on the right-hand side of (11.43). In the case of the sum rule (11.37), for example, we see that the coefficients of the finite energy sum rules in (11.38) are rather simple, whereas the weight function is an incomplete beta function.

The same ideas can also be applied to the conventional dispersion relations to obtain a new family of sum rules. We shall outline the derivation of such sum rules for a crossing-antisymmetric amplitude, noting that the crossing-symmetric case can be treated in an analogous way, with certain minor modifications.

As usual, we assume that a Regge pole representation holds for the scattering amplitude when $|v| \geqslant W$ for some energy W, not only for real v, but in all directions in the complex v-plane. Thus, we may stipulate that for sufficiently large $|v|$ the real part of the scattering amplitude as given by the Regge pole model coincides with the predictions of a dispersion relation. In imposing this condition, as in the preceding reformulation of the continuous moment sum rules, we explicitly separate the dispersion integral into its low-energy and high-energy parts. Thus, we have

$$\frac{v}{\pi} \int_0^W \frac{\mathrm{Im}F(v')\,\mathrm{d}v'}{v'^2 - v^2} = \sum_i \left[\beta_i v^{\alpha_i}(\mathrm{i} + \tan \tfrac{1}{2}\pi\alpha_i) - \frac{2v}{\pi} \int_W^\infty \frac{\beta_i v'^{\alpha_i}\,\mathrm{d}v'}{v'^2 - v^2} \right] \quad (11.44)$$

If we now make use of the dispersion relation which holds for each term of the Regge pole expansion,

$$\beta_i v^{\alpha_i}(\mathrm{i} + \tan \tfrac{1}{2}\pi\alpha_i) = \frac{2v}{\pi} \int_0^\infty \frac{\beta_i v'^{\alpha_i}\,\mathrm{d}v'}{v'^2 - v^2} \quad (11.45)$$

we obtain the family of sum rules

$$\int_0^W \frac{\mathrm{Im}F(v')\,\mathrm{d}v'}{v'^2 - v^2} = 2 \sum_i \int_0^W \frac{\beta_i v'^{\alpha_i}\,\mathrm{d}v'}{v'^2 - v^2} \quad (11.46)$$

depending on the complex parameter v. These sum rules are equivalent to a pair of real sum rules depending on the modulus ρ and phase ϕ of the variable v.

The sum rule (11.46) can be interpreted as an expression of duality in the complex plane, in the same sense in which finite energy sum rules express duality on the real axis. By expanding the denominators in powers of $(v'/v)^2$, one gets

$$\sum_{n=0}^\infty \left(\frac{W}{\rho} \right)^{2n+1} \exp[-\mathrm{i}(2n+1)\phi]S_{2n}(W)$$

$$= \sum_{n=0}^\infty \left(\frac{W}{\rho} \right)^{2n+1} \exp[-\mathrm{i}(2n+1)\phi] \sum_i T_{2n}(W, \alpha_i, \beta_i) \quad (11.47)$$

where $S_{2n}(W)$ are the usual integrals of the finite energy sum rules and

$$T_{2n}(W, \alpha_i, \beta_i) = \frac{\beta_i}{2\pi} \frac{W^{\alpha_i}}{\alpha_i + 2n + 1} \quad (11.48)$$

11.4. An alternative derivation of the sum rules

For a general weight function $w(v)$, the sum rules which we have derived in the preceding section are of the form

$$\int_0^W \mathrm{d}v\, \mathrm{Im}F(v) \frac{2}{\pi} \int_W^\infty \frac{v_\mp \,\mathrm{Im}w(v')\,\mathrm{d}v'}{v'^2 - v^2}$$

$$= \int_0^W \mathrm{Im}[F_{\mathrm{Reg}}(v)w(v)]\,\mathrm{d}v - \int_0^W \mathrm{Im}w(v)\,\mathrm{d}v \frac{2}{\pi} \int_W^\infty \frac{v_\pm \,\mathrm{Im}F_{\mathrm{Reg}}(v')\,\mathrm{d}v'}{v'^2 - v^2} \quad (11.49)$$

where $v_+ = v'$ and $v_- = v$; the choice between v_+ and v_- in the double integrals corresponds to the crossing properties of the weight function $w(v)$, which are opposite to those of the scattering amplitude $F(v)$.

It is possible to introduce a further modification of the right-hand side of (11.49), so as to express the sum rule in a more symmetric form. To simplify the notation, we first define

$$\langle g \rangle = \frac{1}{W} \int_0^W g(z)\,dz \tag{11.50}$$

and a dispersive operator $\mathcal{D}$ such that

$$\mathcal{D}\,\text{Im}F(z) = \frac{2}{\pi} \int_0^\infty \frac{z_\mp\,\text{Im}F(z')\,dz'}{z^2 - z'^2} \tag{11.51}$$

where the choice between $z_+ = z'$ and $z_- = z$ depends on the crossing properties of $F(z)$ in the same way as for $v_\pm$ in (11.49). It is convenient to define also the operators $\mathcal{D}_1$ and $\mathcal{D}_2$ as those which correspond to the low-energy ($v < W$) and high-energy ($v > W$) parts of (11.51), respectively.

The sum rule will always be

$$\langle \text{Im}(Fw) \rangle = \langle \text{Im}(F_{\text{Reg}}w) \rangle \tag{11.52}$$

where F and w have opposite crossing properties. Equation (11.52) can also be written in the form

$$\langle \text{Im}F\mathcal{D}\,\text{Im}w + \text{Im}w\mathcal{D}\,\text{Im}F \rangle = \langle \text{Im}(F_{\text{Reg}}w) \rangle \tag{11.53}$$

If we replace the operator $\mathcal{D}$ on the left-hand side of (11.53) by the sum $\mathcal{D}_1 + \mathcal{D}_2$, we obtain

$$\langle \text{Im}F\mathcal{D}_1\,\text{Im}w + \text{Im}w\mathcal{D}_1\,\text{Im}F \rangle + \langle \text{Im}F\mathcal{D}_2\,\text{Im}w + \text{Im}w\mathcal{D}_2\,\text{Im}F \rangle \tag{11.54}$$

It can easily be verified that the first term in (11.54) vanishes because of the opposite crossing properties of F and w.

One can operate in the same way on the function F_{Reg}, so that, when only the non-vanishing terms are retained, the sum rule takes the form

$$\langle \text{Im}F\mathcal{D}_2\,\text{Im}w + \text{Im}w\mathcal{D}_2\,\text{Im}F \rangle = \langle \text{Im}F_{\text{Reg}}\mathcal{D}_2\,\text{Im}w + \text{Im}w\mathcal{D}_2\,\text{Im}F_{\text{Reg}} \rangle \tag{11.55}$$

which, after exploiting the asymptotic equality of F and F_{Reg}, reduces to

$$\langle \text{Im}F\mathcal{D}_2\,\text{Im}w \rangle = \langle \text{Im}F_{\text{Reg}}\mathcal{D}_2\,\text{Im}w \rangle \tag{11.56}$$

This equation is obviously completely equivalent to (11.49). We note, however, that it has two advantages over the previous derivation: first, it is much simpler and more elegant, and second, it provides a means of eliminating the somewhat unpleasant (integrable) divergence of (11.49) for $v' = v = W$. Although this divergence, being integrable, presents no problem in principle, it requires some care in the numerical evaluation of the sum rule. Now, if the sum rule is put in the form (11.56), it is clear that the divergence is readily eliminated by subtracting the equality

$$\frac{1}{W} \int_{W-\varepsilon}^{W} \text{Im}F\mathscr{D}_2 \, \text{Im}w \, dv = \frac{1}{W} \int_{W-\varepsilon}^{W} \text{Im}F_{\text{Reg}}\mathscr{D}_2 \, \text{Im}w \, dv \qquad (11.57)$$

from the two sides of the equation, so that the point of the divergence no longer falls in the region of integration of the sum rule.

References

1. P. H. Ng and N. M. Queen, *Lettere al Nuovo Cimento*, **2** (1969), 360
2. C. H. Chan and L. K. Chavda, *Phys. Rev. Lett.*, **22** (1969), 1228
3. A. García and L. Masperi, *Nucl. Phys.*, **B15** (1970), 560

Further reading

An extensive survey of dispersion sum rules and their phenomenological applications can be found in the following reference.

1. C. Ferro Fontán, N. M. Queen and G. Violini, *Rivista del Nuovo Cimento*, **2** (1972), 357

The last two sections of this chapter are based mainly on the following papers.

2. E. Ferrari and G. Violini, *Nuovo Cimento*, **69A** (1970), 375
3. M. Czekalski de Achterberg, C. Ferro Fontán and G. Violini, *Nucl. Phys.*, **B40** (1972), 397
4. E. Ferrari, *Nuovo Cimento* (to be published).

CHAPTER 12

Extrapolation of data by analytic continuation techniques

12.1. Physical motivation

Phenomenological applications of dispersion relations and dispersion sum rules fall into two main categories:

(i) tests of the consistency of theories, models and experimental data (or some combination of them)

(ii) extrapolations of experimental information obtained in a given region of the energy (or other kinematic variable) into another, possibly inaccessible, region.

We shall be concerned in this chapter with problems of the second type. This includes many problems discussed earlier in the book, such as the determination of the residues of the poles of scattering amplitudes in terms of physical scattering data by means of dispersion relations, the determination of high-energy Regge parameters from low-energy scattering data by means of finite energy sum rules and continuous moment sum rules, and the determination of the amplitude for the electron–positron annihilation process $e^- + e^+ \rightarrow \bar{p} + p$ from the analysis of experimental data on elastic ep scattering. The role played by dispersion relations and sum rules in such problems is to provide a practical means of analytically continuing amplitudes from regions where experimental information is available into other regions of their domain of analyticity.

However, the usual techniques based on dispersion relations and sum rules, when applied to certain problems, encounter a number of difficulties. For example, as we saw in chapter 6, the conventional dispersion relations for determining the $KN\Lambda$ coupling constant in terms of physical $K^{\pm}N$ scattering data entail a significant uncertainty due to the contribution of the $Y_0^*(1405)$ resonance below the physical $\bar{K}N$ threshold. In determining this coupling constant from a given dispersion relation, the evaluation of the dispersion integral over the unphysical region requires a specific model for the amplitude in that region. Such models are normally obtained by continuing various parametrisations of the low-energy K^-N scattering data into the unphysical region.

In principle, one may investigate the sensitivity of the results to the choice of the model by repeating the analysis for a large number of alternative parametrisations which give an acceptable fit to the low-energy data. However, the determination of the optimum parameters in any particular case is a major computational task, so that it is not practicable to perform such an analysis for many different parametrisations; indeed, only a small number of essentially different low-energy K^-N parametrisations have been analysed. This raises the question of how to obtain a more objective estimate of the uncertainty in the $KN\Lambda$ coupling constant.

One may, of course, strongly suppress the contribution of the troublesome unphysical region by a careful choice of a weighted dispersion relation. Nevertheless, there is no unique prescription for doing this. There are infinitely many dispersion relations which could be used for this purpose, and different dispersion relations will in general lead to different results. This ambiguity remains even if one considers a more favourable case like the determination of the πNN coupling constant by means of πN dispersion relations, where there is no problem of an unphysical region and where one may practically neglect the uncertainties due to the lack of data in the asymptotic energy region. If infinitely accurate data were available, all the dispersion relations would necessarily lead to identical predictions, since there would be a unique analytic continuation (provided, of course, that the amplitude actually has the postulated analyticity properties); but in the actual physical situation, where only a finite number of measurements exist, all characterised by some finite accuracy, the inexact knowledge of the amplitude breaks the equivalence of different methods, and a range of different predictions may be obtained in practice for the same physical quantity. This fact can be exploited in the formulation of consistency tests, but it also leads again to the problem of obtaining an objective estimate of the accuracy with which the quantity in question can be determined.

To take another example, consider the problem of determining the amplitude for the process $e^- + e^+ \to \bar{p} + p$ from an analysis of data on the proton electromagnetic form factors. In this case, we encounter a problem in addition to possible difficulties of the type discussed above. This is the fact that the dispersion relations provide a natural expression for the form factors in the physical region $t \leqslant 0$ for ep scattering in terms of their values on the cuts for $t \geqslant 4m_\pi^2$ (the region related to the electron–positron annihilation process), whereas one is concerned here with the converse problem of analytically continuing the form factors from the region $t < 0$ to their cuts. A possible procedure would be to adopt some specific parametrisation for the form factors on their cuts and then to determine the values of the parameters which produce the best fit to the data for $t < 0$. However, it is clearly desirable to find a more direct and model-independent procedure for extrapolating to the cuts.

With such problems in mind, we shall devote the remainder of this chapter to the more general problem of analytic extrapolation of functions whose values are known experimentally in some limited range and whose global analyticity properties can be specified theoretically.

12.2. Classification of analytic continuations

The specific problems discussed in the preceding section all involve analytic continuations of certain functions which can be determined experimentally at a number of discrete points within a part of their domain (normally some segment of the real axis). We shall refer to such analytic continuations as continuations *from an arc*, since they are analogous to the mathematical problem of analytically continuing a function whose values are precisely given along some finite curve in the complex plane.

Greater insight is achieved if we study this problem in parallel with the problem of continuing an analytic function *from a point*, in which one has information on some finite number of derivatives of a function at a single point of its domain of analyticity: this is analogous to the mathematical problem of analytically continuing a function when all of its derivatives are specified at one particular point.

A typical example of a problem of this last type is that of estimating a quantity $F(g)$ when some finite number of terms of a perturbation expansion for it

$$F(g) = \sum_{n=0}^{\infty} a_n g^n \tag{12.1}$$

can be calculated according to some theory. We recall that the coefficients of the Taylor series (12.1) are related to the derivatives of the function by

$$a_n = F^{(n)}(0)/n!$$

This means that the problem is equivalent to that of carrying out an analytic continuation from the point $g = 0$ to the physical value of g.

If it is known or assumed that $F(g)$ is analytic in some neighbourhood of $g = 0$, then an exact knowledge of all the coefficients a_n clearly determines the analytic continuation into the circle of convergence of the series (12.1). However, it may be possible to analytically continue the function $F(g)$ even beyond the circle of convergence. For example, the series

$$F(g) = \sum_{n=0}^{\infty} g^n$$

converges only within the unit circle $|g| < 1$ (because of the presence of a simple pole at $g = 1$), although we recognise that its analytic continuation into the entire complex plane is given by

$$F(g) = 1/(1 - g)$$

Let us first consider the idealised mathematical problem of analytically continuing a function when infinitely accurate data exist, either at a single point or along some arc; that is, either the values of the function and all its derivatives are specified precisely at a single point, or the values of the function are specified precisely along an arc. It is well known that this information, in either case, completely determines, at least in principle, the function throughout its domain of analyticity, including all of its singularities.

The situation is completely changed, however, in the actual physical situation, when one has only a finite number of pieces of information about the function: either the value of the function and its first N derivatives at some point (possibly exactly), or experimental values of the function at N different points, all with finite statistical errors. In either case, it is clear that, since the information which is missing can be specified arbitrarily, it is no longer possible to carry out the analytic continuation unless certain supplementary assumptions are made.

In continuations from an arc, for example, once we attach any finite error corridor to the specified values of the function along the arc, there is an infinitely large uncertainty in the determination of the function at any point off the arc. This is so because analytic functions can be found which take any specified value at the point in question and arbitrarily small values along the entire length of the arc, and such functions can be added to a given fit to the data along the arc without destroying either the goodness of fit or the known analyticity properties of the function. The existence of such functions can be seen, for example, from the Weierstrass approximation theorem, which states that a function which is continuous within a given interval can be approximated with any desired accuracy by a polynomial. Without supplementary information on the function (such as an overall bound or some smoothness requirement), such an analytic continuation is intrinsically unstable and we say that the problem is not properly posed, since small perturbations in the input data can lead to arbitrarily large changes in the continuation of the function.

It is convenient to introduce a further classification of problems involving analytic continuations from an arc, since the boundary (B) of the domain of analyticity differs in certain respects from its interior (I). Depending on the position of the arc on which the initial data are given and the point to which the continuation is to be made, there are four types of analytic continuation problems: $I \rightarrow I$, $I \rightarrow B$, $B \rightarrow I$ and $B \rightarrow B$.

We shall now show that, by means of the discrepancy function method (see section 6.4), the problems $B \rightarrow I$ and $B \rightarrow B$ can be reduced to the simpler problems $I \rightarrow I$ and $I \rightarrow B$, respectively. For definiteness, suppose that a function $F(z)$ is known to be analytic in the complex z-plane except for certain poles at positions z_n and certain cuts; we divide the cuts of $F(z)$ into two classes A and B such that the values of $F(z)$ are assumed to be known on A but not on B. Suppose that the function $F(z)$ is to be analytically continued from the region A, either to a point inside its domain of analyticity or to points on the remainder of the boundary B. This situation is shown schematically in figure 12.1.

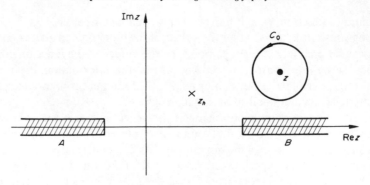

Figure 12.1. A schematic representation of the singularity structure of a function $F(z)$, assumed to be known on the cut A but not on B. The point z_n indicates a typical pole of the function.

For any point z within the domain of analyticity of $F(z)$, we can write Cauchy's integral formula

$$F(z) = \frac{1}{2\pi i} \oint_{C_0} \frac{F(z')\,dz'}{z' - z} \tag{12.2}$$

where C_0 is a small contour enclosing the point z in the anticlockwise sense (see figure 12.1). If the continuation is to be made to some point z_B on the cut B, we can take the limit $z \to z_B$ at the end of the analysis.

For simplicity, we shall suppose that it is known that $|F(z)| \to 0$ as $|z| \to \infty$, so that a contour integral over a sufficiently large circle in the complex plane can be neglected. If this condition is not actually satisfied, but if $F(z)$ is still polynomially bounded, one can introduce a suitable subtraction by dividing $F(z)$ by some polynomial, as for the ordinary dispersion relations, and then carry out the following analysis for the modified function. Alternatively, a finite-contour integration can be used.

By deforming the contour of integration, we can write

$$F(z) = \frac{1}{2\pi i} \oint_{C_A + C_B} \frac{F(z')\,dz'}{z' - z} + \frac{1}{2\pi i} \sum_n \oint_{C_n} \frac{F(z')\,dz'}{z' - z} \tag{12.3}$$

where C_A and C_B are contours around the cuts A and B, respectively, and C_n is a contour enclosing one of the poles of the function $F(z)$ at $z = z_n$ (see figure 12.2). It is easy to see that (12.3) can be expressed as

$$F(z) = \frac{1}{2\pi i} \int_{A+B} \frac{\text{disc } F(z')\,dz'}{z' - z} + \sum_n \frac{R_n}{z - z_n} \tag{12.4}$$

where disc F denotes the discontinuity of the function across the cut, and R_n is its residue at the pole $z = z_n$. Equation (12.4) is simply a dispersion relation for the function $F(z)$.

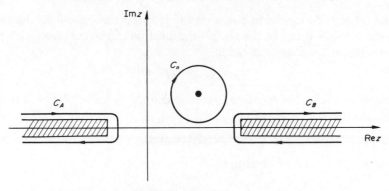

Figure 12.2. The result of deforming the contour of integration in figure 12.1.

We now define the discrepancy function

$$\Delta(z) = F(z) - \frac{1}{2\pi i} \int_A \frac{\text{disc } F(z') \, dz'}{z' - z} \tag{12.5}$$

which can be evaluated in terms of the original data when z lies on the cut A. It follows from (12.4) that

$$\Delta(z) = \frac{1}{2\pi i} \int_B \frac{\text{disc } F(z') \, dz'}{z' - z} + \sum_n \frac{R_n}{z - z_n} \tag{12.6}$$

Equation (12.6) shows that $\Delta(z)$ has the original cut B and the poles at $z = z_n$, but not the cut A. Thus, by subtracting the dispersion integral over the cut A according to (12.5), we have constructed a new function $\Delta(z)$ for which this cut is absent. If an analytic continuation of $\Delta(z)$ is made away from the region A, equation (12.5) then defines the corresponding analytic continuation of $F(z)$. Thus, we have established that the problem of analytically continuing a function from part of the boundary of its domain of analyticity can be reduced to the problem of continuing another function from an arc within its domain of analyticity.

Note that the construction of the discrepancy function requires a knowledge of the discontinuity across the cut. This is possible in practice, for example in the case of the discrepancy function for the forward KN scattering amplitude, when the discontinuity across the cut is purely imaginary and can be determined in terms of the total cross sections through the optical theorem. Of course, a complete determination of the discrepancy function is possible only at those points where the real part of the amplitude is also known.

Certain general statements can be made about the stability of an analytic continuation. Consider, for example, a continuation of the type $I \to I$ or $I \to B$, in which the function $F(z)$ is known experimentally along some arc A. Suppose that the errors on the data are of order ε (for example, ε may characterise the width of the error corridor). Let us assume also that some theoretical bound $|F(z)| < M$ can be imposed on the function throughout its domain of analyticity. Then it can be shown that the function can be continued to a point $z = b$ with an uncertainty of order

$$\delta F(b) \sim \varepsilon^{u(b)} M^{1-u(b)} \tag{12.7}$$

where $u(z)$ is a so-called harmonic measure defined by the solution of Laplace's equation in the complex plane,

$$\nabla^2 u(z) = 0 \tag{12.8}$$

subject to the boundary conditions

$$u(z) = \begin{cases} 1 & \text{for } z \text{ in the region } A \\ 0 & \text{for } z \text{ on the boundary } B \end{cases} \tag{12.9}$$

This result is known as the Nevanlinna principle. Note that the harmonic measure satisfies $0 < u(z) \leqslant 1$ for all z in the domain of analyticity, taking the largest values when z is near the experimental region.

The result (12.7) shows that, provided that some bound M can be imposed on $|F(z)|$, the analytic continuation to points $z = b$ within the domain of analyticity (where $u(b) > 0$) is stable, in the sense that $\delta F(b) \to 0$ as $\varepsilon \to 0$. The nearer b is to the experimental region, the smaller the error $\delta F(b)$ becomes.

On the other hand, the continuation becomes unstable when the point $z = b$ lies on the boundary of the domain of analyticity (so that $u(b) = 0$), since in this case $\delta F(b) \sim M$, independently of the size of the error ε. There are several ways to avoid this difficulty in practice. For example, one may impose certain additional general conditions on the function, such as bounds on its derivatives. Alternatively, one can extrapolate only to *average* values over arcs on the boundary, in which case the stability improves as the length of arc increases.

12.3. The rate of convergence of power series expansions

An obvious method of analytically continuing a function about which certain information is known is to expand the function in a power series about some point, choosing the coefficients of the series to give the best fit to the information which is available. Only a finite number of terms of the power series will be determined in practice. It is therefore important to be able to say something about the rate of convergence of a power series, that is to estimate the truncation error when only a finite number of terms are retained.

Let us consider for definiteness a power series about the origin,

$$F(z) = \sum_{n=0}^{\infty} a_n z^n \tag{12.10}$$

assumed to be valid within a certain finite circle of convergence of radius R about the origin; the value of R depends on the distance from the origin to the nearest singularity of the function $F(z)$. According to Cauchy's integral formula, we can write

$$F(z) = \frac{1}{2\pi i} \oint_{C_R} \frac{F(z')\,dz'}{z' - z} \tag{12.11}$$

where C_R is the circular contour $|z| = R - \varepsilon$, just inside the circle of convergence. The derivatives at the origin are given by

$$F^{(n)}(0) = \frac{n!}{2\pi i} \oint_{C_R} \frac{F(z')\,dz'}{(z')^{n+1}} \tag{12.12}$$

If it is assumed that some bound $|F(z)| < M$ can be imposed on the function over the entire circle $|z| = R$, then

$$|a_n| = \frac{1}{n!}|F^{(n)}(0)| < M/R^n \tag{12.13}$$

(Note that the maximum-modulus principle for analytic functions implies that this same bound holds throughout the region $|z| < R$.) Equation (12.13) means that each term in the power series (12.10) satisfies the bound

$$|a_n z^n| < M\,|z/R|^n \tag{12.14}$$

so that the error in truncating the series at a given term is bounded by

$$\left| F(z) - \sum_{n=0}^{N} a_n z^n \right| < M \sum_{n=N+1}^{\infty} |z/R|^n = \frac{M\,|z/R|^{N+1}}{1 - |z/R|} \tag{12.15}$$

Thus, the rate of convergence of the power series is governed by the ratio $|z/R|$; as one would expect, the nearer the point z is to the origin, the better the convergence.

The fact that the rate of convergence of a power series depends on the distance R to the nearest singularity can serve as a test for nearby singularities of a function when the terms of its power series are known, since the coefficients of the power series are expected to obey a bound of the type (12.13). For example, if one plots the numerical values of $\log |a_n|$ as a function of n (see figure 12.3), then according to (12.13) the resulting points should be bounded asymptotically by some straight line, whose slope is equal to $-\log R$.

Further insight into the nature of power series expansions can be gained by considering the relationship between the full power series (12.10) for a given function within its circle of convergence $|z| < R$ and the approximation given by the truncated series

$$F_N(z) = \sum_{n=0}^{N} a_n z^n \tag{12.16}$$

assuming that the coefficients $a_0, a_1, \ldots, a_N$ are known exactly. For simplicity,

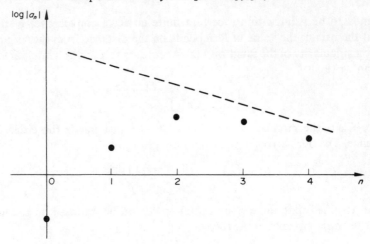

Figure 12.3. A typical plot of the coefficients of a power series as a test for nearby singularities.

we shall suppose that $R \geqslant 1$ and compare the exact function $F(z)$ with its approximation $F_N(z)$ at points on the unit circle $|z| = 1$.

It is convenient to introduce the polar angle θ in the z-plane, so that $z = \exp(i\theta)$ on the unit circle. Equations (12.10) and (12.16) then become

$$F(\theta) = \sum_{n=0}^{\infty} a_n \exp(in\theta) \tag{12.17}$$

$$F_N(\theta) = \sum_{n=0}^{N} a_n \exp(in\theta) \tag{12.18}$$

Recognising that (12.17) is a complex Fourier series for $F(\theta)$, we have

$$a_n = \frac{1}{2\pi} \int_{-\pi}^{\pi} F(\theta')\exp(-in\theta') \, d\theta' \tag{12.19}$$

so that (12.18) becomes

$$F_N(\theta) = \frac{1}{2\pi} \int_{-\pi}^{\pi} F(\theta') \sum_{n=0}^{N} \exp[in(\theta - \theta')] \, d\theta' \tag{12.20}$$

This shows that $F_N(\theta)$ is equal to a certain average over $F(\theta)$, namely

$$F_N(\theta) = \frac{1}{2\pi} \int_{-\pi}^{\pi} F(\theta')K(\theta - \theta') \, d\theta' \tag{12.21}$$

with the weight factor

$$K(\theta - \theta') = \frac{\exp[i(N + 1)(\theta - \theta')] - 1}{\exp[i(\theta - \theta')] - 1} \tag{12.22}$$

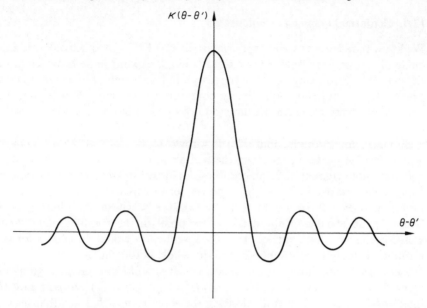

Figure 12.4. A typical form of the weight function (12.22); only the real part is shown here.

A straightforward calculation gives

$$|K(\theta - \theta')|^2 = \frac{1 - \cos[(N + 1)(\theta - \theta')]}{1 - \cos(\theta - \theta')}$$

$$= \frac{\sin^2[\frac{1}{2}(N + 1)(\theta - \theta')]}{\sin^2[\frac{1}{2}(\theta - \theta')]} \tag{12.23}$$

We see that the function $K(\theta - \theta')$ has an oscillatory character, with a central positive peak of height $N + 1$ at $\theta - \theta' = 0$ and a series of smaller peaks on each side (see figure 12.4); the first zero of this function occurs at

$$\theta - \theta' = \pm 2\pi/(N + 1)$$

The larger the value of N, the higher and narrower the central peak becomes. However, with any fixed value of N in (12.18), it is clear that one cannot hope to reproduce local structures in the function $F(\theta)$ which extend over an angular range of order less than about $2\pi/N$, which can be thought of as the 'resolving power' of the truncated series. In other words, we have found an estimate of the number of terms in the series required for a given resolution. For the original derivation of this result, see J. E. Bowcock, W. N. Cottingham and J. G. Williams, *Nucl. Phys.*, **B3** (1967), 95, where an application is made to the problem of extrapolating electromagnetic form factors to their cuts.

12.4. Conformal mapping techniques

We know that a power series expansion such as (12.10) converges only within its circle of convergence, that is the circle about the expansion point which passes through the nearest singularity of the function. It is therefore necessary to find a practical procedure for analytically continuing a function $F(z)$ beyond this circle of convergence when the function is known to be analytic in some larger domain.

Suppose, for example, that $F(z)$ is known to be analytic in the complex z-plane except for two cuts along the real axis for $z < -R$ and $z > R$ (if the cuts were not symmetrically placed, they could be symmetrised by introducing some new variable $z' = z + c$). A power series expansion of $F(z)$ about the origin such as (12.10) would then be valid only within the circle $|z| < R$. Similarly, an expansion about any other point in the complex plane would converge only within some circle and consequently would be useless for performing an analytic continuation into the whole of the plane.

One way of obtaining an expansion which is valid in a larger region is to carry out a conformal mapping $w = w(z)$ of the entire cut z-plane into the interior of a circle, say the unit circle, in the w-plane in such a way that the cuts of $F(z)$ are mapped onto the circumference of the circle. As is readily verified, a transformation which achieves this is

$$w = \frac{\sqrt{(R + z)} - \sqrt{(R - z)}}{\sqrt{(R + z)} + \sqrt{(R - z)}} \tag{12.24}$$

The function (12.24) maps the points $z = \pm R$ onto the points $w = \pm 1$, while $w(0) = 0$; the interval $-R \leqslant z \leqslant R$ corresponds to the diameter of the circle $-1 \leqslant w \leqslant 1$ in the new variable. If the function $F(w)$ is expanded in powers of the new variable w, the result can be mapped back into the original z-plane to yield an expansion

$$F(z) = \sum_{n=0}^{\infty} c_n [w(z)]^n \tag{12.25}$$

which is valid in the whole of the original cut plane.

We shall now argue that the conformal mapping procedure which we have described gives not only an expansion which is convergent in a larger domain than the power series in the original variable, but also a more rapidly convergent expansion in the region where both expansions converge.

Let $w = w(z)$ be a conformal mapping having the property $w(0) = 0$ and suppose that the expansion of $F(z)$ in powers of z is valid within a circle $|z| < R$, while the expansion of $F(w)$ in powers of w is valid within a circle $|w| < R'$. Then the results of the preceding section show that, for any particular point z, the convergence of the second expansion is asymptotically better than that of the first if

$$|w(z)/R'| < |z/R| \tag{12.26}$$

that is if the mapping $w = w(z)$ brings the point z relatively closer to the centre of the circle of convergence.

Let us compare the effects of different mappings in this respect. Let $w = w_1(z)$ be an analytic function which maps a certain domain D_1 of the z-plane into the unit circle and its interior $|w| \leqslant 1$ of the w-plane, and let $w = w_2(z)$ be another function which maps a domain D_2 of the z-plane into the same region $|w| \leqslant 1$ of the w-plane. Suppose further that $w_1(0) = w_2(0) = 0$ and that the region D_1 is entirely contained within D_2 (see figure 12.5).

Under these conditions, it can be shown that

$$|w_2(z_0)| < |w_1(z_0)| \tag{12.27}$$

for any point z_0 contained in the region D_1 (and hence also in D_2). In other words, the image of the point z_0 under the mapping $w = w_2(z)$ lies nearer the origin than the image under the mapping $w = w_1(z)$ (figure 12.6).

We conclude that, the larger the region of the z-plane which is mapped into the unit circle of the w-plane, the more rapid the convergence in powers of w will be; this holds for *all* points in the region of convergence. The optimum mapping is obviously the one which maps the entire z-plane into the circle. In fact, if one knows that the function in question is analytic on a certain part of another sheet, a further improvement is possible if that region is also mapped into the circle.

Numerical examples have shown that such conformal mappings can significantly accelerate the rate of convergence of power series in practice, thus reducing the number of terms required for a satisfactory fit to a given set of data.

It should be mentioned that the conformal mapping of a given region into the unit circle is not unique, since the unit circle can be mapped into itself with

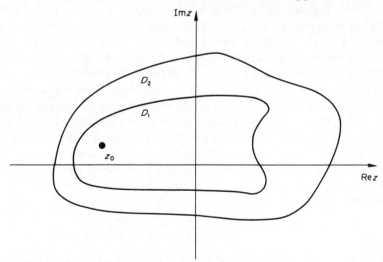

Figure 12.5. Two regions of the z-plane which are mapped into the unit circle.

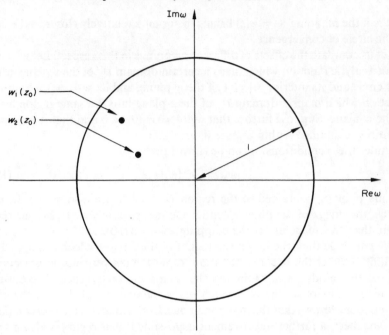

Figure 12.6. The images of the point z_0 under two mappings which map
different regions of the z-plane into the interior of the unit circle.

$z = \pm 1$ as fixed points. In fact, there exists a one-parameter family of such
mappings

$$w'(w) = (w - \lambda)/(1 - \lambda w) \qquad (12.28)$$

where λ is an arbitrary real parameter in the range $-1 < \lambda < 1$. The mapping
(12.28) has the property $w'(\lambda) = 0$. This means that any selected point in the
interval $-1 < w < 1$ can be transferred to the origin in the w'-plane. It is
evidently desirable to choose λ so as to map the region being analysed as near as
possible to the origin, where the rate of convergence is best.

As an example, we shall indicate how the conformal mapping technique can
be applied to the analysis of the discrepancy function for KN scattering defined
in section 6.4. If the total cross sections are assumed to be known over the entire
physical region, the only singularities of the discrepancy function are the Λ
and Σ poles and the short unphysical cut over a certain energy range
$\omega_0 \leqslant \omega \leqslant m_K$. For simplicity, let us treat the two poles together as a single
effective pole at some point $\omega = \omega_Y$. Now it is easily verified that the transformation

$$\xi = \frac{\sqrt{(\omega - m_K)} - \sqrt{(\omega - \omega_0)}}{\sqrt{(\omega - m_K)} + \sqrt{(\omega - \omega_0)}} \qquad (12.29)$$

maps the cut of the discrepancy function onto the unit circle in the ξ-plane;
moreover, the cut-free portion of the real axis in the ω-plane, including the

hyperon pole, is mapped onto the interval $-1 < \xi < 1$, while the remainder of the cut ω-plane is mapped into the circular region $|\xi| < 1$. The pole term can be removed from the discrepancy function by multiplying it by the factor $\xi - \xi_Y$, where $\xi_Y = \xi(\omega_Y)$. This leaves a function which is analytic throughout the region $|\xi| < 1$, and the experimentally determined values of this function in the physical region can be fitted to a truncated expansion in powers of ξ. Such a fit defines a continuation to the point $\xi = \xi_Y$, from which the residue at the pole can be determined.

Another possible application of conformal mapping techniques is to improve partial-wave expansions, which are valid only in a limited region of the variable $z = \cos \theta$ (namely, the Lehmann ellipse).

Conformal mappings can be used to accelerate the convergence of power series expansions for continuations from either a point or an arc. In the second case, however, a possible objection can be raised to the methods discussed so far. Consider, for example, a power series expansion

$$F(w) = \sum_{n=0}^{\infty} c_n w^n \tag{12.30}$$

assumed to be valid within some circle $|w| < R$, with $R > 1$. Suppose that data on the function $F(w)$ are available in the real interval $-1 \leqslant w \leqslant 1$. In order to eliminate any uncertainties due to the finite accuracy of the experimental data, we shall consider the idealised mathematical situation in which the function $F(w)$ is known with infinite precision on this interval.

Suppose now that the coefficients of a truncated expansion

$$F_N(w) = \sum_{n=0}^{N} c_n w^n \tag{12.31}$$

are fitted to the data according to the method of least squares. A simple re-arrangement of the series shows that the result will be equivalent to a least-squares determination of the coefficients b_n of a truncated series in Legendre polynomials

$$F_N(w) = \sum_{n=0}^{N} b_n P_n(w) \tag{12.32}$$

Now the theory of expansions in Legendre polynomials tells us that the coefficients b_n determined in this way are actually equal to those of the full Legendre series

$$F(w) = \sum_{n=0}^{\infty} b_n P_n(w) \tag{12.33}$$

This series is known to converge only within a certain ellipse, namely the largest ellipse with foci at $w = \pm 1$ which does not enclose any singularities of the function $F(w)$. Consequently, the procedure of fitting the data to a truncated power series (12.31) and then taking the limit as $N \to \infty$ will lead to a convergent continuation only within this ellipse. Since the function $F(w)$ has singularities on the circle $|w| = R$, the interior of the ellipse will not include all of the circular region $|w| < R$.

This conclusion may appear surprising at first sight, since the original power series (12.30) is certainly convergent throughout the circular region $|w| < R$. It should be noted, however, that the coefficients c_n determined by the procedure described above, unlike the coefficients b_n of the Legendre series, vary with the truncation point N, so that the procedure does not, strictly speaking, determine the correct power series expansion.

A simple way of avoiding this objection is to map the domain of analyticity into an appropriate ellipse[1] instead of a circle and then to expand the function in Legendre polynomials. This method also offers certain further advantages over the mapping into the circle: the expansion is made in orthogonal polynomials, so that the coefficients of the truncated series as determined by a least-squares fit are equal to those of the complete series; convergence is ensured in the entire domain of analyticity; and, finally, the expansion of this type can be shown to be the most rapidly convergent polynomial expansion when the original data are specified on a finite interval.

Although a mapping into an ellipse is to be preferred from a theoretical point of view when making an analytic continuation from an interval, in many practical applications of the conformal mapping technique the ellipse is found to be very close to a circle and a careful analysis shows that the use of the ellipse offers no real advantage over the much simpler mapping into a circle, since the two methods lead to almost indistinguishable results from the numerical point of view, particularly when the size of the statistical errors is taken into account.

Reference

1. R. E. Cutkosky and B. B. Deo, *Phys. Rev.*, **174** (1968), 1859

Further reading

More detailed surveys of the methods of analytic extrapolation can be found in the following references.

1. J. Pišut, *Springer Tracts in Modern Physics*, **55** (1970), 41
2. J. Hamilton, *Springer Tracts in Modern Physics*, **57** (1971), 41
3. O. V. Dumbrais, *Problems of Elementary Particle and Atomic Nucleus Physics* (to be published).

The following paper contains some interesting remarks on the general problem of analytic continuation.

4. S. Ciulli and G. Nenciu, *J. Math. Phys.*, **14** (1973), 1675

Some applications of analytic continuation techniques to KN scattering are reviewed in the following reference.

5. N. M. Queen, M. Restignoli and G. Violini, *Fortschritte der Physik*, **21** (1973), 569

Padé approximants provide a very powerful alternative method of carrying out analytic extrapolations; a good discussion of this method can be found in the following reference.

6. J. L. Basdevant, *Fortschritte der Physik*, **20** (1972), 283

Index